In *The Law of the Wild*, Ian Swingland offers a unique window into his life as a world-renowned conservation biologist. Captivating the reader with his adventures, exploits and near-death experiences, as well as sharing insights gained from advising powerful individuals in government and commerce, this is a book for those who are passionate about wildlife, biodiversity and its conservation. It is also a cracking good read as he shares stories from his close relationships with key figures in academia, business, charities and the bush.

From modest beginnings to worldwide authority, Ian has been at the centre of conservation for half a century – working with exotic (and humble) plants and animals, such as giant tortoises and komodo dragons – and setting up world-class institutions training future conservationists.

The book describes how our relationship with wildlife affects our behaviour and vice versa. This book is an inspiration to conquer the many threats to life on Earth and to take better care of the natural world.

———•●•———

An inspiring story about an extraordinary ecologist that has changed the world for wildlife and people.

Ameenah Gurib-Fakim, *biodiversity scientist, entrepreneur and former President of Mauritius*

An amazing man whose exploits have blazed the way for others.

Tim Coles OBE, *Operation Wallacea and Trust founder*

Ian is a good friend of mine, deeply impressed by his intelligence, thoughtfulness, a first class and wide-ranging mind, happy to throw himself into a course of action if he believes it is of long term importance and underpinned by sound ethical principles.

Sir Christopher Wates, *construction, development, philanthropist*

Ian was brilliant to work with in a tricky situation. He had loads of energy, gets stuff done, made decisions, pushed people but does not understand that humans sometime lie to get their way.

Chris Mathias, *entrepreneur, environmentalist, philanthropist*

I have always admired Ian's energy and vision. The Institute founded by Ian Swingland, is a first class scientific and conservation organisation.

Sir Ghillean Prance FRS, *former Director, Royal Botanic Gardens, Kew*

Ian is a leading eclectic campaigning scientist in the world with great scientific integrity and personal passion achieving a considerable eminence in the environmental world.

Robin Hanbury-Tenison OBE, *explorer, former President of Survival International, and Chief Executive of The Countryside Alliance*

Some people have exciting and colourful lives, some people are good story tellers. Ian Swingland does both of these.

John Craig ONZM, *Emeritus Professor of Environmental Management, Auckland, conservation biologist and landscape ecologist*

Ian Swingland has made a huge difference to conservation and training the leaders of tomorrow, forging essential links between conservation and economics. This is how to do it!

Ian Redmond OBE, *ape and elephant specialist and Ambassador, UN Convention on Migratory Species*

The Law of the Wild will interest professional ecologists and amateur enthusiasts; it will appeal to anyone who loves animals and wildlife. It is fascinating, enthralling and worthy of entering the lists of 'can't bear to put it down' titles.

Pat Crawford, *journalist*

For Fiona, Anna and Kieran

Atque inter silvas Academi quaerere verum

The Law
of the Wild

The Law
of the Wild

An Ecologist's Life

Ian R. Swingland

First published in 2020
www.ianswingland.com

A CIP record for this book is available from The British Library

ISBN 978-1-8381855-0-3

Printed by Lightning Source

Cover design: Bob Carling
Typographical design: Bob Carling
www.carling.org.uk

This book is also available in eBook form

Contents

PREFACE

I have resisted writing this book for over 20 years for a very simple reason. I already know the story, so sitting down and writing it all out, making sure all the facts and details are checked, that I have all the evidence about everything I say, seemed a very boring exercise.

Once I got started and digging into the family archives, where everything is stored, I began to uncover memories and facts that I had long forgotten, only a quarter of which are described in this book; nearly all concerning animals of different sorts and behaviour.

I've always been my own worst critic, ignoring nearly everybody else's views which normally told me more about them than me. I have been very specific about what I've written in this book as until now my work and publications have been solely about science and research. So to turn my hand to retrospective narrative has been quite difficult and using editors did not help as I began to lose my own 'voice'.

Being a zoologist was not something I aimed at as all the jobs involving zoology, such as veterinary surgery (dealing with people!), museum taxonomist (boring!), or university don (I was not good enough!), were I thought either beyond my reach or something I did not want to do. So becoming an academic was not something I set my sights on but it enabled me to pursue what I loved – animals.

Biodiversity conservation was at the heart of all my work and trying to make the world a better place both for animals and plants and humans. What I hadn't bargained for was all the politics and skulduggery that humans inject into something that was beautiful, fascinating and innocent, the wild world of nature; that disease nearly killed me in 1999. As I became well-known I was sometimes taken for a 'ride', my name used for others' purposes without my knowing, or my ideas hijacked by others; an innate naïveté and occasionally misplaced belief in others' honesty and integrity was my bugbear.

I have many true friends and former lovers worldwide who have been major factors in my life, all of whom I respect for their accomplishments and contributions not only in my life but in others'. Two of my family thought of a title, *Darwin's Darling Chain*. Of course this is an anagram which I never solved after being challenged by them, being misled by thoughts of the famous zoologist and DNA. It's an anagram of Ian Richard Swingland. So enjoy *The Law of the Wild: An Ecologist's Life*.

———————— ● ● ————————

I want to thank: Mary Geddie, John Creedy, Barry Goater, Brian Chirgwin, Dafydd Evans, Ronald Muwenda Mutebi II, Nigel Leader-Williams, Bob

Smith, Jim and Bea Lockie, Richard Griffiths, Humphrey Lyttelton, Edward Whitley, Alan Bevan, Norman Crossland, Jim Thompson, Marshall Halliday, Tony Russo, Peter de Groot, Hemanta Mishra, Iain Colquhoun, Paul Racey, the Ghurkas, Sven Ullring, Stanley Johnson, Charles Taylor, George Dunnet, John, Jean and Marion Baird, John Hanks, Gunnar Sønsteby, Berit Viig, Kate Lessells, Sue Dawes, Kimberly Leighton, Peter Moss, Bruce Carrad, Bent Juel-Jensen, Frank Ansell, Cecil Evans, John Smith, Brian Child, Peter Scott, David Attenborough, Kenneth Kaunda, Fred Topliffe, Astrid and Sven Viig, Angus Bellairs, Malcolm Coe, Alan Newsome, Peter Fullagar, Christopher Perrins, Mark Stanley-Price, Robin Buxton, Robin Lines, Joan England, Malcolm Potts, Harry Charles, Bernard Legae, David Griffin, Len Mole, George and Pat Zug, Carl Gans, Ron Nussbaum, Kantilal Jivan Shah, Peter Nicholls, David Stoddart, David Lloyd, Gerald Durrell, Lee Durrell, Jeremy Mallinson, David Waugh, Robin Hanbury-Tenison, Nigel Winser, John Craig, Miles Barton, Lindsay Saunders, Mike Walkey, Ian Stone, Bob Carling, Earl of Cranbrook, Crackers, Rosa, Neptune, Buster, Dillon Ripley, Paul Ehrlich, Unga Paren, Nyapun, Tony Jack, Ilkka Gobius, Chris Matthias, Clare Rewcastle Brown, Niu Zhiming, Richard Dawkins, Ghillean and Anne Prance, Cairns Nelson, Jonathan Lennon, Chris Walton, Charles Bott, Richard Sandor, John Ashworth, Colin Spedding, David Stubbs, Lynda Lee Potter, Marc Cheylan, Les Mayonnaise, Paul Greenwood, Terry Coulthard, Craig MacFarland, Gerald Rutter, Dick Southwood, Neil Wates, Jenifer Wates, Chris and Georgie Wates, HE Mohammed Ahmad Al Bowardi, Danny Dempsey, John Kesby, Claudio Ciofi, Robert Worcester, Will Travers, Avis Talbot, Virginia McKenna, Bill Dawson, Mike and Helen Radock, Ibnu Sutowo, Whit Gibbons, Richard and Daisy Fitter, David Ingram, Jackie Datlen, Owen Swingland, Sandy Alexander, John Fairbairn, John Knowles, Walter Wehrmeyer, David Galbraith, Georgina Mace, Vincent Weir, Susanna Paisley-Day, Sheila Bliss, Bob May, Keith Lampard, John Swire, Nicholas Baring, Guy Weston, Jacqueline McGlade, Paul Luetchford, Sandy Bruce Lockhart, Mick and Joan Clout, Richard Meade, Liz Rath, Deborah Dowager Duchess of Devonshire, Robert Barrington, Herschel Post, James Kinyaga, Ian Craig, Whit Johnson, Ameenah Gurib Fakim, Dane Gobin, Richard Phillips, Tahir Qadri, John Wigley, Freddie Chitambo, David Summers, Shaun Russell, Alberto Simonetta, Francesco Dessi Fulgheri, Laura Beani, Nils Stenseth, Peter Gottschalk, John Gummer, John Illman, Chris Brown, Dale and Irma Allen, Ara Monadjem, Sumith Pilapitiya, Lei Guangchun, Pat Crawford, Des Gould, Bill Aylward, Julian Steven and HRH the Prince of Wales.

And finally my parents who encouraged my fascination with animals at whatever cost.

CHAPTER 1

The Nest – A Shunting Yard 1946–1953

Setting the Seal

I was born in November 1946 but the beginning wasn't exactly promising; within six weeks I was half my birth weight and close to death. Pyloric stenosis was not helped by an incompetent GP who didn't get a clue from projectile vomiting in a first-born male child. My parents: two young people with no money emerging from the intelligence service in the worst winter in living memory. (Later I was told the deep, deep snow and icy pavements went on for five months.) Eventually they rushed me up to Barnet General Hospital where I was operated on immediately and spent the next few weeks apparently asleep on my father's chest at night – a first-class human incubator.

"Don't do that Ian" – words that were to become familiar as I stirred the goldfish with my three-legged lead milk horse while looking out at the milkman with his horse and milk float. The milkman's horse had a bag under his tail to catch the dung and another with bran to keep him going at the other end; 'a nosebag'. In the background was the shunting yard at Oakleigh Park North Station, North London where Mallard thundered past daily. Designed by Sir Nigel Gresley, the world famous locomotive engineer, Mallard had achieved a world record for a passenger steam train – 126mph, albeit on a very slight downward incline. I would stand on the station bridge when I was 6 years old as the Mallard and the Flying Scotsman flew past covering me in steam and coal smoke. What fascinated me was the milk horse and how it faithfully – and very precisely followed – the milkman in his daily rounds between houses and was always in exactly the right spot to minimise the man's walking. Compared with the goldfish, here was my first lesson in animal intelligence. (Little was I to know how intelligent goldfish really are. That came twenty years' later.)

We lived in Temple Lodge in North London, a grim block of flats now selling for £250,000 but then Council property. 'No pets allowed' – but I did have my goldfish and the shunting yard to amuse me, along with a Tri-ang 00 gauge railway. The Royal Mail train with a Travelling Post Office coach whizzed around the track and was very special, picking up and dropping the mail bag automatically. My father had used a rug to create scenery to enhance the backdrop.

My Dad – Maurice – was an electrical engineer who had served on North Sea minesweepers as the 'Sparks' – or electrical rating – and had

Express milk float and horse (Courtesy Alan Hare)

been working at Standard Telephones and Cables Ltd (STC), New South-gate in the latter part of the war. He worked on the *'Oboe'* project involving a British aerial blind-bombing targeting – system based on radio tran-sponder technology developed in World War II.

My father regaled me with stories of conflict and war from his time with the North Sea Convoys that had been tasked with supplying Russia – our allies from 1941 to 1945. He also frightened me with his tale of a mine with protuberances near the top called Hertz horns, which triggered the mine to detonate when hitting a ship. As 'Sparks' he knew only too well how mines worked – especially the magnetic varieties. They needed a degauss-ing cable (another British invention) around the hull to stop them from exploding. Normally the crew would line up with .303 Lee–Enfield rifles and aim at the Hertz horns on the surfaced mine, once they bobbed up af-ter the saw-like projections on the sweep wire had cut their mooring cable, with the promise of a double tot of rum for every dead shot. My father still possessed a pipe, rum and huge tins of tobacco from his days in the Navy.

STC was a different kettle of fish altogether but Maurice learnt a lot from his time there, not least how to use his innate ability to be stoic – especially when all the young women baited him. He was an attractive 24-year-old young man who, being something of a 'backroom boy' wasn't particularly worldly-wise. Reflecting on the ladies lifting their dresses when he visited the factory floor – at that time considered very risqué – he told me, "Many didn't wear knickers and I was embarrassed but, looking back, it was no worse than the harmless high jinks of ordinary seamen on board ship."

Numerous electrical gadgets were dropped on Britain in the early stages of the war such as the first magnetic mines accidentally discharged in the mudflats of Shoeburyness in Essex. They were new to the Ministry of Defence, as were many other bits of equipment which exploded, interfered with telecommunications or were listening devices. They needed examining and understanding and my father soon found himself working in the Ministry of Defence for the rest of his life starting, he told me, in a section that was so secret it didn't even have a name. Much later he was appointed as Director, Procurement Executive, Ministry of Defence (D MOD PE), a highly sensitive job where he had to exercise extreme caution.

My paternal grandfather Charles Swingland. Obituary 1941

During my father's tenure as a director at the MOD PE, Harry Houghton, Ethel Gee, Gordon Lonsdale and Morris and Lona Cohen were discovered spying at the Admiralty Underwater Weapons' Establishment and HMS Osprey at Portland, England, where the Royal Navy tested equipment for undersea warfare. John Vassall pinched details of British radar, torpedoes and anti-submarine equipment and Frank Bossard routinely took classified documents for the Soviets, mostly involving missile systems (my father's speciality) and radars. He photographed the documents in his hotel room during the lunch break, returning them the next day. For every packet of photographs delivered, he received £2,000. Today that would be in excess of £38,000. My father said it was a lady's fur coat hanging in Bossard's office, far above his income, that caused suspicion, similarly with Vassall's overspending. They weren't the only ones: Michael John Smith leaked the details of the XN-715 radar fuse for the British WE.177 free-fall nuclear bomb[1].

Other missile systems that came under my father's responsibility were Blue Steel, a British air-launched, rocket-propelled nuclear armed standoff missile, and Firestreak, a passive infrared homing (heat seeking) air-to-air missile, that sidestepped the jet exhaust and exploded near the cockpit as the pilot was more valuable than the plane. Dad took me to see the annual Farnborough International Airshow, a trade exhibition for the aerospace and defence industries, and while I looked into the Firestreak's eight-faceted conical 'pencil' nose I could see it tracking the lighted cigarette of someone 500 yards away! The nose was made by Barr & Stroud in Glasgow who only served water at lunch! His other big involvement was Blue Streak, a British Intermediate-range ballistic missile (IRBM) to replace Vulcan bombers, and later the first stage of the Europa satellite launch vehicle by what is now the European Space Agency. Blue Streak's stages were made by different European partners (with Rolls Royce making the first stage and not coming to the co-ordination meetings as their *stage always worked*). It was assembled at Spadeadam, Cumbria and test fired at Woomera Test Range, Australia. A message from Dad to take apart a Blue Streak in Cumbria and ship to Woomera was misunderstood. The word 'disassemble' was used in the telex and instead of shipping the stages they took the whole thing apart!

A typical trait of my family; don't blab. Remember that endless debate or conversation about a topic or problem often makes things worse. Years and years' later I reflect that this may be what's wrong with politicians who talk endlessly – solve little – and precipitate wars. They then prognosticate that conflicts can only be resolved through political solutions; a rhetorical circle. Politicians start the wars, millions are killed in some conflicts and politicians then say it is only them who can stop them! Talking did not stop World War I nor World War II and, sadly, still doesn't stop today's ongoing conflicts such as those occurring in the Middle East.

My mother, Flora, was small and very spoilt by her parents. She grew up to become an extremely tough, determined and intelligent woman – a warrior while my father Maurice was a gentle, handsome, tall man who wasn't up to my mother's intellectual abilities and no match for her unforgiving nature. They met over a game of ping-pong at the Barnet Young Conservatives' Club where young people went as one of the few places to meet in 1945. For the rest of their lives neither was interested in, or com-

---

1   West, N. 2009. *The A to Z of British Intelligence.* London: Scarecrow Press.

mented on, politics but their relationship was certainly a sometimes acrimonious and bitter 'game of ping-pong' with me squashed in the middle, the ball that didn't always bounce.

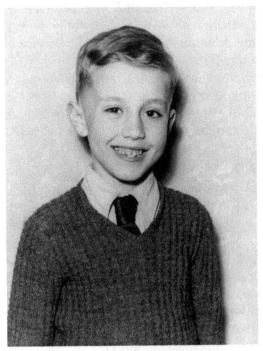

Ian Swingland 6 years old 1952

Thinking back, when I was growing up I could have done with a sibling or two to help me with my parents as their conflicts often terrified me. So I amused myself when young with breeding three-spined sticklebacks from Totteridge Long Pond. I fed them daphnia from the Orange Tree pub pond in Totteridge Green. I had the joys of Dollis Brook – it ran the length of my grandparent's road – to mess around in too, although it was never as full of wildlife as the other ponds.

I also kept black garden ants in a home-made formicarium I fashioned from plaster of Paris with a thin depression, one ant thick, which I covered in actinic glass to ease observation (the ants thought it was dark). It was essential to catch the queen when digging up an ant's nest so I dug up the whole area threw it into a light-coloured bucket of water and scooped up the ants as they floated to the surface with a tea strainer. They would be unconscious by now and I would plonk the sodden mass of ants in the formicarium, smoothing out the pile of bodies, and replace the glass. In 20 minutes they would be running around and with luck I'd have a queen.

The legs (6-inch nails) of the mini-table, the foraging area, on which my ant colony rested, sat in DDT powder so the ants couldn't escape. I also had many other invertebrates, like stick insects which are parthenogenetic and laid eggs that hatched, plus a miscellany of gadgets like an under-floor system of detecting movement (home-made pressure switches) through-out the Temple Lodge flat.

Sixty five years later I have Mediterranean harvester ant colonies on my desk as I write. The species continues to fascinate with its soldiers, its mid-size morphs that make ant bread from canary seed and a very tiny morph that runs around and helps. All controlled by a massive Queen.

Special Operations Executive

My father's secret work was matched by my mother's. She was also a 'spook' and worked in the Special Operations Executive (SOE), created when Churchill wanted an outfit to "set Europe ablaze". She had been recruited at the age of 19 from Mrs Hoster's Secretarial College, famed for "turning out gels for the establishment", opposite the Natural History Museum in London – how young to take on so much responsibility. From then on she was based in SOE's Baker Street headquarters working for Colonel James Butters and receiving decoded signals carried by dispatch riders from Bletchley Park. The messages required the help of SOE's multi-linguists to decipher and translate them into understandable reports.

Mother had to be careful of fifth columnists who were abroad in London during the war and were famously known to target those working in SOE. She was also obliged to secure the platen roller of her typewriter in a safe each night since what she had written could be deciphered. After the war she was invited to join MI6 but had to decline as she was pregnant with me. For the rest of her life she was silent about her experiences and involvements and only slightly opened up in old age. She did, on one occasion, mention The Thatched Barn which had been built in 1932 as a roadhouse for the new A1 Barnet bypass. I passed it every day in a coach from High Barnet tube station to Haberdashers' Aske's school in Elstree. Apparently, for six years The Barn was secretly used by the SOE to develop gadgetry, explosives and disguises. Prior to the SOE taking over the building in 1942, the film studios at nearby Elstree used it. Mother was sworn to secrecy and never even told her parents where she went nor what she did during the war and they, in true British spirit, never asked.

Flora (as Miss Fernie) was present at one of the last meetings the SOE held in the Council Room and took the minutes of the Working Committee on 5th June 1945[2] which effectively founded the Special Forces Club. (It

---

2 Original memo of SOE meeting, London, which Flora Fernie attended.

MINUTES
of the TENTH MEETING of the WORKING COMMITTEE
held at 16.00 hours on the 5th June, 1946,
in the Council Room 64 Baker Street.

Chairman: Lt. Col. Barcroft.

Present: G/Capt. Redding   In attendance: Miss Fernie

Major Boughton Leigh

Major Snow

Major Turner

Major Nipe

Major Boxshall

S/Ldr. Park

1.   Major Sherren and Major McKenzie were unavoidably absent.

2.   The General stated that, although he was of the opinion that the Committee had done all that was possible, the membership could be greatly increased if more encouragement was forthcoming from the senior officers.

India is not, at the moment, in a state of mind to be approached on the subject of Post-War Association.

Officers leaving London H.Q. should be reapproached and encouraged to join.

As regards practical means of furthering the needs of the Association he suggested; firstly, that he would talk to the Council and tell them where their duty lay; secondly, to talk to the Monthly Meeting on the same lines and thirdly to have the Committee's suggestions.

The General will speak of the matter of support from the senior officers for the Association at the next Monthly Meeting.

3.   Distribution of another circular.

It was unanimously agreed that a follow-up circular,

signed by Major General Gubbins, should be sent out direct to overseas Missions. It was agreed that enrolment forms should be attached to outposting papers.

4. Premises for the Association

It was agreed that something tangible should be offered (especially for the officers in the Far Eastern H.Q.) to increase the membership of the Association. After considerable discussion it was decided that a flat in Chiltern Court under the stewardship of Mr. and Mrs. O'Connor might be a suitable start. Major Boughton Leigh agreed to enquire into this possibility.

As an alternative it was agreed that G/Capt. Redding would enquire into the possibilities of accommodation at some Licenced Establishment.

5. Constitution of the Council

It was decided that the Committee should select a Council of, say, eight or ten members (four to constitute a quorum) and a Chairman. Some of the nominated members of the Council should, if possible, have already left S.O.E. This Council should be established before Major General Gubbins sent out the proposed Circular.

6. Appointment of a new Chairman

Major Mips accepted the position of Acting Chairman, pending the appointment of the Chairman referred to above.

7. Appointment of Treasurer and Secretary

It was agreed that Capt. Nunes be approached as regards the position of Treasurer and Secretary.

Minutes 10th meeting Working Committee 5th June 1945 SOE Council Room.
In attendance Flora Swingland (née Fernie).
Founding Special Forces Club

still exists today and I was a member but, as I now rarely visit London, I resigned from this Club and also from the Athenaeum.)

Major-General Sir Colin Gubbins KCMG, DSO, MC was the focal point of the Special Operations Executive. He also set up secret Auxiliary Units, a commando force based around the Home Guard, to operate on the flanks and to the rear of German lines if the United Kingdom was invaded during Germany's planned invasion code-named Operation Sea Lion. My mother met him on many occasions and said he was the most focused, analytical and strategically-minded person she ever met. He remained in touch with people in many of the countries he had helped to liberate and supported the Special Forces Club which he had co-founded. His oldest son, Michael, served in the SOE and was killed at Anzio in 1944. Major-General Gubbins died on the Isle of Harris in the Hebrides.

My mother also knew Maurice Buckmaster who was in charge of F section and did not recognise that some Resistance networks had been compromised for over a year near the end of the war, and had sent many agents to their arrests and deaths. It was extremely difficult to determine who was a collaborator or traitor, and who was not, and what had been compromised. In France this was particularly difficult as many citizens during the war believed that the Germans ran the country better than their previous governments according to my mother! Vera Atkins[3], Romanian in origin, recruited, trained and watched over the legendary British secret agents who parachuted into France to sabotage the Nazis during World War II. She was also Buckmaster's personal assistant.

It was said that Ian Fleming used Buckmaster as his model for M and Vera Atkins as Miss Moneypenny. Vera Atkins stood on the runway to watch every take-off of those who were going to parachute into France. After the

3 She is the basis for the character of Hilda Pierce played brilliantly by Ellie Haddington in ITV's *Foyle's War*.

war, when the tally of lost agents turned out to be a little worse than 1 in 4, Ms Atkins pushed to be assigned to investigate each of them and brought their surviving killers to war crimes trials. The confessions she obtained from the Auschwitz commandant, Rudolf Hoess, were used as evidence at the Nuremberg Trials. She always shuddered at Hoess's reaction to her suggestion that 1.5 million people had been killed in Auschwitz. "Oh no," he said as if offended, "it was 2,345,000." Four of the agents Vera Atkins controlled were captured. Violette Szabo GC, who was tortured and shot, became famous. Her bronze bust is the official SOE memorial opposite Lambeth Palace. Odette Sansom GC MBE who refused to

Fernie family and friends. Ladies row L to R Agnes 2nd, Flora (last), Men's row Jock (last right nearest pillar), Bill (2nd back row centre). Middelkerke August 1936. Agnes Fernie, my maternal grandmother

talk even when the Gestapo pulled out her toenails one by one – survived. Vera Atkins settled in a cottage left her by an aunt at Winchelsea from where she could see France.

Hitler said, "When I get to London I am not sure who I shall hang first – Churchill or that man Buckmaster."[4] My mother told me that General Charles de Gaulle had insisted that the SOE did not recruit French citizens, whilst also demanding that he control the agents

Agnes Fernie, my maternal grandmother

4   Beryl E. Escott, *The Heroines of SOE: F Section, Britain's Secret Women in France*. The History Press, 2010.

operating in France. His protestations were ignored. He returned to France after the war, triumphantly walking down the Champs-Élysées but only after insisting yet again that all foreign agents should have left the country to ensure the fiction that the French Resistance alone helped win the war. Most of those selected were half-French British citizens. One agent[5], recounting how she had reacted to a male agent falling in love – again – said, "Oh, the bloody English! We never have bother of this sort with the French. They just copulate and that is that."

Golf

My mother had fallen out with her father and her brother for complex reasons. She snobbishly looked down on her father, John ('Jock') Sinclair Fernie, because in those days, golf professionals were far down the social scale – very unlike the status they enjoy today. When I asked my mother about the fallout she said, "It was because he stopped me from joining the Spanish Civil War on the Republican's side. Fascism can be on the extreme right or extreme left of politics and it was this kind of bullying and dictatorship which I objected to. Maybe that's why I ended up in SOE although it was father who directed me to Mrs Hoster's Secretarial Training College so I could earn my living during the war. Maybe my sentiments against bullying and being pushed around caused the SOE recruiters to aim at me."

Jock had provided for his family at 12 Marriott Road, Barnet close to Old Fold Manor golf course where he was the professional. They had a maid and there was enough money to allow my grandmother, Agnes, to spend a lot, especially on her daughter Flora, whom she spoilt. Their son, Bill, was promoted Major at Monte Cassino in 1944 and later became one of the first actuaries. From early days he had to fend for himself and I think

---

5   Millar, G. *Road to Resistance.* Little, Brown, 1980.

always resented how much was lavished on my mother.

Jock came from a dynasty of golf professionals and course architects who had won The Open Championship and designed many golf courses. He enlisted with the Northumberland Fusiliers in WWI in 1914 and was commissioned as a Lieutenant with the King's Own Yorkshire Light Infantry in January 1918. To deter the Germans he sent out Ghurkha patrols that crept up behind enemy sentries and lopped off their ears with their kukris.

Returning in early morning, the Ghurkhas received a reward for each ear they threw on the duty officer's table. Later that same year my grandfather was injured and spent time in a Liverpool hospital with shrapnel wounds.

The South Moor course (Durham) was founded in 1923 and consisted of just 3 holes cut on the west side; a further three holes were added later that year on the north side of the main drive. The club engaged the services of Jock to further develop

Shrapnel 16 September 1918 right elbow
(British sixpence=US penny)

Captain J. S. Fernie, KOYLI 1941

POST OFFICE TELEGRAPHS.

N.B.—This Form must accompany any inquiry respecting this Telegram.

If the Receiver of an Inland Telegram doubts its accuracy, he may have it repeated on payment of half the amount originally paid for its transmission, any fraction of 1d. less than ½d. being reckoned as ½d.; and if it be found that there was any inaccuracy, the amount paid for repetition will be refunded. Special conditions are applicable to the repetition of Foreign Telegrams.

Office of Origin and Service Instructions.

19th of 8·35 Boulougne SM   Handed in at } 10·36 a.m.   Received here at } 3-0 P.m.

TO { Fernie Ryton-on-Tyne Durham England.

Wounds slight England shortly writing

love

Fernie

POST OFFICE TELEGRAPHS.

N.B.—This Form must accompany any inquiry respecting this Telegram.

If the Receiver of an Inland Telegram doubts its accuracy, he may have it repeated on payment of half the amount originally paid for its transmission, any fraction of 1d. less than ½d. being reckoned as ½d.; and if it be found that there was any inaccuracy, the amount paid for repetition will be refunded. Special conditions are applicable to the repetition of Foreign Telegrams.

Office of Origin and Service Instructions.

York OHMS.   Handed in at } 12·50   Received here at } 1-55 x.

TO { Mrs A S Fernie Ryton on Tyne Co Durham

KOY 17 aaa regret 2nd Lieut J S
Fernie 4 KOYLI was admitted 14
General Hospital Winereux 15·9·18.
Gun shot wound right arm slight
attesto York

Official Telegrams alerting Agnes Fernie to
injury 16th and 19th September 1918

Letters 16th October 1918 to his wife Agnes and 16th October 1918 to Bill his son on his 2nd birthday from Croxteth Hall Hospital, Liverpool

GOLF CLUBS AND GOLFERS

THE OLD FOLD MANOR G.C.—By "MEL"

One of the best judges of golf clubs as they ought to be (Mr. G. W. Stevens) has said that he considers it an achievement to hit upon a golf club that is "above the average," and he considers that he has done so in the case of the Old Fold G.C. which is at Hadley Green, Barnet, Herts, and has for its President, Lord Strafford, and amongst its members the most proper gentlemen whom "Mel" has collected in his excellent pictures. It is a club well within reach of the harassed city worker and one of its best attributes is the excellence of the turf and the subsoil, the latter being principally gravel and sand so is never impossible even after one of those heavy downpours for which this land was at one time famous

107

Characters of the Old Fold Manor Golf Club, Barnet.
July 1934 *Tatler* (Grandfather bottom right.)

the course into an 18-hole course measuring 4995 yards. The course, opened in 1923, is situated between the villages of Craghead and Stanley and was owned by the National Coal Board and British Coal until 1995 when it was bought by the members for £200,000. Today that looks like the bargain of the century. Jock was no slouch at building golf courses and was considered one of the greatest golf course architects.

In 1924 Jock became the professional at Old Fold Manor, Barnet, North London remaining there until the end of his career. His handicap was 6 under par. He won dozens of competitions and prizes, partnered Edward VIII 1935–1936 and had numerous Dunlop Hole-In-One silver trophies. Any ballgame, he was always the winner and I well remember a full-sized billiard table where I was taught to play snooker using an ivory and inlaid wood cue given Jock by Joe Davis, 15 times world champion at billiards. The table, which required a dozen men to lift being made of solid slate, was used by the family as an air raid shelter during the war. It became a great hiding place for me when the family wanted me to do something I didn't care to do!

Rats were a problem at golf courses and chewed anything like leather, especially if coated with animal oils. Jock live-trapped them and threw them in a box in a shed with food and water. When he was not busy playing golf he used to go into the shed, lock the door, and release the rats. Using a No. 4 wood, a driver, he would practice his driving and only got bitten once – on the thumb.

A very self-contained man, Jock was physically very tough and quiet. He mixed with all kinds of characters from the highest to the lowest in society and

was unmoved by all of them. Jock partnered HRH the Prince of Wales and later when he became Edward VIII before abdicating. Some of the holes on the Old Fold Manor course ran alongside the bottom of people's gardens, including Jock's son's house, and knowing the good-looking Royal was at the course, many women were leaning over the back fence, cooing and waving at him. Jock never forgot the somewhat derogatory reaction this caused from the heir to the throne who was a hedonist and disliked the duties imposed on royalty. A total contrast to the current Royal family, most of whom are genuinely attached to the public and carry out their duties with great sincerity.

One of many friends' drawings from Great Aunt Vi's album Christmas 1915

The Fernies

Violet Fernie, Jock's sister, was a highly intelligent, even remarkable, woman who lived in Penarth, Wales. She went through two husbands; the first was studying to become an ophthalmic optician and she was so bored she did the exams with him. He failed; she passed. Then, after she had become a Liveryman of the Worshipful Company of Spectacle Makers and obtained the Freedom of London, she divorced him. The second husband owned a string of butchers' shops across Wales and died of throat cancer. Violet had a wonderful sense of humour and taught me how to arrange my facial expression to discomfort those riding opposite on the London Underground: a kind of Mona Lisa smile, not quite complete but giving the impression one was slightly unhinged. In 1918, at just 22 years of age, she had become one of the first women to obtain a Bachelor of Arts cum laude from the University of Cardiff. She smoked Du Maurier cigarettes and was a fiend at bridge and poker.

However my great aunt Vi Fernie had a sense of humour:

A SHORT FORM OF SERVICE FOR THE CIVIL SERVICE AND ALL GOVERNMENT

DEPARTMENTS

Not excluding the Co-operative (Soc.) Movement.

PRAYER
        Let us pray,

                O **Lord**, grant that this day we come to no decisions, neither run into any kind of responsibility, but that all our doings may be ordered to establish new departments, for ever and ever, AMEN.

HYMN.
        O Thou who seest all things below,
        Grant that thy servants may go slow,
        That they may study to comply,
        With regulations 'til they die.

        Teach us O Lord to reverence,
        Committees more than common sense,
        Impress our minds and make us plan
        And pass the baby when we can.

        And when the tempter seeks to give
        Us feelings of initiative,
        Or when alone we go too far
        Chastise us with a circular.

        Mid war and tumult, fire and storms,
        Strengthen us we pray with forms,
        Then will thy servants ever be
        A flock of perfect sheep to Thee.

BENEDICTION.

        The peace of Whitehall, which passeth all understanding, preserve your mind in lethargy, your body in inertia, and your soul in coma, now and for evermore,

                AMEN.

A Short Form of Service for the Civil Service
and all Government Departments. ca. 1941

Jock's brothers also served during the WWI, Robert with the Queen's Own Cameron Highlanders and William was awarded the Military Cross. During WWII another brother, Norman, was killed in London during an enemy air raid. Jock also served in the 4th Royal Tank Regiment in WWII but he suffered ill health and had to resign his commission in 1941.

'We are pleased to hear that Sub-Lieut. Wm. Alexander Fernie, second son of Mr and Mrs Fernie, of Stanwell Road, Penarth, has been awarded the Military Cross for conspicuous conduct in France. He is serving with the Royal Naval Division, and has been in France for the past 18 months. He has two brothers serving in H.M. Forces, viz., Lieut. Robert S. Fernie, of the Queen's Own Cameron Highlanders. He has been in the first line trenches for many months and took part in the many big encounters which has of late characterised the fighting on the Western Front. Another brother, John S. Fernie, has been with the Northumberland Fusiliers for the past two years, and is now Signal-Instructor at Clacton-on-Sea. The youngest brother, who is 18 years of age this month, is joining up and is endeavouring to get into the Sutherland Highlanders. A son-in-law has also joined up and Mrs Fernie's brother, who, although 43 years of age, has also enlisted.'

In 1957, when I was 11 years old, my mother overcame the objections of her brother – who held power of attorney – and got her father, Jock, out of the nursing home for Christmas despite the fact that he had had a major stroke which left him almost completely paralysed. My father went to collect him from Barnet, carried him into the house and sat him down in the sitting room. Dad said, "My goodness, he's quite a small chap but he's bloody heavy and still fully muscled." My parents went into the kitchen to prepare the Christmas lunch while I sat with granddad. I was conscious of the fact that, far from watching the television with me – on because I couldn't figure out what to say to him – Jock spent his whole time watching me, unable to move or speak. Tears ran down his cheeks and after we had eaten lunch, little of which he could chew, my father carried him back to the nursing home. He was still crying.

I loved him and Nana (she had died from mitral stenosis in 1955) but I knew he would think it 'soppy' if I showed my feelings as he was a true Scot, fairly stoic and a tough nut but with a rich emotional make up. Some years earlier Jock had walked from his home in 78 Longlands Drive in Totteridge to our house at 30 Chiddingfold, a 15-minute trudge, only for Flora to make Maurice tell him to go away, unprepared to face him herself. Jock died in 1959, aged 69, and left half his estate to me when I reached 25 years old unless his daughter, my mother, was widowed, legally separated or divorced from her husband before that date. The dividend from the investments was to be used for my education or re-invested but, in the event, my father paid for my education and my mother, who felt disinherited, kept the dividend. Jock directed that a main artery be severed before cremation to make sure he was dead; he had seen too many buried alive during WWI.

Jock Fernie and grandson Ian 1948. In uniform 1953

It was against this mixed, interesting and often turbulent background that animals became my best friends. They fascinated me with their behaviour and, as my parents didn't exactly get on, they afforded the companionship I badly needed. Quite early on I realised that observing animals for days and days enables one to learn what they are doing and begin, very gradually, to figure out why.

No. 307

The Coronation of Her Majesty
Queen Elizabeth II
Tuesday, 2nd June, 1953

The bearer _Mrs Y. M. Swingland_

is authorised to proceed to
WAR OFFICE,
Whitehall, S.W.1

G. W. TURNER,
Permanent Under Secretary of State for War

Animals became my best friends

My parents continued to fight each other constantly and I was the one thing that united them, their only child.

As I grew a little older I escaped by breeding animals in the shed at the bottom of the garden. From my hamster breeding income I was able to buy the shed, stock it with foreign finches, build a pond and water-fall and buy a bicycle – plus a kit to build an International Cadet dinghy. Through back-crossing my cream male hamster with females I had developed cream hamsters with a white band across the shoulders. The pet shop in Whetstone offered me six shillings for six hamsters but I discovered that Harrods Zoo would give me six shillings for each hamster (equivalent of £10 today): I had become an entrepreneur!

My private world in my shed and bedroom encouraged me to become highly resilient, nearly immune and capable of handling fear, hurt, and adults' idiocies and idiosyncrasies: a desert island in troubled seas. I used to read all the exciting books by Jim Corbett[6] (by torchlight under the bed clothes with my Pembroke corgi, Crackers) who became famous for tracking down man-eating tigers and leopards many of whom had killed hundreds of lives especially women! He was born and worked in the Indian Himalayan region of Garhwal. Another one who had a lonely childhood, brought up by his widowed mother, but his exploits in tracking down these highly intelligent killers, that often turned him into the hunted, were more exciting than anything. His books were beautifully and simply written and filled with unpatronising love for India and its people. He fought Afghan raiders with his local Kumaon troop on the North West Frontier in 1919, and volunteered to train Chindit jungle soldiers when he was 64

---

6   *Man-eaters of Kumaon, The Man-eating Leopard of Rudraprayag* and many others.

in WWII but never married and retired to Kenya with his sister Maggie in 1947. Another exciting author was J.H. Williams[7], otherwise known as Elephant Bill, who wrote passionately about Burma, elephants and the extraordinary life he led in the forests with the same love that Corbett had for his homeland. They both died in the 1950s.

Animals fascinated me, absorbed me and made me happy. I learnt something new every day and this turned out to be immensely valuable in the career I was to follow. Animals learn from humans and also need a safe haven to which they can retire. They are relatively tolerant and adaptable while pursuing their selfish individual needs. I discovered that animals can sense emotions and the physiological state of humans as well as other animals. Many humans are pretty awful, domineering and deceitful while animals calm human turmoil and enrich life; so much more civilised. Nature is stunningly beautiful. Humankind fails, time and again, to fulfil its potential.

Every day new questions arose; some answers I discovered as a small boy, others it took me much longer to fathom. Why did some animals need to have sex to multiply and others did not? Why did yet others have only one individual reproducing? Although rather shy, and certainly not precocious, I did listen. When adults around me were talking about sleeping together it seemed it meant more than just that but I couldn't work it out, if it was more than just that, how was it they copulated while asleep!

While the sex life of ten-spined sticklebacks is fascinating – as Desmond Morris found out doing his DPhil on homosexuality in sticklebacks at Oxford supervised by Niko Tinbergen – parthenogenetic reproduction or virgin birth is an asexual form of reproduction that, much more recently, has been researched in the Amazon molly[8].

Evolution depends on genetic variability which comes from male and female genes. In parthenogenesis no such combining of parental genes occurs and the assumption is that, without this genetic variability, changing environmental circumstances would cause the ultimate extinction of species.

The genome of the Amazon molly (*Poecilia formosa*), a parthenogenetic fish species, shows little genetic decay and a high degree of diversity. The genetic health of this asexual vertebrate is surprising given the accumulation of genomic damage that is expected to follow from asexual reproduction. In addition to the Amazon molly's usual complement of chromosomes, the cells contain fragments of black molly chromosome. Schartl and

7   Elephant Bill, Bandoola.
8   Clonal polymorphism and high heterozygosity in the celibate genome of the Amazon molly. Wesley C. Warren, Raquel García-Pérez, Manfred Schartl et al. *Nature Ecology & Evolution* (2018).

his team[9] have shown that these fragments contain the gene responsible for the black molly's characteristic dark colour. They have also found that around 5 per cent of wild Amazon mollies carry similar 'microchromosomes', presumably taken up from sperm produced by related species. This may explain how the Amazon molly has avoided extinction.

Similarly with ants: when virgin queens and males take flight during the mating season, it is likely that the queens will be inseminated by the males from the same nest but female (worker) ants in a colony are usually closely related, however, they're not clones, they're sisters. Because of the way their genetics works[10], that means they're on average 75% related to each other (rather than 50% as in human siblings). They're also only 50% related to their mother, and 25% related to their brothers (which are generally rare and don't stay in the colony). With more than one queen, or multiple-matings, worker-relatedness would be lower.

Watching behaviour

Very early on I began to recognise humans and animals desire dominance. The social status of female humans in England seventy years' ago was most often determined by the status of the male partner or husband; women often exercised their concerns and beliefs not directly but through the male. This is mirrored, to a large degree, in the animal world and, even today, in the human world.

In recent times, way beyond the era when men in the UK insisted that their wives did not work, women are far more able to represent themselves and have come to realise that men are fairly superfluous except for the business of reproduction and possibly companionship. Women are still subjugated in some countries, even in places where they do the majority of the work to support the family such as in the rural areas of Africa and in Muslim communities. They suffer many injustices to 'keep them in their place' such as female genital mutilation, exclusion and having to stay apart each month. The irony is that women and female animals invariably have a strong, even controlling, influence on what happens in society and in their empirical or extended families.

The female red-legged golden orb-weaver spider (*Nephila inaurata*) on Aldabra Atoll (where I lived for 2 years) spins webs that are amongst the strongest known, so much so they are capable of enveloping a human;

---

9 Incorporation of subgenomic amounts of DNA as compensation for mutational load in a gynogenetic fish. Schartl, M., Nanda, I., Schlupp, I., Wilde, B., Epplen, J.T. et al. 1995 *Nature* **373**: 68–71.

10 Haplodiploidy is a sex-determination system in which males develop from unfertilized eggs and are haploid, and females develop from fertilized eggs and are diploid. Haplodiploidy determines the sex in all members of the insect orders Hymenoptera (bees, ants, and wasps).

birds and bats also get caught in the webs. The females are very large and eat their tiny mate while copulating. Female Barbary macaques (*Macaca sylvanus*) are extremely vocal during copulation, for a surprising reason: they are looking to attract other males to mate with because, by copulating with multiple mates, the female decreases the likelihood of paternal infanticide as the males cannot tell which babies are theirs.

One in every 25 human fathers may not be the biological parent of the child they believe to be theirs[11]. The latest studies, ranging in date from 1991 to 1999, quote the following incidence rates of paternity fraud: 4.0% (Canada), 2.8% (France), 1.4% and 1.6% (UK), and 11.8% (Mexico), 0.8% (Switzerland)[12]. Young lions, taking over a female pride, kill all the young to ensure the lionesses come into season and give birth to their progeny. Fostering the offspring of other males is not generally acceptable in the animal world in contrast to humans who remarry and raise each other's offspring although with difficulty. Even female ducks have clockwise-spiralled vaginas, with sharp twists and turns. Since male ducks have counter-clockwise spiralled penises, it was suspected that the evolutionary purpose of the female duck's labyrinth arrangements was to prevent insemination from unwanted suitors. Students at Yale[13] tested this suspicion and confirmed that female ducks can indeed block unwanted penetration.

At a dinner party at my Kent house Flora, my mother, was sitting next to a rather bumptious and egotistical man, the husband of a female guest. He kept pestering my mother having discovered she had worked at SOE. Exasperated, she eventually turned to him and very quietly said, "I was trained in self-defence and there were seven different ways of killing a woman unarmed but nearly twenty for a man." Transfixed by this unimportant – and probably false – information, he gulped and requested a drink. Having realised what my mother was up to, I unearthed a highly decorated bottle of Chinese spirit called Baijiu, a very strong distilled, deadly alcoholic beverage used liberally at Chinese banquets. Usually sorghum-based, it was very cheap at 9p a litre. Sometime later his wife said, "Ian, have you seen Charles?" so I looked under the table and there was nothing there. Thankfully his wife, who was clearly used to this sort of thing, took him off abruptly when he was discovered in the pond in our surrounding woodland. My mother had a devilish grin on her face, and since she looked somewhat like Yoda towards the end of her life, it was obvious she had taken some delight in the effect and couldn't care less about

11   https://www.theguardian.com/society/2005/aug/11/childrensservices.uknews
12   Bellis, M.A., Hughes, K., Hughes, S. & Ashton, J.R. (2005) Measuring paternal discrepancy and its public health consequences. *J Epidemiol Community Health* **59(9)**: 749–54.
13   Brennan, P. L. R., Clark, C. J. & Prum, R. O. 2010 Explosive eversion and functional morphology of the duck penis supports sexual conflict in waterfowl genitalia. *Proc. R. Soc. B* **27**: 1309–1314.

the result. Afterwards her verdict was, "What a ne'er-do-well, do-nothing, layabout, and slob. We avoided the 'gung-ho brave' and 'Hemingways' in the secret services as they were too risky. We preferred those who were frightened, who assiduously assessed the risks, moved behind the scenes, recced the whole situation and then carefully executed the plan ensuring their escape was as near full proof as possible. Intelligence is preferable to macho behaviour or bridge aces poker."

'Fear has its use but cowardice has none.' Mahatma Gandhi

I was often taken to my grandparent's house in Totteridge where my education in animal behaviour was further enriched. My grandmother was large and always cooking (rather like Ma Larkin from H.E. Bates' masterpiece 'The Darling Buds of May' – which he wrote in seven books from one snapshot glimpse of the boisterous Dell family shopping in Kent. The iconic ITV series was to follow). As the only grandchild, I was enveloped by her love and by that of my grandfather until, 'helping' in his workshop, I upset a box of gold dust which he used to sign his much sought-after golf clubs. Even then, his ire did not last for long.

The lawn was perfect and I wasn't allowed to walk on this hallowed turf which grandfather weeded with a special tool called a daisy-grubber that only extracted the weeds. He was an unusually famous professional golfer whose achievements and handmade clubs are still renowned – the last wooden club of his I sold fetched £7000. When I was left with my grandparents, while my mother disentangled herself from SOE, I picked up some of the expressions they used from the Gaelic and Northumberland colloquiums. Although forgotten now, I remember the Gaelic being beautifully smooth with a rhythmical sound. One word my grandfather used sounded like *'gouch'*; he pronounced it with a soft intonation and always applied it to some individual who was being a bit of an idiot. Collins recently defined it as *'to be oblivious of the obvious, to be mentally impaired either naturally or by some substance'*.

My grandmother was also strict and I can remember my stubbornness when refusing to eat some of the meals. These would be presented on the next occasion – the same but in an unheated condition. I left them with the same result, a trait my son Kieran seems to have inherited from Fiona, his mother, and me. Maybe it's a Scots' gene. My classic act of bizarre stubbornness was to eat two jars of Heinz Sandwich Spread which had predictable results. I was able to demolish full English breakfasts smothered in Heinz Ketchup and Lea & Perrins Worcestershire sauce; these have been staples in my diet for 70 years. Heaven!

A lady friend, visiting my grandparent's house in Totteridge, spent the first half hour closely inspecting the fence and putting her finds into a small bag. She went out to her car, a great black hearse-like Rolls Royce which she drove very badly, and, returning indoors, she released her marmosets who scampered about the place eating her 'finds' – lots of spiders. The marmosets always rocketed back to the safety of her stole which was some sort of dead fox. I was entranced and fascinated by her hat which had a very long pheasant feather. I grabbed the feather and pulled her hat off. When admonished, I defended myself by repeating what adults told me – hats were not to be worn indoors. They hadn't told me women were excused this rule!

My first paradise – Ibiza

Flora led the family just as females do in elephants, lions, ants, honeybees, killer whales, bonobos (pygmy chimpanzees), spotted hyenas, and octopi (the female octopus sometimes strangles her mate once the deed is done). Flora organised family holidays to far-flung places including Ibiza where I watched the division of labour between soldiers and workers in harvester ants on Ibiza. That was in 1954, a time when Ibiza had about 10 pre-war taxis, a few kilometres of tarmac and 'coffee' was ground acorn beans. In 1957 I saw dejected leopards in cages at Agip petrol stations in Italy; I was continuing to learn about animals and their often strange relationships with humans.

My first visit to Ibiza in 1954 involved flying from London to Barcelona and then taking an overnight steamer to the island. The main port of Ibiza was the old town where the ship would tie up right next to the main road and the houses. The town square, not far away, had the Café Montesol where they made superb sandwiches and great *double vase de café con leche*. My parents had rented an apartment right beside the harbour and made friends with an old British inhabitant of many years who was a tour company representative and an imbiber of large quantities of gin. I was often sent downstairs to the bar which had fantastic tapas – especially the sausage called sobrassada, a raw, cured sausage from the Balearic Islands made with ground pork, paprika and salt and other spices. I was told by the barman that it was made from chillies and donkeys. I am pretty sure he used the word 'burro' as my Spanish was quickly developing but he could have said something else. I was also warned by my mother not to eat pork as in those days *Taenia solium* (pork tapeworm) was widespread. My main task was to get a large pottery jug filled with gin which cost 9p. Sometimes we visited Santa Eulària des Riu. A favourite haunt of my parents, it was a delightful village with a great restaurant.

Most of the older women on Ibiza wore black skirts down to the ground with a white apron and a black shawl. By stark contrast, the younger women wanted bright colours but, on Sundays, dressed in their best white lacy dresses. This was very similar to those in Las Ramblas, Barcelona in the 1950s who came out of hovels along the street to promenade. In Barcelona their children were amused by vendors selling fortunes involving little finches trained to hop out of their cage and pick a small card from a tray. Another pastime involving crabs tied at the end of a stick allowed the children to get amusement from irritating their parents.

In those days Ibiza was back in the 19th century, as was mainland Spain. Having recently suffered a civil war shortly followed by World War II, everything was basic, cheap and redolent of the real rural Spain. As a result of enjoying more EU investment than any other country, Spain has been dragged into the modern era. Having been through so much, the Ibicencos were positive, cheerful, helpful, tough and fun loving. They had wonderful dogs (the Ibizan hound) which looked just like those models found in Tutankhamun's tomb. Elegant, agile and with pronounced ears, predominantly female packs were better hunters than male packs. Surprisingly, there is no genetic evidence that they descended from the pharaoh's hounds. We also visited Las Salinas where the islanders made salt; great mountains of pinkish-white salt were collected from the salt pans by men whose bare feet looked pickled and dehydrated. Since my ability to speak Spanish was developing quickly, I learnt that after work they would have to bathe their feet in freshwater.

Unsurprisingly Ibiza has been made a UNESCO World Heritage Site because of the interaction between the marine and coastal ecosystems. The dense prairies of oceanic Posidonia (seagrass) support a diversity of marine life. It has archaeological sites at Sa Caleta (settlement) and Puig des Molins (necropolis) testifying to the important role played by the island in the Mediterranean economy, most particularly during the Phoenician-Carthaginian period. The fortified Upper Town (Alta Vila) is an outstanding example of Renaissance military architecture.

We made many excursions to Ibiza where the sea was just 50 feet away from the apartment and I spent countless pleasurable hours exploring the water and snorkelling for octopus. Using a trident, I was taught by the locals to kill them by everting their bodies through the siphon and turning them inside out. I also sailed the International Cadet dinghy I had built, after we had disembarked from the steamer, and which my father, using our Standard Eight 800cc car, towed all the way to Barcelona. Going home, car and boat were hauled onto the steamer for the return journey. Not too surprisingly, we only did that once! Even the flights from London had exceptional moments. An Avianco flight used a pre-war DC 3 which flew at quite low altitudes, skirting round the Pyrenees. As we approached Barcelona airport I noticed a hole between my legs where I could see the sea.

On a later occasion – in 1965 – we were on a BEA flight back from Barcelona to London in a de Havilland Trident that was one of the first to use Autoland. This fully automated landing system was developed at the UK Royal Aircraft Establishment (RAE) with which my father was involved. He casually mentioned it to me as the engines were vacillating alarmingly and the flaps were overly active so that the plane was bucking around in quite dense fog.

On one of our trips our return to the UK was delayed by a day. In those days, without mobile telephones and only a very unreliable Spanish telephone system, it was almost impossible to contact the UK from Ibiza. I was surprised to find a number of smartly suited men in our house in Chiddingfold searching the premises. Neither of my parents reacted with any surprise as there was a concern that we had been kidnapped. Both my mother, from her wartime knowledge, and my father, in his current job in the Ministry of Defence, had sensitive and secret information of some importance. I was banned from visiting a communist country until my parents were dead with the exception of Dubrovnik (for a 1970s conference on herpetology where I met Roger Avery who taught zoology at Bristol University for 37 years) when President Tito was still in charge. He had worked with SOE as leader of the Partisans, often regarded as the most effective resistance movement in occupied Europe.

For me Ibiza was heaven where I got to know an island's natural history, its culture and way of behaving – and I made good friends. I visited it for 11 years and for me it was like the Corfu of Gerald Durrell's childhood days. Sadly, unlike Corfu, it has been ruined and turned into a giant nightclub. The latest news is that Corfu might be going the same way. I haven't visited Ibiza for over 50 years and never will again.

A taste of Asia

I didn't have any siblings because my parents were advised that I was their 'Achilles heel' as children can be used as weapons against their parents. If I was kidnapped or sabotaged in some other way, it could be dangerous, especially given the secret intelligence material known by both parents. Anyway their relationship was so bad that when my mother said to me when I was 8 years old that, "We are staying together for you." I replied, "Please don't. You keep fighting and it scares me."

Not surprisingly, I developed various counter-espionage habits – for example, in my entire world travels I have always double-locked my hard-cased suitcase. I shrink-wrap it-and any other items – to ensure that nothing is slipped in which could cause trouble such as drugs, copies of Playboy or anything that would give authorities an excuse to apprehend me. I usually travel business class on my four favourite airlines who got to know me quite well, especially later in my life when I was travelling hundreds of thousands of miles by air[14] which helped me keep control of my luggage, ensuring nothing untoward happens with customs when I landed. I prefer, if possible, to constrain myself to cabin luggage. More than once I have stuck a hair or two across the joint between the door and the jamb to see if my hotel room has been entered in my absence or invested in mini-alarms only to discover it was only the maid that came in!

This latter idiosyncrasy has proved useful in a number of Asian countries. I was invited by one of my postgraduate students to give a speech at a zoology conference in Bangladesh. He put me in a one star local hotel in Dhaka where I was the only European. This 'innovation' caused a crowd to develop outside my room where the door, that could not be locked, seemed to be open most of the time. Within minutes of closing it yet again, there was a knock and I was asked, "Are you all right Sir, would you like some company?" Behind him were a lot of very good looking young girls in saris. Obviously not content with my negative answer, the hotel porter came back again and asked, "We have some very good boys if you would prefer?" The porter, obviously much concerned with my strange behaviour, returned after half an hour with, in his view, a more superior offer. "Would you like a boy and a girl at half price?" My hosts, on learning of this experience, moved me to a somewhat better hotel.

On this particular trip I flew economy Biman Bangladesh Airlines and all the passengers were Bangladeshis. We stopped at Dubai where all the free seats were taken up by Bangladeshi labourers and servants who are largely responsible for keeping everything going in that city. We were delayed because of immense storms over Dhaka, as a result all the Europeans were herded onto a coach to spend the night at a hotel while all the Bangladeshis were made to stay in the transit lounge. Many Bangladeshis took exception to this; suddenly Emirati men in white *dishdasha* and *ghutrah* appeared with long whips and separated the majority from us, herding them away into a corner of the departure lounge.

The men with whips were clearly used to this kind of performance – it was obviously a regular occurrence. The next morning we had to face the animosity of the crowd, particularly bad for me since I was the only European not in business class. Interestingly, many of the Bangladeshi passengers, all of whom could speak English, encouraged the staff to treat me well and trolley loads of excellent Bangladeshi cuisine served from open dishes arrived. They were embarrassed and engaged me in conversation and did their best to defend me against the barrage of insults which were expressed in Bangla (Bengali) not English. They were probably venting their frustration at being away from home without their families for years

---

14 On British Airways alone I have flown 453,970 miles and spent 908 hours in the air in the last 20 years alone.

– demeaned by the job – and by the treatment they experienced in this foreign country.

Despite the kind concern of my fellow passengers, I still ended up with Dhaka diarrhoea from a salad I had stupidly eaten in the Sheraton hotel just before I boarded the plane home. At one point during the meal I was sure one of the small lettuce leaves moved and I pointed at it with an exclamation. Immediately my hosts covered my sight of the plate with their hands and the offending dish was rapidly removed. Once home I was in a bad way and, since it was the weekend, an acquaintance – the veterinary surgeon from the local zoo, Howletts – came over with very large pills to deal with the problem. He told me this treatment worked on tigers! The pills certainly did: my gut was pretty much paralysed for 10 days.

Twenty years later that same Sheraton Hotel was to become my base as a member of the World Bank Panel of Experts for the Gorai River Restoration Project, a river which supplied all the freshwater into the Sundarban forest from the north. Just before the border with Bangladesh, India had built the Farakka Barrage to divert water to the Hooghly River. This had effectively starved Bangladesh of water for the previous 50 years and resulted in severe siltation at the offtake of the Gorai River from the Ganges leaving it dry through most of the year. Before the project was dropped, $80 million had been spent on expert engineering works at the headwaters of the Gorai River to try to develop structures that would cause scouring currents within the Ganges, cleaning out the Gorai source, as it ran from India due south to the Bay of Bengal. The Gorai runs parallel to the Ganges straight down Bangladesh and into the Sundarban, a World Heritage Site of the largest mangrove forest in the world. With the Gorai dried up, communities have suffered with no water to drink or irrigate crops and no fish. It has made the Sundarban more saline which, along with illegal human settlement and activities, has ensured the deterioration of this habitat, the very last refuge of the Bengal Tiger.

Worldwide I have found that most ordinary rural people, even in the poorest and most corrupt countries, have a sense of the civilities, the difference between right and wrong, and are helpful. In all the countries I have visited there were extremists, those with irrational beliefs and illogical obsessions and those who were dominated by politics particularly in the cities. Nevertheless, as in Bangladesh, there was a strong core of humanity to be found in Abu Dhabi, China, Sri Lanka, Indonesia, New Zealand, Australia, Zambia and the other countries where I have worked. People in the countryside, out in the field, have very pronounced, I suppose, old-fashioned values.

CHAPTER 2

Haberdashers' Prep School 1953–1957

We got a television for the Coronation in 1953 like so many other people which later provided me with an education about animals (Zoo Quest, David Attenborough's first television foray[15] in 1954 with indri and Komodo dragon which I worked on much later). Wildlife and animals in particular became television's main money spinner over the 68 years I have been a TV addict such as Blue Planet II (2017) by Sir David Attenborough watched by 14m. We have been personal acquaintances for well over 30 years and he has brought the world an understanding, appreciation, and delight in the behaviour of animals and plants with superb photography and explanations that anyone would understand. My passion for animals is the same as Gerald Durrell's and even Sir Peter Scott loved birds in particular in his own quiet and somewhat shy way. Sir Peter was the one who got me involved in conservation when he urged me to set up a Specialist Group for tortoises within the Species Survival Commission (IUCN) but it was David who fired me up to make animals the rest of my life along with a maidenly lady Miss Mary Geddie, more of whom later. But David and I were also fascinated with social anthropology which we both studied at University. The explanations for much of what primitive and preliterate peoples do is often inadequately explained by anthropologists whose viewpoint is largely opinion where evolutionary ecology has a much sharper quantitative perspective.

My grandfather gave me a pet bitch Pembroke corgi called Crackers. She was so excited when given to me she piddled all the way up the hall and became my bosom pal. She became my constant companion. When she was 14 years old my father took her to the vet and came back alone with tears in his eyes. Carcinoma.

I started breeding hamsters in a tall condominium-like structure of individual female apartments which I made from an old fruit box with individual doors, and sold the cream and white striped babies at six shillings each (£10 today) to Harrods, rather than six shillings for six locally. I had a

---

15   In 1952, having left the navy, the University of Cambridge graduate began a career in broadcasting at the BBC. Zoo Quest is a series of multi-part nature documentaries broadcast on the BBC Television Service between 1954 and 1963. After studying a postgraduate degree in social anthropology at the London School of Economics, in 1965 David became the controller of BBC Two. Four years later, in 1969, he was promoted to director of programmes, making him responsible for the output of both BBC channels. David has since narrated Wildlife on One (1977 to 2005) and more than 50 episodes of Natural World. He is also famed for his narration on The Blue Planet (2001), Planet Earth (2006), Frozen Planet (2011) and numerous other programmes.

cream male hamster called Jim and by back-crossing I was able to 'manu-facture' this colour form.

The Rare Carpets Department in Harrods had Isfahans, Safavids, Louis XV Savonneries and Barodas laid out on the extensive flooring. The formal-ly suited and tight-lipped assistants glowered as my hamster's skittered sawdust all over them when Dad and I carried this large condominium to the Harrods Zoo next door that cared for my breeding colony when we went on many holidays to far flung places organised by my mother. Offers to clear up the mess were met by, "That's quite all right sirs. No problem at all!", with icy facial expressions belying their vocal niceties.

My grandfather, who smoked an upside-down pipe when playing a round of golf so it didn't go out in the rain and even had a cigarette alight when he went swimming, said, "It'll do those carpets good, tobacco ash is good for Persian carpets", and promptly 'accidently' dropped some on his carpet at home and ground it in with his foot: "That'll get the wine stains out." Years later I was hired by the Harrods' Zoo and asked to dissuade local glitterati from buying exotic pets which could kill them or be killed by these ignoramuses.

We moved when I was still at Prep School in the early 1950s to a new house built by the Leyland Construction Company on the extensive land towards Totteridge. Fred Ingram, the builder, originated from Sussex and took great pride in naming the thoroughfares, cul-de-sacs, crescents and closes after the quirkily named villages and hamlets in that part of the world, with the 'Sussex Ring' parade of local shops comprising the corner-stone of Woodside Park with even a kosher butcher[16]. Everyone in Chid-dingfold was a Jew except us, and I found them very engaging and learnt some Yiddish in self defence and as humour or to swear properly. They found it amusing that the nickname for the road was 'Yiddingfold'. They worked extremely hard in Covent Garden getting up at three in the morn-ing like Mr Landau, or had very tall small black vans which had clothes hanging on either side, but this attracted thieves and one morning all the vans were having a 'powwow' in the centre of the field in the middle of Chiddingfold, empty. Their handbrakes had been released and the robbers had just steered them down the slope to the middle. One of our neigh-bours, the Caplins, was also very industrious and had their house com-pletely covered in marble.

Leaning over the fence one day, watching my father digging trenches for groundwater drains in the garden at number 30, through thick London clay, knee deep in water, Mr Primack observed, "Oy vey, I'd move if there was that much water under my house." At this point my father discov-ered a newt which further disturbed our neighbour who professed to the

---

16   http://woodside-park.com/the-history-of-woodside-park-garden-suburb/

notion that, "The best way to garden is with a cheque book." We were not in such a lucky position and the garden was a precipitous slope so my father, who insisted on having a flat lawn, built an extraordinary wall across the garden using any materials to hand, bricks, tiles, stones, shells, anything that would reduce the cost. I released a Green Lizard (*Lacerta viridis*) behind Dad's wall were it was warm and built a shed and a pond with a waterfall. The shed became a mini zoo where I bred all kinds of animals. Foreign finches like violet-eared waxbills, zebra, Gouldian, Bengalese, Java sparrows, red canaries, cockatiels and other avian wonders where I could maintain a modest temperature during the winter with a cheap heater.

The hamsters were kept on top of the fridge in the kitchen in their condominium. After keeping hamsters and birds when I was young I have become increasingly intolerant of caging animals unless in the most exceptional enclosures for conservation's sake. I remember the Old Lion House at London Zoo especially at feeding time when great hunks of meat were pushed through the bottom of the bars. It seemed to me that the lions weren't particularly hungry just angry.

I commuted to Haberdashers' Aske's Preparatory School in Mill Hill on the little single-decker 251 from Totteridge Green for 6p (also one sown into my trouser waistband for an emergency) and had a wonderful four years of real help and support which inspired me to become a zoologist. The headmaster Roy Lewin, the maths teacher Mr Manning or 'Eggo', and Miss Mary Geddie especially set the mould of what I became; even started a sort of club which everyone joined but, for the life of me, I can't remember its purpose.

Miss Mary Geddie was a tall, elegant, maidenly lady of some erudition and discipline. She inspired me as my natural history teacher and used a small simple microscope which I still have. "Ian, we've looked at lots of things through the microscope like beetles, butterfly wings, soil, and anything else that looked interesting. Come over here and look at this snowflake which I caught on a slide. What do you think?" What I saw was a beautiful geometric pattern which was designed by some mathematician using a laser.

"Now look at this other snowflake I caught." This time it was the same beautiful shape but of a totally different geometric pattern. So I immediately asked the obvious question

"Why are they different?"

She was ready for the perpetual questions of a 9-year-old:

"Most are six-sided shapes, but others are much more complex in their shape. Snowflakes have intricate patterns and designs because of their exposure to different atmospheric conditions falling through the sky, almost all snowflakes are unique."

From that day on Miss Geddie had me trapped into a lifelong love of nature and its amazing diversity. I invited her nearly 30 years later to attend The Royal Society meeting about Aldabra Atoll when I presented the results of my work. I wanted to thank her but I think she was somewhat overwhelmed by the invitation and declined but said, "I'm so very pleased that my modest efforts and your enquiring and perceptive nature and love of natural history has given you a lifelong pursuit. Thank you so much for your invitation but I shall be thinking of you when you stand up and speak."

However Mr Peebles who was our physical education master as well as our maths teacher was of a different disposition. His idea of discipline, when we laboured silently over maths questions so he didn't have to teach, was to put a large lump of plasticine on the end of a foot-long ruler and anyone talking during the maths lesson was invited to come up and put their nose on his desk so he could hit them on the back of the head with his home-made truncheon. His gym classes were similarly sadistic and I can well remember a boy who was fat called John Stern being made to climb down the inside of the wall bars, between them and the wall, for some minor infringement if any. I was appalled at the inequity and pointless cruelty of humiliating John who I liked and ached to save him. He got stuck, much to Peebles' embarrassment.

Miss Wozencroft stood out in my memory as someone who made me learn in the first form all of my times tables up to 12 when I first joined the prep school. She had a times table on the wall for each of us with 12 columns where she stuck stars each time we succeeded faultlessly in repeating out loud the times table from 1 to 12. I shared a desk with Colin Blessley who had a trick of being able to lick snot on his top lip when he had a cold as like me he never had a handkerchief but I could never copy him. He became the President of the Old Haberdashers' Association. Roy Lewin, the headmaster, was wonderful and my four years at Haberdashers' Prep School was exceptional as I liked everybody there with one exception, Mr Peebles. But then there was Eggo, whose head was completely bald, and perfectly egg shaped, the 4th-form master who showed a more sophisticated form of discipline in making maths fun by solving everyday questions of 10-year-olds. He always used a sharpened pencil for his work and wielded a penknife with great skill.

I became School Vice Captain and was House Captain of St George's 1957–1958 according to *The Skylark*, the Hampstead School's magazine while also playing Lotus Bud in a production of The Hungry Tiger. I was also selected to attend the opening of Haberdashers Hall in June 1956. I failed the 11+, mainly because I couldn't find a given name quickly enough in the massive London telephone directory, which would have got me into

Queen Elizabeth's Boys School Barnet but retrospectively relieved that I carried on in the Haberdashers' Main School (means tested in those days with the Company using Direct Grant to subsidise what my parents could contribute) using trolleybuses 651/660 from Tally Ho Finchley to Westbere Road, Hampstead.

Assorted badges given to me over 60 years. The Preparatory School ones are red. The enamel fracture in the House Captain badge was caused by crashing into another pupil

CHAPTER 3

Haberdashers' the Main School
1957–1965

Hampstead

The Main School in Westbere Road was a forbidding 19th-century building with desks in pairs with bench seats, ink wells, and the engravings of tortured youth to inspire. I can remember firing ink bombs onto the ceiling so they dripped and using blotting paper inside shoes to assist fainting in morning assembly but I was never sure if it worked.

Playing in a rugby team was tricky as my eyesight deteriorated since I began tackling my own side so I was guided to rowing where I didn't need to see but did not have the muscular bulk of my crewmates who were well-built being much older and Tarzans, although I did have the skill. I was put in position 4 normally occupied by the most powerful and heaviest rowers, colloquially known as the Fuel Tank, Engine Room, Power House or Meat Wagon. It was an especially long haul to the rowing club on the Thames by Green Line when we all moved to Aldenham Hertfordshire in 1961 and breaking the ice in winter with embedded drowned rats was part of the rigours of the sport. Haberdashers' competed in Schools' Head of the River Race from Mortlake. Needless to say it was not long before the strain made me feel ill and I ended up with tachycardia in St Thomas' Hospital. This unfortunate accident coloured my remaining time in the school. Rowing ceased at Haberdashers' sometime later. I can remember playing Eton Fives with Nick Rose, the brother of Steven Rose a professor at the Open University, which is a most eccentric game played in a court somewhat like a squash court but with a buttress, and two levels, and no bats but reinforced gloves to hit the ball.

Elstree, Hertfordshire

Getting to the new school meant taking the tube from Totteridge and then coaches from Barnet. My mother, who was bursar of the Queen Elisabeth's Girls School Barnet (QEGGS) right beside the coach stop, having left SOE/MI6, liked me to drop by in my boater causing derision from the daunting and clever girls. However the boater was useful military hardware and I was handy at using its stiff brim like Oddjob at the golf club in 'Goldfinger'.

I can remember that we seemed to be forever changing clothes and our shoes not just for sport but in everyday wear. Black shoes outdoors, brown shoes indoors and boots or shoes for rugby, squash, rowing and cricket. At one point I can remember waistcoats were required, and certainly uniforms for every occasion including the CCF. The Combined Cadet Force (CCF) was entertaining for a bit. The sergeant major was a sixth former called 'Red' Butchart who was very smart and spent his spare time being a session's drummer in recording studios where he could no doubt earn substantial 'pocket money'.

From 1957 to 1964 my mother was the bursar at Queen Elizabeth's Girls Grammar School and then went on to teach at the Holborn College of Law, Languages and Commerce which turned into the Polytechnic of Central London and is now the University of Westminster. Helen Moser wrote from Germany where she settled about knowing my mother at the girl's school and then later at Holborn: "I hope you don't mind me writing, but I just wanted to tell you how much we liked your mother. What a great teacher she was. She was a truly remarkable woman. I have never regretted my commercial training and probably earned more money with that

Haberdashers' Aske's School, Westbere Road, Hampstead circa 1958.
Front row David Shemuel, Vijay Singh and Shulman. Second row behind Shemuel is me.
The desks were deeply carved, opening lids, bench seats, with inset ink wells, useful for anything
except writing

than with my degree. I remember groups of girls from QEGGS, including me, being taken by coach to Haberdashers' for social evenings from 1962 to 1964. We were supposed to dance and socialise, but I found the atmosphere rather strained and awkward – clammy hands and stilted conversation on both sides. I suppose they thought that as there were no males at QEGGS in those days with the exception of an elderly and toothless caretaker (no risk there!) they might be wise to let us get used to the opposite sex under supervision!" She is absolutely right on all counts especially the artificial socialising sessions amongst a lot of randy boys and tentative girls.

One sport I did enjoy was sailing on the Rickmansworth Reservoir. My eyesight was no deterrent although my spectacles had to be tied at the back of my head since we capsized on occasion. The drive down the side of number 30 Chiddingfold was too narrow for a car yet it had a garage at the end which I used to build a small sailing dinghy, an international Cadet originally designed by Jack Holt in 1947 who also designed the Merlin Rocket owned by the school. The Rocket was beautiful, with rolled decks; carvel-built in mahogany marine plywood with Elvstrom self-balers, all varnished, and went like the 'bats out of hell' often with the crew on a trapeze. It made up for being sidelined from sport although Rickmansworth Reservoir was too small for such a thoroughbred.

I really enjoyed classes in Zoology taught by Mr John Creedy which were always interesting and involved dissecting real animals to learn how nature worked. Our religious instruction teacher nicknamed Spike often forgot to secure his flies. So we couldn't resist playing jokes on him; we used to dangle rats guts tied together down to the classroom windows where he was teaching. Botany classes were also riveting and Barry Goater was an inspiration. I can remember a field trip that we took with him to the Cairngorms which was great fun and led without question to my making such forays to far-flung and exotic places throughout my life. I can remember one boy called Peter de Boer who was well over 6 feet and was unable to place his feet accurately on the ground and frequently put them in potholes in the path, poor lad! Another memorable field trip was to the Norfolk Broads where we sailed around, or should I say mucked around, in boats. Led by Mr Dudderidge, I spent some time together with a friend called Shapiro (now a GP) convincing another that the word connoisseur was pronounced 'conossa'.

My performance at Mathematics was the worst and caused my parents in panic to hire a private tutor in the form of Wilf Hewitt who was in fact the Haberdashers' master in charge of Strouts which was my House. He was an excellent teacher but I found trying to learn mathematics in abstract on my weekly visits to Finchley, where he lived, driven there by my mother, rather than applied to real life problems, very boring. I quite enjoyed Physics although the master who was also my form master professed the opinion in my last report that, "Ian has reached the limit of his academic potential." It is curious how such verdicts are arrived at since it could have stopped my career in zoology and ecology at that point.

I know little of his background but it's another example of having to survive teachers by adamantly ploughing your own furrow, a belief in yourself driven by a passion for a subject, and Haberdashers' own propensity for being impressed by precocious boys, many of whom achieved far less than us middle rankers later in life. Another plank was laid in my psychology 'helping the underdog' and his concerns for my potential also resulted in my efforts while involved in continuing education at Kent University to open universities nationally to older unqualified students of any age without O- or A-levels; a program now called Access which allows people without traditional qualifications to gain entry and study at university. It also meant that I supported Oxford in the annual boat race as they kept losing against Cambridge, and as soon as they started winning I changed sides.

My time at Haberdashers' Aske's was a mixture of inspiration, basic biology, hierarchies, control, uniformity, aggression, bullying, reciprocal altruism, ignorance, privilege, badges, perception, *Brave New World*, rules, misconception, imperfect evolution, emotional support, and the beginnings of an understanding of how the world of animals and humans were not that far apart.

All animal societies can provide examples of precisely the same aspects of their communities as I observed in Haberdashers' Aske's; for example, the wall that divided the adjacent Boys' School from the Girls' School had a shiny top improved by boarders. Neither School has boarders any longer!

History is often repainted through ignorance or privilege or the need for hierarchical control. Robert Aske who died in 1689, a dealer in raw silk and a Freeman of the Haberdashers Company, bought a piece of land within one mile of The City upon which was to be built a 'hospital' (almshouses) for 20 poor members of the Company and a school for 20 sons of poor Freemen of the Company. The remaining cash was left to form the Haberdashers' Aske's Foundation, of which the Company is Trustee. An almshouse and school, Haberdashers' Aske's Boys' School, were built on 21 acres in Hoxton by 1692 to a design by Robert Hooke where both my father Maurice and Uncle Owen studied. A further 1,500 acres (6 km²) in Kent were acquired to provide an annual income.

Newbrough Swingland Snr, one of my forebears who had escaped from the Low Countries as a Protestant against the Catholic hegemony, had become the largest cork merchant in England at 10 Rood Lane in the City of London, now the 'Walkie-Talkie' building. He was successful enough

Expedition to the Cairngorms. Barry Goater (extreme right), Peter de Boer (the tallest) and I'm the one with spectacles

to provide religious silverware for his local church St Margaret Pattens, one of the City's guild churches, further down the Lane that are now kept in the Victoria and Albert Museum. Newbrough undoubtedly must have been well established for in 1744 he presented to the Church a silver chalice and a silver paten in a red morocco case inscribed on the chalice, "The gift of Newbrough Swingland, Parish Clerk St Margret Pattens 1744", and on the paten, "The gift of Newbrough Swing land, Parish Clerk 1744". These gifts could still be seen at the church in 1939 but I understand they are now in the V&A Museum.

He was also a Freeman of the Haberdashers Company like Robert Aske. They both had this vision of the company subsidising the best education for boys from families who could not afford the cost. John Wigley's history[17] of the Haberdashers' Aske's Boys School is an excellent compendium of the facts and activities of the school from the very beginning until 2007.

I was a beneficiary of this philosophy since my parents didn't earn much between 1953 and 1965, and could only afford a Standard 8 800cc car bought during the Suez Crisis in 1956 when petrol was extremely expensive! They paid Haberdashers' as much as they could and the company bore the rest of the cost. This policy is one that I have carried on through all the students I have helped and was happy to select the best and then worry about the money afterwards. Today the school is one of the best in Britain and attracts people from across the world who arrive for their interviews in Rolls-Royces and Bentleys. They of course can afford any fees and do not require the Company's largesse. Thankfully there has been a

17   Wrigley, J. (2007) *Serve and Obey. The Story of the Haberdashers' Aske's Boys' School*. James and James, London.

world class headmaster in charge Peter Hamilton who used his discretion in making sure that the best of the poor can be helped. I've had the pleasure of meeting him and he's an enlightened, modern man who reflected what's needed in the world today.

Animal populations invariably have a structure based on hierarchy. Individuals gain perceptions of their position in those hierarchies and indeed the relative dominance or subordinance of another individual. Misconceptions between individuals or communities of animals can lead to death and is a good example of how evolution can fail. Evolution is not perfect which really doesn't matter as selection will function as usual. Larvae can be fed differing foods to achieve differing outcomes described by Aldous Huxley in *Brave New World*. Animals work by rules invariably dictated by genes although the environment influences outcomes.

Aggression is a waste of energy and dangerous since it can lead to death if the individuals do not assess their chances of success accurately. Bullying is also evident in many species, for example, the bonobo chimpanzee use copulation as a means of conflict resolution. Moreover reciprocal altruism has been observed on many occasions when for example two male apes observing an attractive female can cooperate so that while one engages the male partner the other slips in and engages the female. The expectation being that next time around the other male will enjoy some reciprocation.

But I was bored most of my time, exacerbated by being let off games when rowing had put me in St Thomas' Hospital, and so I worked in the Special Service Unit (SSU) tending the incredible gardens and exotic shrubs of the previous owner, Lord Aldenham.

What I really wanted to invest my time in was studying animals, their ecology and behaviour and not Latin, French, Ancient History, Geography, or English although the latter was taught by Simon Stuart a man of exceptional intellect and abilities. He dubbed me with the nickname ' Ironside ' and could be found on occasion teaching Shakespeare, sitting cross-legged on his desk with a chair over his head. He knew that teaching teenagers required their attention and engagement and as I have learnt in my teaching career, it's a performance. After Eton Simon went up to Trinity, Cambridge where he began to deepen his love of English literature and to generate it in others, through his gifts as a teacher. Simon inspired, encouraged and was a great teacher. Simon also loved the environment and the earth. He nearly kidnapped me to the arts and English.

Otto 'Porky' Pask was another memorable character who dressed beautifully over his portly frame, had my full attention and could play honky-tonk and ragtime on a piano. John Carleton was my chemistry teacher and I remember that he used blakeys on his shoes, saving wear and tear on all types of footwear, so he could be heard from some distance away as he approached. This was useful as he was the target of a number of practical jokes such as putting coins in the hubcaps of his new Austin Mini.

There are those who can teach like Simon Stuart and those that cannot. You cannot teach someone to be a good teacher; maybe a better one but not good. Good teachers are born not made. Many will disagree but one of the many tricks I have learnt is that if you engage with humour, like Simon, you engage the audience and they listen. Most valuable when teaching in adult education classes and audiences of varied educational backgrounds and skills, not dissimilar to the students from across the world found in my Institute DICE[18]. School teachers and university lecturers generally have to be survived. As in most professions some are incompetent and put you off a subject you love. The trick is avoidance.

I couldn't see the point of learning something unless it helped towards a goal, e.g. learning statistics without an interesting problem to solve, preferably ecological or behavioural, drove the learning. I made some great friends at school who like me were not the sparkling show-offs but just ordinary pupils. I was also attracted to those who were different and therefore interesting.

My mother observing the group of us remarked, "Ian, you seem to have a lot of friends of every other colour, shape and size rather like the United Nations." I thought this a rather obvious comment since my varied friends were far more engaging than most and also somewhat sidelined by the popular mainstream just like me. "They're much more interesting and fun, Mum, and like me different from the rest." David Shemuel, Georg Haller, and Salatullah Baig Sufi who all enlarged my understanding of Judaism and their practices, how the Swiss live and develop in isolated communities, and how Islam functions, the behavioural diktats, and how Sufism is the phenomenon of mysticism and asceticism within Islam. It became clear to me that they had much in common since Judaism, Swiss culture and Sufism are all ways of living in the environment in which they arose. An evolutionary adaptation by communities to the ecosystem they were born in and not just a religion.

Animals have show-offs in their populations and this behaviour can be used to an advantage or disadvantage. For example male birds of Paradise are famous for their spectacular courtship displays and have evolved the most amazing plumage to dazzle and bewitch likely females. But show-offs can also attract unwanted attention especially from predators and there are many examples where death is the consequence.

Equally human show-offs also attract undue attention which is either deception or valid, and the consequences are unpredictable. Other than the entertainment industry, where show-offs abound, most working in

---

18   https://research.kent.ac.uk/dice/

professions do not have to advertise as their skills and abilities become quickly evident and exceptional humans are in my experience normally quite quiet self-contained individuals. Just like the four or five geniuses I've met in my life; two out of the three who are mathematically extraordinary are Sri Lankan.

Harrods

I was briefly hired by Harrods's Zoo about 1964, while still in the sixth form, and asked to dissuade local glitterati from buying exotic pets which could kill them. I remember a jaguar, leopard, lion and an anaconda all residing in the Kensington and Chelsea area of London.

A Canadian couple who were famous on British television for appearing together on talk shows said to me, "Isn't he wonderful, he matches the furniture and the carpet", as she pointed to her male lion cub. Another, this time an exotic dancer, bought an anaconda, one of the largest snakes in the world capable of giving one a good bite although not poisonous but a good squeeze to death. Her reasoning was, "He's so lovely and impresses the audience which means that I get hired more often. He's really good."

Two young men also bought another male lion cub[19] and they became famous because when the cub grew they took it back to Africa and released it. After some years they returned and their fully grown lion came back to them, recognised them and romped with them. The melanic jaguar and the leopard were acquired by an African multimillionaire who clearly thought they adorned his status.

The problem in this summer job with Harrods was that convincing the new owners took time and involved getting them into your confidence and realising that wild animals grow up, get bigger, and have hormones which could result in them harming their unwitting keepers. The difficulty was that it was the individuals' egos that drove them to acquire such exceptional and beautiful animals. After painting a picture of what might eventually transpire I suggested that perhaps they donate the animal to a zoo which might be a better place for their pets and would be welcomed as in those days even London Zoo was advertising itself as having the largest collection of animals in captivity on earth. The Harrods clients that gave away their animals could visit their pets at any time, not have the responsibility or costs of upkeep, and be welcomed as a generous donor. The anaconda was given away when it squeezed too tight, the jaguar and the leopard frightened the maids, and together with the lion cubs, were either donated or released in the wild.

Most of these animals were captive bred and could not be returned to

---

19   http://www.telegraph.co.uk/finance/newsbysector/retailandconsumer/10564375/
Harrods-pet-department-to-shut-after-nearly-100-years.html

their natural habitat. Semi-domesticated wild animals habituated to humans are dangerous especially when released into the wild. Today London Zoo emulates Jersey Zoo in trying to conserve habitats as well as animals, to put nature back.

The debate was taken up on BBC Radio 4 in a live transmission between me and John Aspinall who owned two Kent zoos. His first was merely a house that he had won by gambling in 1957, a substantial win on the Caesarewitch (a famous horse race) allowed him to buy Howletts country estate in Kent, and to amuse his weekend guests he bought some wild animals. This turned into a zoo where he encouraged his keepers to get close to their animals. This resulted in some tragic accidents[20]. Five zookeepers were killed in 20 years, three of them mauled to death by tigers. Yet Aspinall maintained his belief that keepers should be allowed to enter the enclosures where tigers roamed and bond with them. Although he was undoubtedly successful in breeding animals, his efforts in conservation would have been hampered by releasing stock that were friendly to humans. They wouldn't have lasted long.

I couldn't understand my job since it would be easier not to sell these very exotic and dangerous wildlife in the first place. Harrods eventually got the point and 12 years later closed the exotic end of their business pushed by the 1976 Endangered Species Act[21] concentrating on canaries and hamsters, and finally shut in 2014.

I went back to the sixth form at Haberdashers. I was relieved that this summer job was a temporary one but was now better versed in the whole business of keeping animals in captivity. While the public's education has been a strong plank for zoos to justify their existence, which cannot be proved, and some zoos even tried reintroducing species back into their natural habitats, zoos have been attacked for decades just as money-making exercises where animals are used to attract people and not treated well, a *'cut-flower scam'*.

Some species only exist in zoos such as the New Guinea Singing Dog, Pinta Island Tortoise (Lonesome George in now dead so this species is extinct), Kihansi Spray Toad, and Micronesian Kingfisher; some are on the edge of extinction in the wild where zoos are helping such as Amur Leopard, Bornean orang-utan, Mountain Gorilla, Western Lowland Gorilla, Pika, Giant Otter, Black-footed ferret, South China Tiger, Darwin's Fox, Sumatran and Javan rhino, White-rumped vulture, Pangolin, Saola, Vaquita, Yangtze Finless Porpoise, Hawksbill Turtle and Peruvian Black Spider Monkey.

---

20 https://www.theguardian.com/uk/2000/jun/30/keithperry#:~:text=The%20millionaire%20and%20controversial%20zoo,also%20secretly%20struggled%20with%20leukaemia

21 http://www.dailymail.co.uk/news/article-2537568/Harrods-pet-shop-sold-alligators-lions-baby-elephant-Ronald-Reagan-set-close-100-years.html

Ten species that zoos saved are Arabian Oryx, California condor, Prze-walski's Horse, Corroboree Frog, Bongo, Regent Honeyeater, Panamanian Golden Frog, Bellinger River Turtle, and Golden Lion Tamarin. Most animals in the world are invertebrates[22] many of which are threatened but bacteria and other microbes exceed even them.

What career?

I thought I should go to University but I wasn't convinced. Having spent a year at weekends as a surgery assistant in a veterinary practice in Totteridge when not at school, I realised dealing with bumptious clients would be hell, especially after a large tweed-suited lady with a pheasant's feather poking out of a hat came bursting in with her fat Pekinese under her arm, with her clothes similarly on the point of submission, and demanded, "Where is the vet, at once young man?"

"What's the problem, Madam?", I said hardly able to contain my laugher at this preposterous apparition.

"My Pekinese is not well. There is something wrong with his eyes." At which point both the poor animals' eyes popped out dangling down his face.

"Oh my God, oh my God, send for the police. Anybody! An ambulance," she whispered in a stentorian gasp.

At which point the tremendous female vet who I worked with emerged, took the dog in hand and beckoned me into the surgery.

"Ian, please try and calm her down or stop her. She'll frighten the other animals let alone the other clients in the waiting room."

"How?"

"Well you're an attractive capable young man and I'm sure you can think of something that would distract her enough to stop making so much noise."

I decided there and then, I was not going to become a veterinary surgeon and that I would always have a female GP as my doctor. I went back to reception, gave the tweeded lady a cup of tea and then much to my distaste sat next to her holding her hand. The veterinary surgeon must have pushed the eyeballs back and sowed the lids together advising the overstuffed client to feed her overstuffed pet less food.

The old vet who owned the practice in Totteridge was a fairly grumpy character and qualified when the acquisition of a veterinary degree was not necessary to be a member of the Royal College of Veterinary Surgeons (MRCVS). I recollect one day in 1964 I went into the surgery and he was smoking his usual cheroot while castrating a young cat and the ash was falling into the incision. The cat was fine.

---

22 https://www.zsl.org/sites/default/files/document/2014-02/spineless-lr-2039.pdf

On another occasion some young male, a smooth slick individual, of the same age as me came by with superb A-levels and said that he chose a veterinary career, "to make money". This finally put me off pursuing a veterinary career. I didn't want to deal with the nuisance of the public nor pursue a career for money.

My father once told me, "Whatever you do as a job don't have anything to do with the public. They complain, argue, misbehave, obstruct and think they are in the right. Like politicians they cause wars. People get over-emotional about obsessions and unworthy causes célèbres. Rich people use their money to influence what happens. They are often nonentities or glitterati who want their own way."

I was bored after being at Haberdashers for 11 years and I needed better GCSE results. Alan Bennett's stage play *The History Boys*, for which Simon Schama, an historian and Old Haberdasher, has written a preface, catches something of Haberdashers' atmosphere and mentions the school by name. Bennett's fictional headmaster reflects on his own school status:

"We are low in the league. I want it up there with Manchester Grammar School, Haberdashers' Aske's. And Leighton Park. Or is that an open prison?"

Schama, now a professor at Columbia University in New York, remembers three bad teachers at Haberdashers': "One was a monster. I actually hated another two who took pleasure in humiliating kids."[23]

In those days you needed O-level in a foreign language and a dead language but the modern languages teacher would not put me in for French! So I went to a crammer called Southgate Technical College 1965 to improve my language O-level grades and zoology and botany A-level grades and for the first time I was in a coeducational atmosphere at 19 years old. I was learning the business of working with, and having relationships with, the opposite sex. Gladwin, an excellently organised and very clear teacher, succeeded in getting my grades up. A-levels in those days did not require an analytical brain but simply memorising several thousand facts and regurgitating them on demand. This was not the way my brain worked as I believed that facts can always be looked up in a book, library or on the internet today. If I wanted to identify a plant or animal I looked it up whereas most people mistakenly and wrongly believe that I can't be a real zoologist if I can't identify every bird.

23 Wigley, J. (2007) *Serve and Obey: The Story of the Haberdashers' Aske's Boys' School*. James and James (publishers) Ltd.

CHAPTER 4
The Mile End 1966–1969

Queen Mary College

I had left it rather late for UCCA (University Central Council for Admissions) so with the help of my father, but I'm not sure how, I was interviewed at Queen Mary College (QMC) by three academics; Mike Walkey (who was my oldest friend and died 2018 who became Executive Director of my Institute, DICE, which I created 23 years later), Davis a theoretical physicist, and a lady called Dorothy who was an organic chemist whose wig was askew.

I had one of the best times of my life at QMC, or QMUL as it is now, being involved in subjects I loved, being part of something which gave me the freedom to do interesting things, and learn the basics of zoology, botany, ecology, behaviour and parasitology with a touch of social anthropology in an era when one dissected real animals and got down to the nitty-gritty. The atmosphere between the zoology staff and students was exceptional and although we were in grotty dirty old buildings in the tired old Mile End did not matter.

Being in the Mile End Road itself was an education and soon after I went up I was able to get a place in the South Woodford Halls of Residence. This was difficult as my home was within 6 miles of Charing Cross, the cut-off parameter for being eligible for University accommodation, but the discord between my parents made it impossible to study, apart from commuting long hours, much of it on the Misery Line otherwise known as the Northern Line Underground. The Wardens took pity and gave me a bedroom. Brian Chirgwin (mathematician) and Dafydd Evans (Romance philologist) were the wardens of Creed and Beaumont Halls respectively and were both highly intelligent and charming people. Being in Dafydd's Beaumont Hall, involved in PopSoc and Friday night gigs at the People's Palace, parties, convincing a classmate that dried banana skins would give him a high, and having my 21st birthday with two pals then, Martin and Ken in the ruins of a nearby listed building, Elmhurst House, were all part of the kaleidoscope for three years while getting a zoology degree. The college bar was a magnet for zoology staff, postgraduates and undergraduates. Amongst others, Ken Simkiss, who headed the department after Gordon Newell, was a lively aquatic biologist and Bryn Williams, who claimed he fell in a coal crusher when he was a miner, standout for quite different reasons.

Dafydd himself was an education for me as he was a very particular short rotund man like a bumble bee; a Romance philologist who unsurprisingly was a homosexual. He was quite attracted to me and I can recollect after a hard night's partying I would be asleep in my room and he would use his pass key to come and have a look very quietly and then leave. He stopped when it was clear I had a girlfriend. He offered me the use of his penthouse apartment whenever he was away which was quite often where I could enjoy real coffee but like all homosexuals I've known he was much more interested in the wider aspects of life, art, design and indeed had more taste than most heterosexuals. Homosexuals are very attractive to women for a whole variety of reasons not least their ability to cook and their engaging conversation and also quite safe since they would have few ulterior motives.

I cannot think of, nor observed, any species which doesn't indulge in homosexual behaviour except those species that never have sex at all because they are hermaphroditic. Most animals are bisexual, practicing same-sex sexual behaviour to assert dominance or dissipate possible conflict, while also engaging in opposite-sex or heterosexual behaviour for procreation. I have observed the same in humans. Both animals and humans also perform sexual acts on themselves; one might also say 'as do hermaphrodites'.

Nightly excursions

I have a significant element of Scots genes in my makeup which means that waste is something that really annoys me whether it's human potential or material items. Hundreds of sandwiches were discarded each night when they reach their sell by date at Queen Mary College so I gathered them up for nothing and took them down to Bethnal Green, Whitechapel and Wapping areas especially Cable Street for the meths drinkers and other down-and-outs. There were many bombs sites still vacant and it was easy to distribute a pile of sandwiches around the fires always burning from the scraps of timber and rubbish around.

One day there was a passing African who looked somewhat down on his luck but had a most educated accent. I gave him some sandwiches which I thought, given his obvious respectability and bearing, might be rejected but he accepted them saying, "I'm sure my wife will be grateful as she has quite a number of youngsters to take care of. Thank you so much. Good night." Later I got to know him as Freddie and would give him what I had.

I learnt much later that Freddie Mutesa died of supposed alcohol poisoning in his London flat, just across the river, in 1969. Many claim that Freddie may have been force-fed vodka by agents of the Obote regime in Uganda since he was interviewed in his flat only a few hours before his death by the World Affairs Editor of BBC News, John Simpson, who found that he was sober and in good health[24].

He was certainly an embarrassment to the British Government trying to maintain reasonable relationships with Uganda during the Obote and Amin reigns, and had not afforded Freddie any special comfort. The kingdoms of Buganda and Bunyoro were abolished by Uganda's first Prime Minister Milton Obote in 1966. Following years of disturbance under Obote, and the dictator Idi Amin, as well as several years of internal divisions among Uganda's ruling National Resistance Movement under Yoweri Kaguta Museveni, the President of Uganda since 1986, the kingdoms were officially restored in 1993.

Sir Edward Frederick William David Walugembe Mutebi Luwangula Mutesa II was the Kabaka of the Kingdom of Buganda, in effect a king and to my first-hand knowledge held in the most enormous regard within modern Uganda. I had great pleasure in meeting the current Kabaka, Freddie's son, Ronald Muwenda Mutebi II, or Ronnie, on 20 November 2007 for whom I have great respect since it can't be easy holding a kingdom together in modern Africa especially within a Republic ruled by a long-standing President.

Ian Swingland 22 years old, Queen Mary College, University of London 1968

---

24   https://allafrica.com/stories/201005160015.html

We agreed to meet at the Speke Hotel Kampala but he told me on the telephone that one of his people would pick me up since if he walked in it would cause a bit of a commotion with people wanting to show their deference and respect. He does a lot for his people and much later on we did meet with his representatives in London in the hope that we could help. He must have been one of those youngsters that Freddie referred to 40 years before. It was ironic that at the same time as meeting Freddie on a few occasions I was studying social anthropology at College and in particular conflict resolution in the Bunyoro, neighbouring Buganda, which also has an advanced governance system.

Mating and social systems

Such highly organised, sophisticated and involved societal systems which governed the behaviour of all the people, frequently hierarchical, and involving penalties for infractions and methods of dealing with conflict in such a way that blood was not spilt, is reminiscent of many animal societies.

Many primitive and preliterate societies have not surprisingly evolved the way they function by adaptation to their environment and what works. We talk about how sophisticated our western society is, and how our systems of law and governance are advanced, but my experience of both delivers evidence of corruption on a daily basis and how the law is bent by subjective argument to meet the aims of others. Both are rife in every country. However in many old hierarchical societies, what ignoramuses called primitive societies, their manner of governance, rules and methods of resolving conflict and succession can be very sophisticated.

One society in the foothills of the Himalayas practises polyandry which is where one woman will marry several men. This occurs in an environment which is quite hostile to humans as primary production and natural resources are quite low. In order to survive and given that there is likely to be the same number of boys and girls born, which the society could not support if marriage consisted of one woman and one man, this society ensures stability and sustainability through the bottleneck of many men, always brothers, producing progeny through one female.

If a significant proportion of the males are involved in polyandrous marriages as they are in Limi, Nepal, which is linguistically and culturally part of Tibet, one would expect there to be a surplus of unmarried females barring other neutralising factors such as higher female mortality[25]. Although fraternal polyandry does not affect individual fertility it does have a significant depressing effect on aggregate fertility and functions, unper-

---

25 Goldstein, M.C. (1976) Fraternal polyandry and fertility in a high Himalayan valley in Northwest Nepal. *Human Ecology* **4(3):** 223–233.

ceived and unintended, as an important mechanism for reducing population growth, obviating female infanticide. Anyway, the very rare unmarried single women don't reproduce. Since brothers marry the same woman every child she delivers is related to all of them, none of the husbands knowing who the biological father is. A textbook example of inclusive fitness (defined by W.D. Hamilton in 1964) which is the number of offspring raised by an individual regardless of who begets them.

Fundamental to the recently-proposed hypothesis that females mate with more than one male as a hedge against genetic incompatibility is the premise that mechanisms are available to polyandrous females which enable them to safeguard their reproductive investment against the threat of incompatibility between maternal and paternal genomes[26]. Polyandry[27] occurs in less than one percent of all bird species, and is found mostly in shorebirds. Here one finds a whole variety on the main theme; females may mate with all of their consorts in one day and provide each male with help in defending his nesting territory such as the Northern jacanas where a female mates with a male, lays eggs, and then terminates the relationship with that male, leaving him to incubate the eggs while she goes off to repeat this sequence with another male. This also happens in the Spotted Sandpipers, Red-necked and Red Phalaropes.

Governmental structures called 'superorganisms' within animals, probably caused by the nature of the environment in which they are evolved, can be seen most notably among insects of the orders Hymenoptera (ants, bees and wasps) and Blattodea (termites) which show an extreme form of sociality, involving highly organised societies, with individual organisms specialised for distinct roles and where individuals are not able to survive by themselves for extended periods. These are called superorganisms. In termites, labour is divided amongst different castes, including reproductive 'queens' and 'kings', and non-reproductive workers and soldiers. It is also seen in several species within the orders Thysanoptera and Hemiptera, as well as one species of weevil, *Austroplatypus incompertus*. Outside of Insecta, only two rodent species, the naked mole-rat and the Damaraland mole-rat, are known to be superorganisms.

Fun and getting down to it

I was involved in organising, or at least helping, quite a few socially bonding events such as quizzes, a rugby match, and other gatherings under BioSoc (the student society for those studying biology). We also organised

26   Zeh, J.A. & Zeh D.W. (1997) The evolution of polyandry II: post-copulatory defences against genetic incompatibility. *Proc. R. Soc. Lond. B.* **264:** 69–75.

27   http://www-personal.umich.edu/~phyl/anthro/polyandry.html; https://web.stanford.edu/group/stanfordbirds/text/essays/Polyandry.html

a Rag which invaded the Mile End and raised considerable amounts of money for kidney machines with the help of ransom money having kidnapped most of the University of London College mascots including a concrete gorilla and the mummified body of Jeremy Bentham the founder of University College. A Trojan task undertaken by our heavyweights in the rugby teams. They were also useful during our Friday night gigs in the People's Palace. A venue owned by the College which seated over a thousand people and without the seats danced more.

We had many famous bands and I can remember that we had the stunningly good-looking Francoise Hardy one night and she requested some protection which the rugby team were only too willing to supply. When the Modern Jazz Quartet (MJQ) was playing I was standing at the back and realised that Humphrey Lyttelton was beside me, a friend of Milt Jackson whose group it was. We also had Procol Harum, The Kinks, Joe Cocker, Cat Stevens, The Small Faces, The Who ('fresh from the Marquee Club' as PR people put it where I watched Peter Townsend go crazy and smashing things up), and Cream. They all had their particular needs; MJQ wanted a specially tuned Steinway, Joe Cocker's team wanted free beer, Ray Davies of the Kinks, I was told, wanted white wine, Cream wanted mineral water (virtually unheard of in those days in Britain), and The Who wanted to be protected as did we and our equipment! Humphrey Lyttleton played at the Pizza Express Maidstone 2007 where we met again and reminisced about Barnet where he lived close by me in Arkley and had to build a soundproof room to practice as small-minded neighbours complained.

The Marine Field course led by Dr Mike Walkey (who much later helped create DICE with me) was held in what was the Royal Native Oyster Stores Whitstable (now a restaurant) and The Prince Albert pub next door, together with field courses in Wales on algae, and a Field Studies Centre called Slapton Ley, Devon, established by the Whitley Wildlife and Conservation Trust. The Whitleys created Paignton Zoo whose animal catcher was Gerald Durrell and later were involved in DICE insofar as its alumni have won nine Whitley Awards, the 'Green Oscars' of conservation. During end of year exams I was told by Bryn Williams that I got 100% for the Marine course paper mainly responding to questions about the physical nature of the marine environment and so they were waiting for me to trip up, he said, at the practical exam to see if I knew anything about actual marine organisms! I didn't believe him.

All the staff and students were a highly gregarious bunch which improved performance and camaraderie on all sides; the rugby songs about threshing machines that I learnt in Whitstable were very blue, the algal field course in the Gower Peninsula had to be weathered (led by Prof. Maud Godward, a single lady of some years who drove the latest sports cars, an MGB), and coping with a live mink caught in a trap in Devon all added to the rich jamboree in getting a degree in zoology. It was sometimes peppered by a fascinating course in social anthropology which attracted me enormously not least because of the conflict resolution and governance systems of some primitive and preliterate societies and the seemingly utterly inadequate subjective explanations of the social scientists. I wanted to pursue social anthropology but I could not see it being useful then in making the world a better place as a university or museum career was the only pathway. I didn't want either then.

For the first year and a half at Queen Mary College I pretty much coasted, enjoying the subjects I found fascinating such as social anthropology, parasitology, marine ecology, and behaviour. But in 1968 I thought I'd better concentrate and apply myself more seriously. In particular Dr George Savage, a brilliant young researcher who trained under Prof. J.Z. Young, University College London, had joined the college and was a breath of fresh air intellectually, even if his attire was somewhat démodé, double-breasted suits or 'super-throaters' as some student wags dubbed his trousers. He was also a gifted teacher and I was very stimulated by his lectures on behaviour and neurophysiology. In the summer of 1968 I worked away in his laboratory with goldfish.

Imagine an aquarium with the goldfish at one end and at the other two signs, + and -. These signs were switched about in a Gellerman sequence (statistically random) and the fish conditioned to approach the + each time they were released by a bit of beef heart as a reward. When they had got it pretty much perfect George did a remarkable operation by removing their forebrain without cutting the optic nerve from which they quickly recovered. Fish brains are not like ours but clearly separated into fore, mid and hind sections. When we retested the same fish they had clearly forgotten what they had been trained to do. This was published by George in *Nature*[28] and he generously made me co-author. We hadn't found the location of memory in a vertebrate brain but perhaps something akin to the alarm clock.

This research in my second summer vacation on memory in a vertebrate was published in *Nature* 1969 but I still only got a 2:2.

London University had invented a new system started in 1966 (when I started) of course units where you finished courses at the end of each year and were examined; if you passed the maximum number of course units (12) you got a 1st, or if did the least number (9) but at a high average mark you got a 1st. I aimed at the maximum units (passed 11.5 units) being a bad examinee but the University couldn't get their heads round the system

---

28   Savage, G. & Swingland, I.R. (1969) Positively reinforced behaviour and the forebrain in the goldfish. *Nature* **221**: 878–879.

they invented! I chose the wrong strategy. Sue Dawes my girlfriend from Nottingham was a great companion and smart enough to go for 9 units (the minimum) and got a 1st in zoology.

CHAPTER 5

Department of Forestry and Natural Resources, University of Edinburgh 1969–1973

Shell Oil Company, Agrochemical Research, Sittingbourne, Kent

The question was: did I go into the private sector, into business, or pursue my own way working on animals? But how and in which way? I had tasted the veterinary and retail business and academia and neither was my bag. So I gave industry a taste after I left Queen Mary College.

Dr Clive Boyce of Shell had synthesised the molecule N-trityl morpholine (a molluscicide called Frescon™ that killed Lymnaeid and Bulinid snails) and contracted bilharzia (schistosomiasis where the secondary host are Bulinid snails) himself on a field trip to the Sudan where the technique of dripping Frescon into canals was being tested by Norman Crossland. Norman hired me in the summer of 1969 to work in Devon with the Product Evaluation team on Frescon's use in controlling liver fluke in sheep by killing Lymnaeid snails, the secondary hosts. Clive subsequently became Head of Organic Chemistry Division and the Research Director at Sittingbourne. Frescon worked well as a snail control agent and was acceptable to regulatory authorities at the time but the product was too expensive for the Sudan and other countries in Africa where bilharzia is endemic. Some years ago the patent for `Frescon™' could have been bought for a few pounds.

While at Shell I met Professor John Cornforth FRS who was the father of a friend of mine at school (J.W. Cornforth who was head boy with David Bucknell whose father was a well-known TV DIY personality). Professor Cornforth had been awarded the Nobel Prize. In the late 1960's his garden and John Fisher's (a source of information about Shell) adjoined and on drawing his bedroom curtains in the morning he often saw Cornforth already out in his garden in his dressing gown with a large mug of tea or coffee, the usual prelude to him practising croquet shots. Milsted Laboratory at Shell Research Sittingbourne had very competitive croquet and tennis competitions that Prof. Cornforth tended to dominate!

While there I was fascinated to hear that the Vapona strip, a yellow plastic strip one hung in one's larder to kill insects, was a source of considerable revenue for Shell. The active ingredient DDVP was first synthesised at the Shell Chemicals Laboratory in Modesto California which I visited with my girlfriend on Aldabra Atoll who was born in that city, much later. John Fisher can't remember where the work on slow release strips was done but recalls that when a very tiny amount of technical DDVP in a bottle was left accidentally uncapped for a very short time all the houseflies waiting to be used in experiments that same day all died in short order. DDVP was profitable but as the cost of insecticide discovery and registration increased, and the 'winners' had to pay for the 'failures', what looked like a large income was soon spent on further research.

A better anecdote arose out of the use of DDVP dog collars to control ectoparasites on dogs. During one Christmas lunch, Doug Yeo, the laboratory director, received an enquiry purportedly from a Scottish Presbyterian minister asking if two Vapona dog collars worn one above each knee would enable him to wear his kilt out of doors during the midge season. Shells' reply pointed out that this was an unregistered use of the product so it couldn't be recommended.

Mike Walkey called me while I was in the depths of Devon where I worked for the Product Evaluation Division, Shell Research based at Sittingbourne hired by Norman Crossland to evaluate the ecological and environmental data on n-trityl-morpholine `Frescon™' used on *Lymnaea* (now *Galba*) *truncatula*, a freshwater snail and secondary hosts to liver fluke *Fasciola hepatica* in sheep. He told me I had only got 2.2 honours and said he was sorry about the system failing me as the Board had recidivistically resorted to the old evaluation i.e. average mark.

We worked from the Fox and Hounds Hotel in Chulmleigh, North Devon on the banks of the River Taw, and used Romney Marsh seconds (lambs) in multiple enclosures, some treated and others not. I took home beautiful lamb at summer's end after successful trials proved we could selectively kill the liver fluke's intermediate host *Limnaea truncatula*. Quite tough work but occasionally we had a party and I can remember creating a liqueur-like drink from laboratory alcohol and Kummel essence with a crazy Danish scientist who was very good playing the guitar naked with me on drums at the local pub.

One slight shock was the appearance at the hotel of a lot of city folk in expensive cars down from London who professed to be the local otter hunt! Dressed in dark blue velvet jackets and done up to the nines with a number of quite rare otter hounds they went flying into the river each day and then regaled us at the bar in the evening. Thank God they never caught on otter and made it plain that they tried to organise it in such a way that they only ever caught mink, a renowned pest that destroyed the riverside's natural wildlife. They were escapees from fur farms or released by animal rights nutters.

The question of animal rights, feral animals, introductions, hunting, and the ways in which we use wildlife was something which much exercised me from this point on. Not just at Oxford, where we were intellectually engaged in something far removed from this concern, but subsequently when I was on the Council of the RSPCA 30 years later. The hunting debate was at its peak in the early part of this century with those emotional and somewhat ignorant opponents of the age-old practice pushing through a Parliamentary Bill while others recognised the importance of hunting which improves biodiversity in the countryside[29].

Shell offered me a fantastic job that summer; cheap car fuel, cheap mortgage, substantial salary, and worldwide prospects for life. I turned it down for two reasons: it would take me away from animals and I could never afford to resign, trapped by the excellent conditions.

Taking risks

At the end of the summer 1969, when Neil Armstrong stepped on the moon, and said, "That's one small step for a man, one giant leap for mankind", and he did say, "a man", but it was lost in translation, I knew I would have to take risks to achieve anything worthwhile. 'Nothing ventured, nothing gained' was I suppose a pertinent adage but for the next 40 years anything I created which was constructive, beneficial to the environment, useful to communities, and both intelligent and sustainable, always involved a risk, invariably my risk.

Most academics avoid risk at all costs and are happy to do research, publish papers, get a chair and be elected a Fellow of the Royal Society but they are hardly ever found outside the ivory towers applying what they discovered and seeing if it works or if they even got it right; in other words, verify or applying their research. I'm not the traditional academic in any sense.

With utter determination and again at some risk I had applied to do a PhD at the multidisciplinary Department I wanted to do my first degree in three years before, the Department of Forestry and Natural Resources, University of Edinburgh, the only multidisciplinary land-use University Department in the UK. I wanted to study under Dr Jim Lockie[30], a brilliant research ecologist and university lecturer, and a maker of Whim Looms that sold worldwide. His deeply held concerns for the care of the planet were still active at 91 when he wrote to Scottish ministers about the potentially disastrous consequences of the Transatlantic Trade and Investment Partnership aimed at reducing regulatory barriers for big business.

29　Leader-Williams, N., Oldfield, T.E.E., Smith, R.J. & Walpole, M.J. (2002) Science, conservation and fox-hunting. *Nature* **419**: 878.

30　https://www.scotsman.com/news/obituaries/obituary-james-donaldson-lockie-ecologist-1-3883526

The problem was I had no funds except what I had saved, some £540, to survive and an old family car, a Standard 8, which I couldn't drive without a licence. Jim was also taking a risk in accepting a postgraduate student with only just enough funds for one year but I suspect that the fact that Dr Charles Taylor, deputy head of the Department under Prof. John Black, was an Old Haberdasher might have coloured his view. Dr Taylor found out there was an Exhibition on offer from the Haberdashers' Company that might assist, the Throgmorton Trotman Senior Exhibition, but when I won it was an enormous disappointment to discover it was just over £60!

In 1970 I competed for a scholarship to help me survive this time from the Overseas Development Administration (now Department for International Development, DfID) which in those days, during a Conservative administration, was part of the Foreign & Commonwealth Office. Again my father pointed me at this source of funding and during the interview I was asked whether I would work in a developing country afterwards, and whether I could learn Hamitic, to which the answer was, "Absolutely!", not having a clue where that ancient and remote language was spoken

or indeed which country they would send me to. I went from being the poorest to the richest postgraduate overnight!

The project Jim and I devised was to look at communal roosting in rocks and jackdaws and ascertain what went on and why they did it in such vast numbers every winter (hundreds of thousands). My field site was east of Edinburgh in a place called Haddington, a vast communal roost established over a hundred years ago; about the same time a distant relative, a Fernie, won the first golf Open at nearby Musselburgh in 1883 when only the Scots entered. I carried out my research at dusk and through the winter nights up a tower with all kinds of equipment, night vision glasses, and quite a lot of experimental work in the research basement of the Department.

I found a place I could get something to eat at one o'clock in the morning in Edinburgh called the Traverse Club, an experimental theatre club in the Grassmarket, and often had a drink there with one of the greatest mime artists who was equal to Marcel Marceau, the late Lindsay Kemp. The other researchers were working on how grass grew in a wind tunnel (Jim Thompson, later Executive Director at Institute of Ecology and Environmental Management), the inner secrets of salmon and trout (Marshall Halliday, later Director of Esk Rivers and Fisheries Trust, Scott Campbell), ecological models (Prof. Mick Crawley later FRS, Imperial College, London), and the use of sophisticated mathematical approaches to how you successfully manage red deer herds (Prof. Sir John Beddington FRS, later Government Chief Scientist).

This latter work was carried out by John Beddington who shared my room and was funded by the Nature Conservancy. He was quite brilliant, having quiet disdain for anyone with a lesser intellect. He had a bet with me that he could make his sponsors leave his mid-PhD seminar within 15 min and launched into technical explanations of extracting the latent dominant root from population matrices to understand how to maximise the cull from a red deer herd while maintaining a very healthy and productive population. He won!

I, on the other hand, was always trudging over to George Jolly in the Agricultural Research Council, Unit of Statistics, 21 Buccleuch Place to talk about multiple regression analysis and other multivariate statistics to unravel the secrets of what affected what; what parameters underlay the communal roosting of rocks and jackdaws in these vast and traditional gatherings in winter. My PhD thesis was not particularly good and indeed never unravelled why the species roosted together at this time of year. At least I thought so until 10 years later!

Peter de Groot, a scientist who was later to work with me at the Commonwealth Secretariat when I became chairman of the Iwokrama International Centre for Rain Forest Conservation and Development in Guyana 2002, had done his own PhD on this question and had got closer to an answer. He proposed an information centre hypothesis whereby individuals could follow each other to feed each morning, the better off individuals could be identified from their sleek plumage and tracked by those less fortunate who needed food badly.

In evolutionary terms, why would better fed individuals share information about where food could be found? In other words, if you're doing well why go to the roost only to have competition the following day at your food source. Perhaps it was like a trade union? You will need it when you're doing badly and have to subsidise others when you're doing well? And you never know when you are going to be short of something to eat. But animals are not socialist but selfish like most animals and humans!

Patrick Weatherhead in 1983[31] illustrated an alternative to the then popular information centre hypothesis. This hypothesis proposes that different individuals join and participate in communal roosts for different reasons that are based primarily on their social status. Unlike the information centre hypothesis, not all individuals will join a roost in order to increase their foraging capabilities.

This hypothesis explains that while roosts initially evolved due to information sharing among older and more experienced foragers, this evolution was aided by the benefits that more experienced foragers gained due to the fact that as better foragers they acquired a status of high rank within the roost. As dominant individuals, they are able to obtain the safest roosts, typically those highest in the tree or closest to the centre of the roost. In these roosts, the less dominant and unsuccessful foragers act as a physical predation buffer for the dominant individuals. This is similar to the selfish herd theory, which states that individuals within herds will utilise conspecifics as physical barriers from predation. The younger and less dominant individuals will still join the roost because they gain some safety from predation through the dilution effect, as well as the ability to learn from the more experienced foragers that are already in the roost.

Weatherhead describes support for the two strategic hypotheses that have been demonstrated in studies of roosting rooks (*Corvus frugilegus*). A 1977[32] study of roosting rooks (mine) showed that an inherent hierarchy exists within rook communal roosts. In this hierarchy, the most dominant individuals have been shown to routinely occupy the roosts highest in the tree, and while they pay a cost (increased energy use to keep warm) they are safer from terrestrial predators. Despite this enforced hierarchy, lower ranking rooks remained with the roost, indicating that they still received some benefit from their participation in the roost. Interestingly, when weather conditions worsened, the more dominant rooks forced the younger and less dominant out of their roosts. I had proposed that the risk of predation at lower roosts was outweighed by the gains in reduced thermal demands.

Similar support for the two strategic hypotheses has also been found in red-winged blackbird (*Agelaius phoeniceus*) roosts. In this species the more dominant males will regularly inhabit roosts in thicker brush, where they are better hidden from predators than the less dominant individuals,

---

31 Weatherhead, P. (1983) Two Principal Strategies in Avian Communal Roosts. *The American Naturalist* **121(2)**: 237–247.

32 Swingland, I.R. (1977) The social and spatial organization of winter communal roosting in Rooks (Corvus frugilegus). *Journal of Zoology* **182(4)**: 509–528.

which are forced to roost at the edge of the brush.

This work was to lead me on into areas and thinking prevalent in the Zoology Department at Oxford University after I returned from Zambia which is where I went next after Edinburgh. I never thought much of my PhD but it just goes to show that while I've always believed that a person is their best judge, it's interesting how others perceive one's work. Weatherhead published this appraisal of communal roosting in Wikipedia.

Group selection advocated at that time by many Scottish academics such as Vero Wynne-Edwards[33] in Aberdeen was beyond my comprehension. Individuals it seemed to me were in charge of themselves and selection would therefore operate on an individual and not on a group.

The Scots

Integration of Scottish people with their wildlife is much greater than with the English, highlanders and islanders were in tune with nature which they relied on much more. The Scots held on to their traditions and ways and even during my PhD viva my external examiner the late George Dunnet (Regius Professor of Natural History, Aberdeen University) referred to me as a 'sassenach' (an English person) to which I had the pleasure of responding in the Gaelic picked up from my grandparents which he did not speak.

Today multidisciplinary land-use and natural resource Departments are the only way to address global problems and single subject departments are passé. That's why I created a multidisciplinary Institute 30 years ago knowing that the future lay in such cross dissemination of ideas, research and solutions. The Department of Forestry and Natural Resources, University of Edinburgh no longer exists and was carved up into smaller pure science entities to maximise the University's score in the Government Research Assessment Exercise which could not deal with multidisciplinary outfits just like DICE. By destroying my old department they decreased the University of Edinburgh's relevance to the outside world.

It was a huge learning experience about Scotland and the Scots which suited my genetic background and first language, and I left in 1973 with the highest regard for their culture, common sense and fortitude. When I was much younger I had decided that if ever I pursued animals through academia I wanted to study in the capital of England, the capital of Scotland and Oxbridge. But don't be fooled for a moment. Most of my life has been led by happenstance, luck and very hard work.

The idea that I could actually design my future pathway seemed even then both unattainable and ridiculous. I was wrong as you will see later

---

33 Wynne-Edwards, V.C. (1962) *Animal Dispersion in Relation to Social Behavior*. Oliver & Boyd, London.

in the story. John Baird lived in Glasgow with his wife Jean and daughter Marion. He was my godfather, a headmaster and was active in making films to raise funds for a national disability charity now called Scope and in particular for hydrocephalic kids who were particularly bright. He often made the films with the entertainer Max Bygraves; *'Take my Hand'* and the other *'Guide them on Their Way'*. His family and their friends showed me the true nature of the Scots, their generosity, warmth, stoicism and inventiveness.

During my time there Dr John Hanks was a frequent visitor and guided me towards my next undertaking (Zambia). He remains a close friend even today. Whenever he came we went off and drank Glenmorangie malt whisky. There is an extraordinary story which he retells in a book he wrote called *'Operation Lock'*[34], which intended to wage war on rhino poaching, and involved Prince Bernhard of the Netherlands, and David Stirling (SAS founder) who my mother worked with during the war. It had considerable dangers and while the right thing to do, as every other way fails even today, John was very brave to set it up given the risky stakes.

I had a room in Esslemont Road near the Kings Buildings which is the science campus of the University of Edinburgh for the first year and then joined up with Hemanta 'Hamey' Mishra (Nepalese), studying tigers, and three Norwegians, from Lillehammer and Edinburgh who was studying or working in the city. We took a very large flat for my second year in Marchmont and many's the time I would return home to discover the huge living room floor covered in plastic with a fully cooked goat in the middle and many other dishes and cross legged around the food a Gurkha Regiment (guarding Edinburgh Castle) drinking beer and whiskey in the middle of the night.

It was great fun and certainly warmed me up from returning after a night's observations in winter at my roost site. I remember it being a wonderfully warm and very friendly time of my life. I learned a lot from the Nepalese and especially the Gurkhas. For example to keep a diesel vehicle going in the Himalayas first thing in the morning it's perfectly all right to light a fire under the engine block. And when using dynamite to get rid of rockfalls it's important to urinate before you light the fuse in case you trip in rushing away and embarrass yourself! The Gurkhas impressed me with their integrity and strength, and their absolute discipline. Their help and support many years later when I was on an expedition in deepest Borneo was invaluable and also their hospitality at Gun Club Hill Barracks Hong Kong now occupied by the People's Liberation Army, China. As with Yiddish, I learnt a few swearwords in Gurkhali and my friendship with Hamey extends today as he has made a significant impact in the con-

---

34   Hanks, J. (2015) *Operation Lock and the War on Rhino Poaching.* Penguin.

Dr Hemanta Mishra and myself, Herons Hall, 2011

servation of the fauna of his own country.

In my last year my mother helped me buy for £5000 a very small top-floor flat in Morningside and delivered the cash interleaved in a paperback book for some reason. The solicitor, T. Graham Salmon, that helped me buy the place had a Morningside accent, similar to Kelvinside in Glasgow, both quite posh, and was a Writer to the Signet, a private society of Scottish solicitors, dating back to 1594 and part of the College of Justice. He was an imposing, charming gent in black coat in an office straight out of Dickens with towering piles of paper teetering on the edge of collapse if a door was slammed or window opened. Lawyers love lots of paper which they trundle around in wheeled suitcases these days, even in this digital age, and I wonder if we shouldn't start a forest conservation society for the Solicitors Regulation Authority (SRA) and the Bar.

The flat was immediately opposite The Volunteer Arms always known as The Canny Man's in Morningside Road. Along with the bars frequented by the large number of Norwegians in the city, and their mad parties, and the old world beauty of Leslies Bar where the barman wore old-fashioned black aprons, the Canny Man became increasingly risqué to attract custom at odds with the highly conservative and staid Morningside. While the downstairs bar was unremarkable, the upstairs was in contrast quite remarkable since patrons could often find semi naked females dancing between their pots along the bar. Many's the time when working hard to finish my PhD I glanced out the window to see police vehicles with dogs search the pub only to emerge an hour or so later when even the dogs were grinning.

During this time I also learnt how the Scots and their environment, especially the animals and the plants they relied on, were an integral part of much of their culture. The practices, vices and ingrained habits when living off the land and dealing with the English, and such matters as the Highland Clearances, coloured even my views and I can sympathise with their desire to be a sovereign country however impractical.

One of their customs at formal dinners was the loyal toast which involved passing the wine over the water glass! A pledge to the Stuarts namely James II of England, who was deposed from the English throne in 1688 and his grandson Bonnie Prince Charlie, who resided 'over the water ', in other words the English Channel, in France. The mirror embedded in the floor of the guard room at Edinburgh Castle to check they were dressed properly under their kilt *sans pantaloons*! The wild and informative ceilidhs where everyone had to perform were a lesson in binding the community and being generous to everyone; a Scottish trait since while they watch the pennies they are the most generous in the United Kingdom.

The stoic dark haired Scot with few words, Iain Colquhoun, who was a crack shot and could stalk deer crawling for miles and then take the final shot simultaneously with the overfed overblown client so he had the impression that he had a clean kill. Driving across snow covered roads in an Austin Mini he noticed a hated hooded crow perched 300 yards away on an opposite hillside. He got out his rifle with a telescopic sight and resting it on the roof of the car took aim and shot the bird stone dead with one shot. Scottish shepherds would make offerings to hooded crows to keep them from attacking sheep[35]. I learned more during my time at Edinburgh than anywhere else about the basic ecology and behaviour of animals, range and population management, community behaviour, and was drawn into the whole question of applied ecology which was to become a future mission but then it was impossible to get a PhD except in pure ecology.

Norwegian Resistance

I painted the entire flat Norwegian red as I was fascinated by the country, its countryman, and the way this thin strip of a country, the same land area

---

35 Ingersoll, E. (1923) *Birds in legend, fable and folklore*. New York: Longmans, Green and Co. p. 165. Retrieved 2009-08-08.

as United Kingdom, with only 4 million people had achieved the highest standards of living. My mother had a long distance association with the country because SOE had worked with the Norwegian resistance especially concerning the attack on the heavy water plant at Vemork during World War II. Many years later I took my mother to Norway and a friend introduced us to one of the most famous Norwegian agents who played a significant role in fighting the Nazis. The late Gunnar Sønsteby was a member of the Norwegian resistance movement known as 'Agent No. 24' during the German occupation of Norway in World War II. He was the most highly decorated citizen in Norway. He was invited to dinner by an old friend Sven Ullring and his wife Bodil to meet Flora my mother in April 2007. When he came in the conversation between the two of them was so mundane that you would think they had met yesterday instead of only communicating by messages 67 years ago.

"Did the agent wear British army uniforms over their white ski camouflage during Operation Gunnerside [the name of the Vemork attack]?"

"No, they wore Norwegian army uniforms."

"And did they leave the Bren gun lying on the floor to reinforce the impression that the British military had done it and to prevent retribution

Flora Swingland (SOE), my mother, Gunnar Sønsteby (SOE Agent 24 and the most highly decorated citizen in Norway) and myself. Oslo, 2007

against the local people?"

"No. They were running out of time fitting the shortened explosive charges to the principal vessels and they wanted to leave without having to shoot anybody."

I met Joachim Rønneberg, leader of Operation Gunnerside in 2013 when I attended a ceremony at the SOE Memorial on the south bank of the Thames. He expressed himself in the same matter-of-fact way that my mother and Sønsteby spoke about their wartime experiences. All of them were part of SOE and all of them were young. They all felt, "what else could we do?" The Allies and especially SOE were so fearful that Hitler would begin using heavy water to build nuclear weapons that London ordered a series of sabotage missions, culminating in Operation Gunnerside in 1943 in which Norwegian commandos were sent in to blow up the plant. Rønneberg said he made a last-minute decision to cut the length of the fuse from several minutes to seconds, ensuring that the explosion would take place but making it more difficult to escape. Thus the Bren gun was not left even though not a shot was fired! It was only a matter of weeks before the plant was operational again as the Nazis had copied the principal parts of the vessels used to extract the heavy water and stored them in Berlin.

Heavy water vessel

After the raids the Nazis realised they needed to safeguard their remaining stockpile and on February 20th 1944 began moving a year's output of heavy water by train and ferry from Vemork, en route to the reactor site in Germany. On Churchill's orders, Norwegian resistance fighters had attached a time bomb to the ferry to explode and the vessel sunk 1,500 feet to the lake bottom where it was impossible to recover the barrels. In 2018 underwater scans discovered at least 18 barrels which tests showed contained heavy water, and many more are thought to be crushed beneath the sunken boat, enough to put the Nazis closer to becoming an atomic superpower.

Many years before my father once told me he had drunk heavy water; something to do with his work on Blue Steel, an air-launched, rocket-propelled nuclear armed standoff missile. He said his legs felt like lead!

Marriage

I married a Norwegian girl, Berit Viig, in Oslo in 1973. She was doing research in organic chemistry for an MPhil and was the daughter of Sven Viig, who came from lowly beginnings but rose to be the former deputy governor of the Bank of Norway and had become chairman of the Christiania Bank og Kreditcasse, and Astrid, a blue-blooded mother, whose family helped create Norway when it split from Sweden 7 June 1905. Sven had one of the four original paintings by Edvard Munch, as far as I can remember, called 'The Scream' or 'Skrik' on the wall of his office which is a painting or pastel of such force that I would find it impossible to work in the same room. On many weekends a man would visit the Viig household with his poodle, Troll and get into close conversation with Sven behind closed doors. I was told that they discussed the Norwegian strategy for handling the new gas and oil discoveries in the North Sea which incidentally bound Scotland and Norway even tighter. He was Olav V of Norway.

Now it was time to put into practice all my education and training to some purposeful effect starting with Zambia. Unfortunately Berit found the reality of wild Africa rather more than she bargained for and after 700 days we divorced.

Myself, Berit, Astrid Viig, a ship owner, and Sven Viig on the occasion of Astrid launching a refrigerated cargo ship. Oslo 1974

CHAPTER 6
Zambia 1973–1974

I thought I'd heard a knock at the door but when I opened it I was dazzled by the ferocious Zambian sun.

"Bwana, Doctor. She is having a baby."

I raised my hand to my eyes and squinted. A man appeared, silhouetted.

The man stepped aside and a large pregnant woman appeared, beaming with a huge smile. She looked at me, before turning to her husband. He spoke to her and immediately she lay down on the veranda and lifted up her skirt. Sweat pricked my brow as I realised that, doctor or not, I was going to have to assist. There were no medics for miles. Mahatma Gandhi's words, "Fear has its use but cowardice has none," again came to mind just as a group of men appeared carrying logs and dumped them outside the house. Whether this was so that we could boil water for the impending birth or roast me if I failed, I wasn't sure. I racked my brains to try and remember whether cannibalism was part of the area's cultural history but I couldn't recall so I got down on my knees beside the woman. With more gesticulation than words, I asked the husband if her waters had broken and discovered that it had happened hours beforehand. That was the extent of my knowledge on the subject.

I could not see the head but I felt the woman's stomach and as far as I could tell the baby was roughly in the right place, head down. The mother wasn't the slightest concerned about my touching her and maintained an encouraging smile throughout. Her husband and the log-carrying men skulked away. I gestured to the woman to stand and then crouch as though defaecating, aping the position myself, remembering that it was by far the best position to give birth – opposed to lying flat on one's back as initiated by King Louis XIV. The mother and I crouched and I made straining noises to encourage her to push. Within seconds the baby's skull hit the concrete veranda and fortunately the infant started to cry. I ran indoors for my Queen Mary's College zoologist's dissection kit and raced back to find the mother surrounded by women and cradling the child. I cut the umbilical cord after tying off both ends with string.

Elated, relieved, exhausted, I found something to cover the tiny boy then collapsed first into a sitting position before laying lay flat out, thinking of everything that could have gone wrong and the consequences. The assembled women gathered me up, pushed me into a chair and placed a beer in my hands, smiling at me and patting me as they did so. To my horror, a wizened old lady with a handful of dry elephant dung approached the mother preparing to daub the woman's undercarriage, but I knocked her hand out of the way. The logs were set alight and before long a party was in full swing with me as the guest of honour. Young maidens somewhat scantily clad suddenly appeared and started dancing in unison towards me with thrusting and pulsating hip movements. Unfortunately Berit, my wife, was in Norway but I remembered the advice of the little red book[36] about fraternisation given to us by the British Government on our departure and just smiled politely. The next day I was told I'd done women's work and that, although men don't usually attend child birth, they were pleased with what I'd done.

There were several baptisms of fire during that year in Africa of which midwifery was only one. Berit and I were as green as they came. She was a budding organic chemist from a prestigious family whose normal territory was urban Norway. She was game though, and although I had no idea what to expect, I was excited too. This was my first real job with wildlife conservation and I was to be in a country with a rich cultural history where the wildlife was largely intact and plentiful. Although Kafue was the largest and oldest National Park on the continent, like so many throughout the tropical world, it wasn't managed properly. What were missing in those days were not equipment, transport, manpower or organisation but intelligent intent and determination. Personal relationships undermined authority and a wildlife department run by Mzungu (white men), none of whom even spoke the local Bemba language, didn't help. Poaching and corruption were rife.

We couldn't really prepare, so we focused first on our health, the required vaccinations and a briefing document of frankly gruesome information in the red book called: *Preservation of Personal Health in Warm Climates*.

The UK Overseas Development Administration (ODA) became the Department for International Development under the Labour Administration in 1997. Now it's merged into the Foreign Office and called the Foreign, Commonwealth and Development Office after the PM remarked, "We give as much aid to Zambia as we do to Ukraine, though the latter is vital for European security." And China, the world's wealthiest nation, gets £55.6 million; Iran that harasses British merchant shipping in the Gulf, received £16 million and Yegna, an all-female pop group dubbed 'Ethiopia's Spice Girls', received £9.2 million! This profligacy was epitomised during 1997–2003 under Tony Blair, when overseas aid was characterised by sending 'lollipops and frozen chicken' instead of capacitating countries that needed help to be able to do the job for themselves and not charity. The

---

36 *Preservation of Personal Health in Warm Climates* (1971) The Ross Institute of Tropical Hygiene.

left-wing liberal chattering class's idea of overseas aid, their temple to fake compassion and self-righteous preening, was stopped 16 June 2020 and PM Cameron's overseas aid law of 0.7% of GDP having to be spent each year turned to better use.

For the next decade at least the UK needs to save every penny it can, not give it away to rich countries and corrupt politicians, since charity begins at home! However it supported me for my PhD when the Overseas Development Administration was folded back into the Foreign Office under a Conservative administration and was the agency through which the Republic of Zambia offered me a job.

It was ODA who gave me the book, small and red, which had been published by the Ross Institute of Tropical Hygiene. It was full of horrific medical details of all the diseases, fungal infections and parasites that could afflict us. These included, but were not limited to, smallpox, diphtheria, lockjaw, measles, hepatitis, plague, typhus, and rabies. Then there was malaria which came in four different varieties, the worst being Blackwater fever. Yellow fever, dengue fever, trypanosomiasis or sleeping sickness transmitted by the tsetse fly prevalent in the Kafue. Typhus and sand fly were further delights awaiting us.

Then there were the parasites. These were particularly interesting, especially filariasis where the worms block the lymphatic system leading to elephantiasis. I did see a man suffering from this. Poor soul. Fortunately, I didn't have to engage in small talk with him. Where would one start?

Guinea-worm disease is contracted by drinking water that contains water fleas infected with guinea worm larvae. Initially there are no symptoms and after ingestion, the fleas die and are digested, releasing larvae which then penetrates the host's stomach or intestinal wall from where they enter into the abdominal cavity and retroperitoneal space. After maturation, which takes approximately three months, mating takes place; the male worm dies after mating and is absorbed by the host's body. Approximately one year after mating, the fertilised females migrate in the subcutaneous tissues adjacent to long bones or joints of the extremities. The female worm forms a painful blister in the skin, usually on an ankle. From the blister the female worm releases more larvae when the sufferer is paddling in water. The only cure is to wrap the end of the worm round a matchstick and very carefully, day after day, rotate the matchstick slowly drawing the worm out. If you break the worm you have to deal with sepsis.

Berit and I were inoculated against everything possible. I also had additional inoculations against rabies. Morbid rabies is a danger since even infected saliva on a branch or fence can carry the disease and if you inadvertently touch it with a hand that is scratched or cut, you can contract it. Dr Bent Juel-Jensen was the Medical Officer of Oxford University and he used to inoculate me before I went out into foreign places with plenty of diseases. I can remember his attitude was quite brisk being a formal Danish naval officer and he used to inject me with everything in one go and suggest I buy a bottle of whisky and lie down for two days!

When we got out to Zambia, we boiled all our water and took great precautions with our food, never eating salads or uncooked meals. We religiously took our malarial prophylactics for breakfast every morning and never walked around with bare feet. In the event, the only parasite experienced was when I got a small swelling on my ankle. I had to dig out dead larvae having first suffocated them using cling film. *Dermatobia hominis* is the only species of botfly whose larvae ordinarily parasitise humans. I did smile at the recent story that surfaced of HRH the Prince of Wales who 'shrieked' and 'trembled' when seeing cling film for the first time[37]. While I don't believe the story, if only he knew of its use as a deadly but imperfect weapon[38] against parasites he would understand.

As well as warning against fraternising with the indigenous community, the small red book of gloom talked about persons of, *'a highly nervous disposition, or with a family history of mental disturbance, reacting badly to the life in the tropics where the heat and the humidity tend to magnify the petty irritations that would pass unnoticed in more temperate regions.'* On several occasions when my 1.5 tonne Land Rover was charged by the same five-tonne elephant who hated that particular vehicle for some reason, I would say to myself, "Such a petty irritation, and made so much worse by the humidity."

My title at Kafue National Park (KNP) was Wildlife Management Biologist. The Park was 22,400 km², four times the size of Devon, and pretty much in the centre of Africa. My job was, among other things, to undertake aerial surveys over the Busanga swamps and floodplains in the northern section of KNP. I saw herds of up to a thousand buffalo and other sdpecies, including lechwe, sable, kudu, roan, zebra, wildebeest, puku, impala, duiker which were well represented. as well as black rhino, honey badger, mongoose, cobras, mambas and fabulous birds. I knew that I would doubtless come across Gaboon viper – the most dangerous snake, well camouflaged, highly poisonous and easily stepped on in the early morning – as well as insects to make your hair stand on end.

At Lusaka airport, the heat slammed into us like a brick wall and we were surrounded by noise, colour, shouting, body odour and bustle.

A wildlife department clerk took us to the department's centre at

---

37   https://www.dailymail.co.uk/news/article-5579833/Prince-Charles-discusses-carry-ing-toilet-seat-Australia.html

38   Bhandari, R., Janos, D.P. & Sinnis, P. (2007) Furuncular myiasis caused by *Dermatobia hominis* in a returning traveler. *The American Journal of Tropical Medicine and Hygiene* **76(3):** 598–9. doi:10.4269/ajtmh.2007.76.598. PMC 1853312. PMID 17360891.

Gaboon viper Zambia. Ambush predator beautifully camouflaged and stepped on often but first thing in the morning too cold to strike although by 10am very dangerous. When bitten the prey is held onto injecting large amounts of venom which is not considered particularly toxic in small quantities. (Courtesy Mike Roberts)

Chilanga where we met Frank Ansell and Bill Astle. Ansell was the Deputy Director, and had written books on mammal distribution and taxonomy, or classification, in Zambia. Astle oversaw research.

Frank greeted us at HQ. "We're sending you to Chunga HQ in the north of the Park. There's a Land Rover waiting outside, with a driver. Radio us when you're in post." The road was new, tarmacked by the Chinese, and dead straight for four and a half hours. It made me go cross-eyed.

I asked the driver why we saw little wildlife, now that we were out in the bush.

"Nyama!"

"What's nyama?"

"Meat, bwana!"

"Do you mean poachers?"

"Outside the Park all animals nyama. So they run away."

Chunga was right beside the Kafue River, smooth as a mirror 200 metres wide, and running for over 250km through KNP.

There were a handful of houses which were for us as well as the northern sector Warden and another employee from Britain whose role I never fathomed. The camp had a workshop where vehicles and machinery could be repaired and a guard's camp with a small office. This housed the radio

Hyena road kill in KNP – vehicles speeding through the Park commonly kill wildlife

A fish out of water 1973.
Newly arrived in Zambia with flared trousers and binocs at the ready!

which, I would discover, was vital for work in the bush. We could use it to speak to HQ in Lusaka and the Park HQ in the south at Ngoma. It was a very basic camp where, as a biologist, it was difficult to do any real work; no laboratory, computer, printer, scanner, telephone and no reference books, maps or files. There was no store or shop for essential supplies for hundreds of miles. We had to be entirely self-sufficient and had no mail or contact with the outside world except via the radio.

Berit and I explored our house. It was a basic bungalow with a bedrooms, bathroom, living room and kitchen. The furniture was government supply and we were pleased to see a new mattress. We had to supply our own soft furnishings and had bought a small paraffin refrigerator before leaving Lusaka. We'd brought cooking utensils with us. We were to cook using wood-burning stoves. A gas range was available but the gas bottle supplier hundreds of miles away.

We unpacked our suitcases. We'd brought practical bush clothing and shorts and flip-flops for wearing around camp but mainly the cases were full of drugs and sealed hypodermic syringes because we didn't want to depend on the local hospital and clinic's equipment in an emergency. Zambian hospitals were generally quite poor during my time in the country and most people subscribed to private medical programs to avoid them. In 1988, 14 years after I left, the HIV virus was beginning to become prevalent and when I returned 37 years later mechanics wouldn't service Land Rovers or Landcruisers that had been serviced by others in case they grazed themselves inside the engine and were infected. We set about killing every kind of bug we could. That evening as we prepared for bed, I heard a snorting noise coming from the back of the house and went to the window.

We watched for a while as the male impala jostled with each other before they found a comfortable spot and settled down. We made our way to bed and crashed out too. At 3am Berit grabbed my hand and I jolted awake. It turned out that it had been monkeys on the roof that first night. We were often visited by vervet monkeys, appealing creatures with petite black faces, fringe-like coats and known for their human-like characteristics and mischievous antics. When the noise was louder then baboons were visiting.

On one occasion I heard the soft and tentative tread of an animal walking across the roof, its claws making a slight clicking noise. I rushed outside with a torch, the beam of which hit the shining eyes of a leopard a few feet in front of me. We were both startled and skedaddled instantly. The last time I had been that close to a leopard was 15 years previously when I had seen the dejected eyes of a caged and skinny leopard on the forecourt of an Italian Agip petrol station. The wild leopard had looked straight into my eyes. The caged leopard could not.

Something of a talking point, the white warden's soup bubbled in a huge pot on the stove by his door 24 hours a day, seven days a week, with the remnant of every meal poured into it. The soup had a life of its

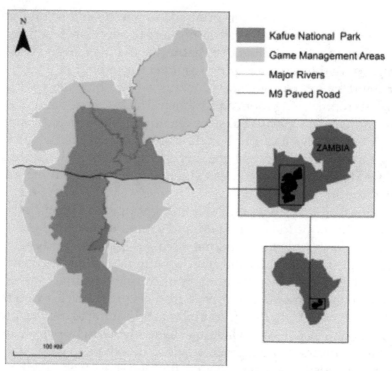

Kafue National Park and surrounding nine Game Management Areas
(where hunting is allowed) today

own and quite remarkably never made the Warden sick. "Ah yes," he said. "That cat is after my soup. I always forget to shut my front door." He was a former hunter approaching retirement that had taken the job as his last before retirement and was, despite some missing fingers, a crack shot when sober. This was not often, hence the Wildlife Guards' comments. Having given up on life, he drank alone and was pretty sour about his own existence. Despite this, I learned a lot from him as one of the last white hunters around. I never worked out what he actually did as most of the workers, Wildlife Guards and drivers seemed to busy themselves effectively like an orchestra without a conductor.

The Warden was what was known as Bush Crazy. This condition has one clear symptom. The sufferer, having been living in very remote conditions, will go into town for supplies and cross the road to avoid someone they know and possibly like. This loss of desire for human connection comes from long periods of surviving alone and feeling out of touch with everything that's familiar and informative. It also breeds a sense of inferiority and a lack of worthiness, where the need to stamp one's individuality is paramount.

"If I can live in a tent, anyone can live in a tent." I knew what Astle was

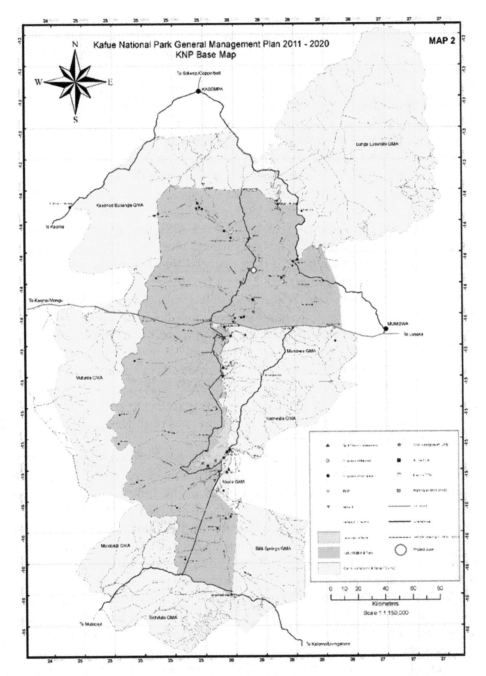

Kafue National Park General Management Plan 2011 - 2020
KNP Base Map

MAP 2

Chunga is where the Chinese M9 road enters the Park from the east, crossing the Kafue River at the Kafue Hook Bridge, and Ngoma is down south next to Lake Itezhi Tezhi

saying: he'd had it rough and now it was my turn.

He was giving me instructions, over the crackling radio, for my first task. I was to build a road of many miles through the miombo woodland. The road was to be a wildlife survey transect – a track that enables biologists to assess species diversity, population size and population movement among other things. I would be accompanied by Wildlife Guards, armed and wearing military uniform. We were to live in the Bush, in tents, surviving on rations and game meat that we shot. We would be miles from camp but it was what I signed up for and even though it was a pointless exercise, since there were tourist roads which could easily serve as transects and I didn't understand Astle's plan, I had to do it.

As we began our work, the tsetse flies were so thick on the spare tyre on the bonnet of our Land Rovers that it appeared to moving. Attracted to anything black, tsetse flies are extremely easy to census. To do so, an employee from the tsetse department would walk through the bush for a standard amount of time with a standardised piece of black cloth attached to their back. The person behind then counted the flies on the fabric.

I worked on the road four days a week for two months. When I was not out building the road, Berit's and my daily routine was quite mundane. We would have an egg and tea and some toast if we had remembered to make bread. This didn't happen if the fridge wasn't working as the butter was just a puddle on a plate. We would sometimes go for a walk and watch the wildlife, the river, and smell the perfumed air of miombo woodland, scented with the Wildlife Guards' cooking and the oily smell of the workshop and hear the wonderful birdsong. Sometimes we would catch sight of the stunning Narina trogon bird. It's blue, red and green plumage was so vibrant that it looked hand-painted.

At 8am I would start work, contributing to the Park management plan. This was being put together by Peter Moss in Ngoma down south, the Park HQ. Peter was an old Zambian hand in the Provincial Administration, the successor of the Colonial Service, straight from Malvern College in Worcestershire at 19. He spoke Bemba and Nyanja, and some Lozi – Zambia has 72 local languages and dialects probably because many tribes ended up in Zambia who lost conflicts elsewhere. I would finish my work with Peter at 2pm, and rest during the afternoon since it was too hot to do anything especially during the rainy season. Berit and I would eat late in the evenings when it was cool. Occasionally we would listen to the radio to hear news or music but generally we had to make our own amusement, much as my parents did when I was born and before. Berit was good at cards and I was good at cheating but she never let me get away with it so we had great fun.

Diversions

As light relief, the local tour operator Cecil Evans and his Italian girlfriend often had barbeques or braais, with guest tourists. There would be chicken, beef and game steaks, sweet potatoes, yams, Heinz Ketchup and Lea & Perrins and large quantities of beer and scotch. He taught me to bark like an angry baboon using a washstand ewer, or growl like a lioness in heat. If carried out properly it gave the tourists a fright, a feeling that they were experiencing true Africa. They'd go very quiet then laugh with embarrassment before listening to whatever it was I was trying to tell them.

Laughter as a weapon was also very useful later in my life when teaching large audiences of students and makes them listen. Cecil also had a speedboat which the tourists liked until he hit a hippo and then they didn't. Cecil was definitely the life and soul of the party with a leopard skin band round his Bush hat and endless energy and bonhomie. In the absence of any other entertainment, Cecil's parties and humour had to suffice for both Berit and I.

We had the occasional visitor. The boss of a very large railway company in North America brought his wife who one night crawled around the fire stark naked and started making noises like a lioness until the big, strong, blond Southern Rhodesian assistants picked her up and took her away. She was embarrassing the other guests and likely to pick up some nasty diseases from the ground. I suspect the young assistants probably took her off to bed. Her husband remained unmoved, seemingly relieved that she had been dealt with.

This somewhat Spartan and curtailed existence at Chunga couldn't last for long. I was essentially a one-man band with no support, and pursuing a pointless exercise. Two months after I arrived, I suggested to Peter Moss that it made more sense for us to be working together in the south. This was true, but in addition Berit had very little to do and although she made the best of it she was bored much of the time. Going south to Ngoma would make a difference to her as there was more activity, a tourist Lodge, and Peter was married with a family.

We settled into a newly built house down south in Ngoma, after I made it abundantly clear I was wasting my time in Chunga being a civil engineer, much to Astle's chagrin. No sooner had we settled in than a wily local chief, who relied on us for batteries and maintenance of his battered Land Rover, demanded that we drive all the wildlife back into the Park which had moved into the tsetse-free zone or Game Management Area (GMA), a buffer area around the Park. This zone of some miles was between the border of the Park and the various human settlements and villages. It had enclosed the few permanent waterholes available during the dry season and of course it attracted wildlife that moved out of the Park. He was within his rights since he knew that some wildlife carried the trypanosomiasis spirochetes that the tsetse fly transmitted to humans but he also knew that

Kafue National Park guards on parade before wildlife drive 1974

it would be virtually impossible to get the wildlife back into the Park. We had seven days to get all the wildlife back otherwise he was within his rights to go in there with his own people and kill whatever nyama they wished. (Nyama is the Bemba word for wildlife and meat which says a lot!)

So we called up the departmental helicopter a Bell Jet Ranger donated by David Shepherd, the artist, for anti-poaching with Jack Uys, the pilot, and the Cessna with John Smith, 20 Land Rovers, 300 armed Wildlife Guards with me helping to command proceedings from the roof of my

Game drive to get animals back into KNP before a deadline passed allowing local villagers to hunt. 1974

Land Rover on a slight hill with a walkie-talkie. Everything went quite well until Jack Uys radio me to say he was trying to get a herd of zebra back in the Park and could I get on the ground with a rifle. I did so only to have the herd stampede directly towards me, driven by Jack, so I fired my .303 rifle and in doing so knocked my glasses off. I spent the next 5 min trying to find my specs since I was so short-sighted it was only by touch I could find them. Afterwards Jack explained that he could only turn the Bell Jet Ranger helicopter to the right and not to the left which is why I got the full benefit of the striped horses! His eccentricities were legion and included swearing in Afrikaans at Zambia Ministers when they got in or out of his flying machine, fearful that they often didn't listen to him and walked towards the rear rotor.

Recovering my vantage point I was able to get this wildlife drive slightly more coordinated and things were going along swimmingly until I got messages that the Wildlife Guards were moving too fast and baby elephants were being left behind. Of course this meant the mothers would turn round and charge the Wildlife Guards who would shoot her dead. So we ended up with two baby orphans who needed gallons of milk a day and we had no cows. They were shipped down to Livingston another National Park where they could be looked after a little better, and had milk, but I learnt later the local vet had mistakenly treated them with a hypodermic syringe containing air.

Berit Swingland, an orphaned elephant and a bottle of powdered milk which was the best we could conjure up

To make things even more exciting I could smell something like burning and I turned round to discover that some bright spark had set fire to the very dry grass behind me from whence the wind was blowing so I was between an inferno which was going too fast and the game drive which was going somewhat slower! The fire certainly was proceeding apace and indeed faster than a man could run. I instructed everybody to stop the game drive turnaround and deal with the fire (by back burning) which was enough of incentive itself to drive the game. By nightfall the fire was out, the game was inside the Park and I was both kippered and exhausted but at least we had saved a lot of wildlife from becoming a stew for the moment!

Day-to-day

The hot water for the house was a 45 gallon oil drum mounted in a brick structure, known as a Rhodesian or donkey boiler, heated by burning wood. We also had running water, but the most important piece of kit was a deep freeze; not from John Lewis in London, who were going to ship a paraffin one, but bought locally from a departing expat. We hired Jonas to help with cleaning, some cooking and as a general houseboy.

The Rhodesian or 'donkey' boiler

Berit found the company of Europeans, the Moss family and Ngoma Lodge guests a godsend as being in deepest Africa was somewhat of a shock being devoid of almost everything that was familiar and commonly available. Rations were a constant headache as we couldn't really function without basics like cooking oil, salt, and vegetables, all of which were unobtainable in the bush. Matches, paraffin for the deep freeze and other items were vital to our survival as Western Europeans, deep inside this vast National Park, which meant a monthly trek of 600 miles return to Lusaka which were often out of the basics when we arrived in those days when strikes and Government mismanagement were rife. The 'jungle drums' of radio information alerted us when a store had a shipment but it was a gamble if there was any left by the time we arrived. Staff rations were of course part of the job and each month we got a leg of the best antelope species (kudu, eland) to eat, as did all the staff. We gave most of it to Jonas.

We frequently had to save tourists in open overloaded Land Rovers who got stuck in sand/mud, offering a delicious target for a notorious local male lion called Shakalonga whose antics involved either charging the front tyre or jumping over the entire open-topped vehicle with tourists shrinking down in horror. While not part of the original job specification, rescuing screaming tourists became part of my work! The Lodge was run by an open-hearted large Rhodesian lady with bleached hair, in love with Star Yamba, a junior Warden. Ngoma Lodge was very popular with both the tourists and the local people. I often joined in drumming parties at the Lodge, and I was absolutely transfixed by the way many of the Wildlife Guards could dance, mimicking the exact habits and postures of wild animals, especially the hamerkop (*Scopus umbretta*).

Ngoma Lodge 2008, 32 years after I lived in the camp

We also had a resident crazy man who was our museum curator and who had collected some of the most bizarre artefacts most of which resembled witchdoctor charms. I learned later that he was indeed a witchdoctor and was called on frequently given he was much cheaper and closer than conventional medicine to the majority in need of 'medical' support.

As the Park biologist I worked for the government and was able to walk around the Park as I chose, occasionally taking tourists with me. Once I took 10 American tourists on a walking safari and told them to keep quiet, keep in line, and if we came across a lion to keep still.

"Don't stare directly at the lion, and especially not at their eyes, don't move, don't try and take photographs, stand stock still and wait until I give the order."

Of course we did come across a lioness directly on the path in front of us.

"Freeze!", I said in a loud whisper.

I was in front with the armed Ranger, but there was no time to shoot a full-grown lioness if she charged as they can cover 30 or 40 yards in seconds. Besides, if the Ranger had only wounded her she would have been more likely to kill quite a few of us.

What paralysed me even further was to hear mewing cubs behind me. We had somehow overlooked the cubs and got between her and her offspring! Hidden in the scrub vegetation just off the path where we hadn't seen them. And then a moron did exactly what threatened us all – a New Yorker stepped out of line and started taking holiday snaps.

John Smith refuelling the Cessna where he used chamois leather filters to prevent dust clogging the engine

She charged and without concern for us she streaked past towards her progeny. The obese, stupid New Yorker collapsed on the ground having either a panic attack or heart attack. Frankly I didn't care which as he had put us all at risk of our lives for his own selfish wishes, and I would have been (pleasantly) unsurprised if she had nailed him.

Our survey pilot John Smith was known to digress from tasks in hand, making occasional visits to see the Litunga (King) in Barotseland in the west of the country. On one such digression I was presented with a carved blackwood (*Dalbergia melanoxylon*) walking stick finished in warthog tusk ivory which I still use today. My Boosey and Hawkes B♭ clarinet is made of the same wood.

The Lozi people of Barotseland live under a highly sophisticated customary system of governance. Barotseland, the Kingdom of the Lozi people, was a protectorate under British colonial rule until it became part of Zambia at the country's independence in 1964; although Queen Victoria had promised the Lozi people their own independent country. The Barotseland Royal Establishment continues to demand independence and their Ngambela, or Prime Minister, has said the Government failed to honour Queen Victoria's deal for the Barotse Kingdom to attain autonomy. The Zambian Government subsequently denounced the call as treason.

On another occasion John flew me down the Kafue River for 100s of miles at a very low level, skimming over the plains and tree tops, zooming over the heads of hippopotamus herds, surprising basking crocodiles, bathing elephants, scattering antelope and other wildlife, leaving me with a similar feeling as when I saw the film '*Out of Africa*' ten years later and the Hon. Denys George Finch Hatton, who was an aristocratic big-game hunter and the lover of Baroness Karen Blixen (also known by her pen name as Isak Dinesen), a Danish noblewoman, flew his Gypsy Moth over great flocks of flamingo in Kenya.

I often used either the Cessna with John Smith or a Bell Jet Ranger helicopter with Jack Uys in my work as well as continuing the transect surveys around the Nkala loop by Land Rover, started by John Hanks years before when he worked in Zambia.

Danger

And then there was a much darker side of being in the Bush in the midst of what is being stolen from Africans on a daily basis by its own politicians and business elite. One has to remember that a poached elephant regardless of the ivory is worth a year's income to the average rural family and so a year in jail is a fair price to pay if you're caught.

The Park Wildlife Guards had planned to raid a poacher's camp they had recently discovered on a foot patrol. Our helicopter had confirmed its

African buffalo, Busanga, KNP. 1974

location from some distance away. We approached this ramshackle look-ing camp in the early evening with a crude conical semi-thatched shaped hut and I moved to duck down and enter the entrance. At which point the Ranger pull me back violently and showed me it was booby-trapped which would have fired some sharp sticks into my guts. We then withdrew quite some distance until the light started to fade and having been completely silent we moved with similar stealth slowly towards the camp again to discover two men crouched over a small fire. For some reason they became alerted to our presence, grabbed their rifles and started shooting. At which point we all started to shoot and there were eight of us, each armed. At the end both were dead and one of our Wildlife Guards was slightly wounded.

The Warden and the deputy Warden in charge of anti-poaching were a class act in their various ways. Neither seem to do very much and I was quite alarmed at first when the Warden walk around the camp with me

Poacher's hideout KNP with Berit peering in guarded by the Ranger and his junior. 1973

hand-in-hand; an apparently perfectly normal and innocent gesture. On the other hand the anti-poaching Warden looked like a hyena and laughed like one. He was a frightening character.

The plumber in my new house at Ngoma was unique and called Nelson. To get from the top corner of a wall to the opposite bottom corner he simply installed the pipe diagonally across the wall while smoking his dagga (marijuana) cigarettes which had turned the whites of his eyes brown.

One day he and others went charging out into the bush when they heard that poachers had shot buffalo in the search of nyama. Then we heard that

The back of my house at Ngoma in 1973 with the wood-burning cooking stove outside and the front in 2008

there had been an accident and rushed out to help. As we drove across the plain towards the riverside rushes bordering the Kafue River we saw a man waving to us. As we approached he removed his hand from his waist and his guts protruded. Unfortunately one buffalo was only wounded, hiding in the rushes, and had gored Nelson. All we could do was to powder the incision with penicillin, roughly sow him up, giving him a lot of marijuana and drove him a long way over the roughest dirt roads to the north of the Park, over the Kafue Hook Bridge and down the other side of the River to the nearest hospital, 200 miles. The Asian doctor wouldn't treat him for fear of retribution should he die and so we had to drive him all the way to Lusaka. Miraculously he appeared 7 weeks later fully recovered and continuing his bizarre plumbing.

Biodiversity thievery

The Convention on International Trade in Endangered Species of Wild Fauna and Flora, CITES, is a multilateral treaty to prevent trade of endangered wild plants and animals. It came into force in 1975. There was also the Species Survival Commission of IUCN, the international group of ecologists who gave their services free. When I was in Zambia, CITES wasn't invented and IUCN operated with the World Wildlife Fund (WWF); IUCN being the brains funded by the money of WWF. IUCN was established in 1948 and in 1961 created WWF to fund its operations.

At the time, wildlife products from game meat, horns, tusks, skins, and every other part of animal, as well as many valuable plants such as orchids, were being snatched from the wild and no doubt shipped out using many ingenious tricks including diplomatic bags; a cover that I was to come across many times in the next few decades. Over the succeeding years I became well aware of the increasingly illegal trade in wildlife. Today it is a multi-billion-dollar business which frequently involves politicians and other powerbrokers in cahoots with international crime syndicates. The depletion of wildlife worldwide is giving new significance and purpose to zoos, and the use of scientific technology such as cloning to recreate extinct species. The world's 7.6 billion people represent just 0.01% of all living things by biomass yet since the dawn of civilisation, humanity has caused the loss of 83% of all wild mammals and half of plant biomass, while livestock kept by humans abounds.

A new work[39] is the first comprehensive estimate of the weight of every class of living creature and overturns some long-held assumptions. Bacteria are indeed a major life form – 13% of total – but plants overshadow bac-

---

39 *Living Planet Report* (2018) Zoological Society of London (ZSL) and WWF. Bar-On, Y.M., Phillips, R. & Milo, R. (2018) The biomass distribution on Earth. *Proc. Natl. Acad. Sci.* **115(25)**: 6506–6511. https://doi.org/10.1073/pnas.1711842115

teria, representing 82% of all living matter. All other creatures, from insects to fungi, to fish and animals, make up only 5% of the world's biomass.

And the days I spent in the Bush alone, as I was permitted to do, since I had the power of arrest and other responsibilities, especially to walk unaccompanied, brought me much closer to nature and to be able to listen to its noises and discover every step I took something fascinating. This is a habit I had pursued for the last 70 years. People never stop talking, mostly vacuously, looking without seeing or realising without knowing what they could experience if only they shut up, paid attention or informed themselves.

I arrested three Cabinet Ministers in their Mercedes at one of the Park gates one evening with trunks/boots full of shot illegal game. I told the Wildlife Guards to take them to our jail. Early next morning I went to the jail to see how much they would threaten me – 'mzungu' – but the jail was empty and I thought they had bribed their way free. They hadn't as the Wildlife Guards and Rangers, drilled by the Provincial/Colonial Administration adage that poaching was the greatest sin, had handcuffed them to the outside of the jail. Shakalonga was roaming with his pride that evening hunting, although they normally slept on my veranda, and the Minsters were white with fear. I let them go after confiscating the game meat, the rifles and let them rush off in their Mercedes Benz.

That evening Shakalonga was at a buffalo kill with a female who had the temerity to approach before he had eaten. She's about to be cuffed by him. I was on foot and I suddenly came across this scene, before retiring carefully

We had been asked by President Kaunda to get him crested guinea fowl for release on his Lion Hill estate outside the capital Lusaka. I used the best poacher we had and got ready; thinking this business with the Ministers would have me hanged. Knowing this I used the Departmental helicopter and flew straight in with the guinea fowl for tea with Kaunda. Having released them I explained they'd die as they only eat termites and there were none on the estate that I could see so he'd need minced meat. Then he broached the business of the Ministers and after 10 minutes he said he'd not fire them as nyama was the customary passion (nyama = meat also same word for wildlife) but he'd fine them one year's salary with a warning. He wanted them still in post to advertise the punishment for killing wildlife that was the future life blood of Zambia's economy alongside copper and other minerals – at least that's what he said after a further 20 minutes with me. He kept his word. Corruption is everywhere and especially amongst the rich and politically powerful. Defeating it depends on what the corrupt want, whether it can be satiated without harm and how scared they are.

Biodiversity sharing

Data harvested by ecological anthropologists about the use of animals and plants provides essential facts for conservation and intelligent management; such as the fruits of the sausage tree (*Kigelia africana*) as replacement springs for an old 'banger' aka car, and vegetation and animals which the rural people can easily survive on sustainably.

CAMPFIRE (Communal Areas Management Programme for Indigenous Resources) was developed by Brian Child[40] (a Rhodesian, who is now Associate Professor, Department of Geography, Center for Africa Studies, University of Florida) with whom I worked. One of the first programmes, started in Zimbabwe, to consider wildlife as renewable natural resources, while addressing the allocation of its ownership and benefits to indigenous peoples in and around conservation protected areas. One of the first attempts to ensure local communities benefitted down to the village level and giving value to the wildlife in their area and not stolen by the hunting companies or politicians; in other words, avoiding the Tragedy of the Commons where nobody owns anything or, if you like, everybody owns everything. During 1989–2001, CAMPFIRE generated over £12 million of transfers to the participating communities, 89% of which came from sport hunting, but, driven by American desire to include endangered species, it faltered and died, helped by political corruption.

Trying to ensure local people and communities benefitted from the natural resources around them has been a mission of mine. Attending the

---

40   http://www.library.ufl.edu/spec/manuscript/guides/child.htm

1990 preparation meetings (PrepComm) in Nairobi for the upcoming Earth Summit 1992, I became involved in drafting the Convention on Biological Diversity (CBD), known informally as the Biodiversity Convention.

Trying to draft tight and comprehensive paragraphs for the treaty to ensure material gain for local people including their detailed knowledge of what plants and animal species could be used for was incredibly difficult. This needed the help of lawyers who were there from some of the most prestigious American institutions trying to define legally who constituted the beneficiaries to stop mass migration should a biodiversity 'goldmine' be discovered. And who would enforce this multilateral treaty since the national wildlife services both in Zambia and Kenya were deteriorating by this time and become battlegrounds between politicians, conservationists and communities?

It is ironic that at the Summit the late President George Bush Snr, who spent just a few hours at the meeting, refused to sign the Biodiversity Convention saying that it would cause unemployment in the United States. This international treaty was adopted in 1992 – one day after the UNFCCC (United Nations Framework Convention on Climate Change) – and signed by every country in the world except the USA. President Bill Clinton, who took office in 1993, did provide his signature, but the agreement failed to get Senate approval. His response was that, "an extensive system of (US) Federal and State wildlife refuges, marine sanctuaries, wildlife management areas, recreation areas, Parks, and forests" existed which protected the natural environment in the USA but overlooked the rest of the world. This remains the situation today and although it has made little difference until now President Donald Trump has had a devastating effect on conservation legislation in favour of industrial growth.

Like CAMPFIRE, if ever these key paragraphs had worked in practice, preventing beneficiaries being inundated by 'gold diggers', local people and poverty, even starvation, would not be so prevalent and perhaps there would be much more wildlife around since the sense of ownership would incentivise local people to conserve what was theirs. Community ownership is a vital ingredient for conservation against politicians and governments grabbing what they can. The objectives of the Convention on Biological Diversity are, "the conservation of biological diversity, the sustainable use of its components, and the fair and equitable sharing of the benefits arising out of the utilisation of genetic resources" (Article 1). These are translated into binding commitments in Articles 6 to 20.

It has been known for some time that Amerindian peoples of the Rupununi area of Guyana, South America chew the nuts of the greenheart tree (*Ocotea rodiaei*) as a crude form of contraception. While I was chairman of

Iwokrama, Guyana I became aware that an individual, Conrad Gorinsky[41], had successfully applied for a patent in America to own the key chemical constituent in direct contravention of the Biodiversity Convention without any known benefit either to Guyana or most especially to the Rupununi who lived around Iwokrama and had used it sustainably for centuries. A similar scam surrounded the Peruvian cat's claw (*Uncaria tomentosa*), a woody vine found in the tropical jungles of South and Central America. The plant root bark is sold as a dietary supplement or slimming aid. Many Peruvian conservation lawyers work very hard to try and ensure this benefited those who had imparted the knowledge of its use.

Biodiversity politics

During the 80s, the conservationist Sir Peter Scott invited me to join World Conservation Union IUCN and in 1984 at the General Assembly, I was in Madrid when HRH Prince Philip, president of WWF International, with the director general Charles de Haes[42], presided over the divorce of the funding arm of the WWF from IUCN, which the public had hardly heard of, leaving all the *pro bono* expertise in IUCN without funds to function, and the well-known WWF with all the money needing to hire masses of expert staff worldwide for every national WWF, which increased their overheads fourfold i.e. less money committed to action on the ground.

IUCN, unknown to most of the world, had to run around finding the funds to survive and becoming, in effect, a consultancy company popping up automatically on World Bank project documentation as the preferred conservation consultant. WWF, known throughout the world, saw its overheads go through the roof as they had to hire a forest officer, a marine officer and many other specialist officers for each country; meaning that only a small percentage of every $1 donated to WWF hit a project since 1984 whereas before it was most of the donation.

Joshua Nkoma's Zimbabwe People's Revolutionary Army was briefly in southern KNP before I left, decimating wildlife to supply his men, and attacking Rhodesia's PM Ian Smith while Robert Mugabe attacked from Mozambique. Robert Mugabe, a Shona, was supported by the Chinese, and Joshua Nkomo, an Ndebele Zulu, supported by Russia. In 1979 the Republic of Zimbabwe was established with Mugabe winning the election. The Shona became a supermajority in the country. I went to visit Nkoma at his camp and his response was that he had to feed his men for freedom so machine gunning water buck was acceptable "even if inedible".

---

41   https://www.theguardian.com/science/2019/sep/12/conrad-gorinsky-obituary
42   https://www.independent.co.uk/news/uk/wildlife-charity-tries-to-end-strife-nich-olas-schoon-looks-at-how-two-years-of-infighting-have-1480622.html

Living in a conservation camp

There were many Wildlife Guards and many wives since polygyny was common and reproduction ran at a high rate – children were in effect their old age pension. On one occasion during the rainy season there was a riot and we had to go into their camp and quell the troublemakers. Unfortunately many freshly dug long-drops (toilets) were still open, and not encased with 45 gallon oil drums and a small cubicle, and had filled with rainwater. Some babies fell off their mothers backs in the panic and drowned. It was a tragedy but I discovered tragedies, danger and death were commonplace in wild Africa.

We locked up one of the miscreants in the biologist's store. The following morning he looked quite white and died for no apparent reason a few weeks later. We were told that the presence of a bloody duiker's skull in the store was a very bad omen and according to the locals would have cast a spell on him causing his death.

The Itezhi Tezhi dam was being built nearby by Impregilo Recchi, an Italian consortium, to control the Kafue River for hydroelectricity and it would flood part of the Park and increase human incursion. The Itezhi Tezhi manager, a very charming Italian, invited us to dinner during which we were called to the hospital to see one of our staff who was badly hurt. He had been to the dam site store to pick up paraffin and acquired two floozies. Returning home the Land Rover went into a culvert. He was with

Land Rover after hitting a culvert off-road with my assistant's body underneath

my scientific assistant whose dead body we found the next morning when righting the overturned vehicle. He had just returned from six months training at Edinburgh University, and his highly educated widow (she had O-levels), in the absence of his income, would be forced to marry his eldest brother under tribal custom whom she loathed. Peter Moss and I managed to ensure that his widow got a pension by saying he was on duty acting on my orders against the negative attitude of the local police chief. The two floozies just disappeared.

Many other instances of working in wildlife management enlarged my experience of how rural communities in central Africa functioned. Rushing north in a Land Rover to catch someone stealing at Chunga caused a back wheel to overtake us; the nuts had not been screwed tight. It took us five hours to find one or two nuts so we could proceed.

A particular bull elephant frequented one of the tourist loops or trails and always charged my Land Rover whoever was driving it. Unfortunately it encouraged some to take out tourists in my vehicle who paid privately to have a 5-ton killer charge for a story to tell back home. This activity was prohibited in Government vehicles with number plates starting GRZ and belonging to the Wildlife Department. Notwithstanding the restrictions, GRZ vehicles were known colloquially as 'Go Round Zambia' vehicles, and their use for private purposes was widespread.

Some alarming customs kept me constantly amused, such as an old lady who greeted me by beating her own chest with her crossed arms and then lying on her back with her head towards my feet. Similarly when men shook hands in Zambia they frequently lightly held their right forearm with their left hand as a gesture of harmlessness. The reason being that in days gone by when someone approached the chief they could prove they weren't armed with a dagger by these performances.

Berit befriended Peter's wife Judy, who was pregnant and not taking malarial prophylactics. She became desperately ill, cerebral malaria as we found out later, and we needed to get a plane to get her to hospital quickly. When I got the news, we were still at Chunga and for some reason Peter couldn't get hold of the Cessna pilot. He contacted me by radio to see what I could do. Cerebral malaria is a severe neurological complication of malarial infection with *Plasmodium falciparum*; sufferers fall into a coma and Peter told me that Judy had lost consciousness.

"Ian, I'm losing her. I'm not sure what's wrong exactly but I think she's got malaria or blackwater fever. We need to get to a hospital pretty damn quickly. Do whatever you can, Bwana! I can't lose her and the baby. I am helpless here. I don't know what to do."

For a man who had faced enormous dangers this was an extreme *cri de coeur* and I ran to the radio shack to call for the pilot. As I darted between a

Land Rover and the garage wall a black-necked spitting cobra rose up and spat its venom into both my eyes, fortunately hitting my spectacle lenses dead centre. I had no time to panic and continued running for the radio room.

I got hold of John Smith, the Cessna pilot, who landed at Ngoma one hour later. He even had a doctor with him. Only afterwards did I look at my glasses which were still dripping with venom. I washed them under the tap but didn't clean my face for fear the poison would get into my eyes. I just patted it with tissue and thanked my lucky stars for my terrible eyesight. Venom in the eyes results in pain, inflammation, eyelid closure and corneal erosions or scarring and blindness. When venom is spat into the eye, the cranial nerve may be affected by local spread of venom. No wonder I ended up in the Royal Eye Hospital, Moorfields, thirty-five years later after going blind in both eyes with retinal detachment after lens replacement.

Judy survived, had her son (who I met for the first time since then in 2017 at 43 years old) and continued to cook great curries on the outside stove at the back door of their house.

I discovered that under extreme circumstances I can remain very philosophical and focused. If something needs doing, my attitude is do it now, do it quickly, and get it right, otherwise chill. As far as the cobra was concerned it had already done its worst and failed.

The longer you spend the more you see

I'd been driving alone and had spotted two intertwined black mambas (*Dendroaspis polylepis*) on the road. I thought they were fighting and since they are the fastest snakes on the ground, able to whip along at 7mph, I quickly leant over to grab my camera. I turned back and came face to face with the snakes. They were inches from the open window and staring right at me. Since they can strike in a second there was nothing to do but freeze. Then it occurred to me that they might have been having sex rather than fighting and I hoped that this distraction might get the better of them. They slowly edged downwards and after a minute or two I looked out of the window and they were at it again.

Being alone out in the bush was not advisable for example when the bloody Land Rover got a wheel stuck and tipped into an aardvark hole with only one front and one back wheel in touch with the ground (in those days you couldn't lock the wheels) and I thought I'd be there forever, alone.

So I sat down to think of a solution and saw a great big, black millipede the locals call a foot long Shongololo worm (*Archispirostreptus gigas*) crawling over my hand. It's a beautiful bit of engineering, all the legs functioning and appearing like a wave down the body. It was glistening and shiny. Quite harmless. Guinea fowl, which are always making a fuss about something, woke me up in the morning and are pretty good at telling you something nasty is nearby. But there's such a sense of eternal peace and order. Danger is only born by the necessity to survive, I think. Almost as if you play by the rules then the forest looks after you. Baboons and leopards seem to have a constant battle going on. I saw a leopard being chased up a tree by a large male baboon several times that was obviously pissed off about something. When it rains in the woodland the smells become stronger. You can smell the trees and the fungi around their roots which help them grow so well in this rather poor soil.

I fixed the stuck Land Rover by stacking everything heavy to get the other back wheel down from spare jerry cans of fuel, spare tyres and anything else while shoving any logs I could find under the front wheel in the aardvark hole. With a lot of swearing and bouncing up and down I was able to edge the machine free.

When we were building the road there was another very clear example of why being alone in the African bush, as delightful as it is, is not the most sensible thing to do. I'd been sleeping outside under the mosquito net when rain started falling on my face. Funny I thought, in the dry season! Then I opened my eyes and look into the eyes of the hyena whose jaws were hovering above me, saliva oozing. The rain that turned out to

Road construction camp. Miombo woodland near Chunga, Kafue NP 1973. The mosquito nets are hanging near the Land Rover where I was sleeping when the hyena took a fancy to me for dinner. I'm wearing a red turtle neck as at that altitude (1350 m) in the dry season mornings were chilly

be foul-smelling hyena drool. The full-blood Zulu who was in charge of the road-building work gang came racing over, half-naked, screaming and brandishing a panga, a machete. He was more terrifying than the hyena who scarpered. The whole camp was on guard the rest of the night.

The Zulu, like me, was pretty pissed off about constructing a road and thought it a waste of time. I decided not to share the fact that I agreed with him as he was covered in scars, a real tough guy. But he kept the camp supplied with plenty of game meat which together with nshima, a type of maize flour porridge made in Africa and part of our weekly rations, kept us going.

In the woods I saw wandering aardvarks and the extraordinary Secretary Bird that looks like a supermodel but can stomp a snake to death. Exactly like a supermodel! My favourite was the honey badger. No bigger than a Welsh corgi, busily snuffling around. Not to be messed with though, kills and eats snakes and is immune to venom. If they get bitten they might be paralysed for a few hours but then they wake up and eat the snake they've already killed.

International 'aid'

The completion of a Kafue Hook Bridge across the river on the Chinese-built Lusaka-Mongu M9 Road saw the arrival of a Chinese minister along with Zambia's first president, Kenneth Kaunda, in a chopper waving his white handkerchief through the window. He was a remarkable public performer who I rather liked. He could cry on demand for effect and once tearfully railed against leading a nation of drunkards. The road was good for getting chillies which grew in clumps every 10 miles or so. Chilli seeds germinate better when passed through a mammalian gut and these bushes of Chao Tian Jiao, or facing heaven chillies, were clearly of the same origin and marked where the Chinese labourers' camps located their toilets.

Everyone was welcome to this public event as is typical in Africa. A lot of local chiefs turned up dressed in termite-eaten leopard skins and a lot of native beer was drunk. This was made by the women chewing cooking bananas and spitting into a barrel. Others, presumably Zambian ministers, arrived in their European suits with chauffeur driven Mercedes-Benz. Kaunda kept repeating the phrase, "One China, One Zambia," as mantras to no doubt further lubricate Chinese investment. The Kafue Hook Bridge was reported to be collapsing in 2015[43] through a total lack of maintenance since its commissioning in 1963. Kaunda, at the time of writing, is the oldest living African president at 96 years old.

China had paid for the road and much else, and Chinese imports such

---

43 http://www.daily-mail.co.zm/hook-bridge-pillars-cracking/; http://www.parlia-ment.gov.zm/node/6332

Chinese Ambassador and President Kenneth Kaunda when opening the Kafue Hook Bridge 1973

as matches and bikes, were everywhere. These did not have a good reputation with the Zambians. The matches were called Double Happiness but since two were needed to make them work, they were quickly nicknamed Double Strike. The pushbikes were also cheap and fairly useless. The Zambians bought British Raleigh bikes as they lasted even though they cost an enormous amount.

It was at this event that I learnt that China offered large amounts of international aid to many developing countries but in exchange for whatever natural resources they had. In subsequent years I saw this happen in South America, the rest of Africa, Bangladesh, Sri Lanka, Guyana and Indonesia. Zambia had copper, precious stones, precious metals and of course an immense amount of wildlife products such as ivory, snakes and other species of biodiversity that the Chinese use in medicine. The Chinese government continues this practice to this day and works on the principle that they'd rather exhaust other countries natural resources before exhausting their own.

Most countries are incapable of enforcing international regulations and protocols in regard of wildlife conservation. Zambia carries one of the highest debts to China in the world which has tripled over the last three years[44]. Greater spending keeps Zambian politicians in power, which in

44 https://www.economist.com/leaders/2018/09/15/zambias-looming-debt-crisis-is-

Zambia's case includes two expanded airports, together with VIP facilities (for politicians and their business elite clients) they don't need. China has threatened to seize back its overseas assets from countries that don't pay up and in Africa's case China has frozen investment. Zambia, along with 29 other African countries, had many of its debts wiped clean since 2005 under the IMF's 'heavily indebted poor countries' (HIPC) scheme, encouraging more profligacy.

Sex

I was almost asleep when I sensed a dreadful smell pervading the humid air. Perhaps we'd left something near the stove and now it was melting? I got out of bed as quietly as I could and was just putting my flip-flops on when I jumped out of my skin. Someone or something had let out a rip-roaring fart on the veranda. What was out there? I didn't want Berit to wake up so I dropped to the floor on my hands and knees. There was another rumble, a deeper note, but much longer. I sniggered and crawled out of the bedroom and towards the mosquito screen. I slowly pulled myself upwards. Could that be? Was it? Yes! It was.

A surge of joy raced through me as I saw that our veranda was completely covered in sleeping lionesses – a whole pride, gently flopped over each other. My heart pumped in amazement as I watched their chests rising and falling, their whiskers twitching and their tails lifting slightly as they happily snored the night away. Finally, my eyes rested on a large black maned lion with only half a tail. Wow!

Shakalonga and his pride often slept on our veranda which didn't make Berit feel any better. We would get up at dawn like Shakalonga and his mistresses, who normally shifted off to get some food early – we all wanted to make the most of the cooler temperatures. From then on, I looked for the lions every night. They were always there and I wanted to know more about them. So, without worrying Berit at the outset, or alerting the Warden, as I didn't know if he would have shot them, I asked the Wildlife Guards.

"Shakalonga," they told me. "His name is Shakalonga. He sleeps here. With his females."

I was enchanted and as the weeks went by we became acclimatised to our surroundings, we nervously accepted the lions. Of course, this was our main entrance and it did mean that we were trapped inside the house all night. We couldn't step outside to look at the full African moon for example. But it was a small sacrifice. And quite incredible to see the impala sleeping so soundly on the other side of the house, so close to their preda-

a-warning-for-the-rest-of-africa

tors and seemingly unbothered.

Male lions compete to take over female prides. When they manage it, they kill all the offspring that aren't theirs. This is so the females will start giving birth to the new male's offspring. The lion doesn't want to bring up a cub that doesn't have his genes. The lionesses produce and rear the young, and are the main hunter killers, while the males take up the laid-back role but have first choice at a kill.

Lionesses can give birth throughout the year, and come into oestrous sooner if their previous litter has been lost. Pride takeover by solitary males or in coalitions of related or unrelated males can result in a drop in the birth rate through lower female fertility in the short term. It is not known why but possibly this is due to having had previous litters killed by the new male.

Females come into oestrus and give birth at the same times as other pride members because birth synchrony results in increased cub survival. The cubs are mature at two years old and are able to defend themselves before another adult male is likely to take over and bumps off cubs. Males have a much longer effective reproductive life if they operate in coalitions[45]. If two males take over they are commonly brothers, so that the cubs are all related to both males. Males are needed to stick around as long as possible by the females, who require about two years to rear a cub to a point where it can more likely survive until breeding age[46], and to protect them from the other males intent on taking over.

Zambian women no doubt want their men to stay around primarily to maintain stability and fend off other men which will upset the social equilibrium. They also want to increase the odds that they'll be able to raise their children to sexual maturity without incident. Fitness in Darwinian terms means having as many progeny as possible and rearing them to the point they can reproduce themselves.

Some years later I was in the Seychelles, working on the Aldabra Atoll coral island, when a letter arrived addressed to Bwana Dr Ian, Indian Ocean. It had a Zambian stamp. How it arrived is a complete mystery but it read, "Dear Bwana, Dr Ian, I want another job as a glader driver as I am very keen and hopeful. I beg to be a caterpillar. Moses." I was confused until the memory of delivering the baby surfaced. The baby's father had been called Moses, the man who with his wife had given me my introduction to life in the raw in the African bush. He was the Park grader driver ('r's are a problem for some Zambians) and used a massive machine for mak-

---

45 Bertram, B.C.R. (1975) Social factors influencing reproduction in wild lions. *J. Zool.* **177(4)**: 463–482.

46 Packer, C. & Pusey, A.E. (1983) Adaptations of female lions to infanticide by incoming males (Panthera leo). *American Naturalist* **121**: 716–728.

ing dirt roads. The grader was made by the Caterpillar Company, hence the man wishing to be a 'caterpillar'. He frequently ran the 12-cylinder engine dry of water causing months of work by mechanics. I pondered that it was probably during this time that he and his many wives added to the population. I hoped that their children arrived safely into the world and certainly with a softer landing than the concrete floor of Shakalonga's honeymoon suite

A bientôt or see you soon

My year in Zambia was a time when I was first immersed in the whole business of wildlife management and community relations which are at the heart of conservation. Most of the civil service worldwide believe that they can manage wildlife, as do pen pushers in many conservation organisations, but my experience is that governments are particularly bad at running *in situ* conservation.

Very often it's the private sector that is very efficient in managing conservation as they have 'skin in the game'. Civil servants do not and cannot be fired easily. Charities are often self-serving, being more concerned with surviving financially, but some are effective as they also have a lot to lose if they don't get it right. And if they get it right and save a species or area, and achieve their aim, do they shut up shop? No! Corruption is endemic in most countries, and this extends to government departments, while the success of the private sector and some charities depends on tight management and weeding out fiddling. That is not to say that the private sector or charities are devoid of corruption.

It is clear to me that short-termism, which is the nature of politics worldwide, as politicians are only concerned with getting re-elected next time round, and not the long-term future, is anathema to the long-term consistency needed in effective conservation. Tribal habits and customs evolve over hundreds or thousands of years to fit the environment are, by definition, sustainable practices from which we can learn. British colonialism recognised this and used the existing tribal governance systems, hybridising it with British civil services practices. However, the invention of politicians, with their short term objectives and selfish intent, overriding the existing cultural practices and natural hierarchies, has caused chaos and conflict.

I have great affection for many Zambians especially rural communities and their culture.

Most five-year plans for agriculture and anything else fail in Zambia, and they relied on international aid especially China to get by, but they are a peace loving people. Their society was a matriarchal matrilineal one, which meant that rural women did most of the work and the men did very little. This business of who really runs the show pervades both human and animal societies. Darwin's theory of natural selection (or survival of the fittest) derives in part from two fundamental observations; males compete, females choose. In Africa especially, men compete for space and access to resources and expect the women to manage these assets for the family once they have chosen which males have succeeded best. Who do you think is actually running the show?

And we returned again in 2008

In October 2008 I visited the Kafue National Park after a 37 year absence to support Peter Moss in writing a visitor's guide[47]. When I arrived in Lusaka I was met by Peter who organised the trip which I paid for entirely. I hosted a meal for a large number of people including Kaj Østergaard (Danish Embassy), Director General Lewis Saiwana Zambia Wildlife Authority (ZAWA), Jean Michel Pavy (World Bank Environment) and Errol Hickey (Zambia Tourist Board). During the conversation the representative from the Danish Embassy confirmed they were no longer able to support the work needed to prepare the visitor's guide and this was confirmed in a letter from the Danish Ambassador Thomas Schjerbeck in a letter to Errol Hickey dated 17 November 2008. I offered to support the project personally on hearing this and Errol Hickey suggested my gift was paid to the Tourist Board which Peter agreed.

We set off early the following day to drive to the Park with Safari Guide Joshua Chisuwo and stayed with Edjan and Robyn-Anne Van der Heide at Mukambi Lodge while visiting Chunga (my original posting) and Shishamba Loop meeting up with the KNP northern Area manager. The next day we drove north visiting Kafwala and Lufupa and overnighting at the Plains Camp in North Busanga. We then returned south staying with Edjan and Robyn-Anne again en route to the centre of the Park and reached Nanzhila via Ngoma (Park HQ) where we met Dr Francis Mkanda Southern Area Manager. We stayed with Steve Smith at Nanzhila Plains Lodge for a couple of nights exploring the ItezhiTezhi area, where the dam was being constructed when I worked in the Park, Ngoma forest (an ancient hardwood teak forest which has now been burnt to the ground) and the Nkala loop where I used to survey wildlife populations following surveys started by John Hanks.

We returned to Lusaka via Mumbwa and met Richard Jeffery, pilot and well-known conservationist, whose son Phil Jeffery, together with Tyrone McKeith, had developed a tourism business in Zambia. They first met

---

47   *A Visitor's Guide to Kafue National Park, Zambia* (2013) Peter Moss (Author), John Hanks (Editor).

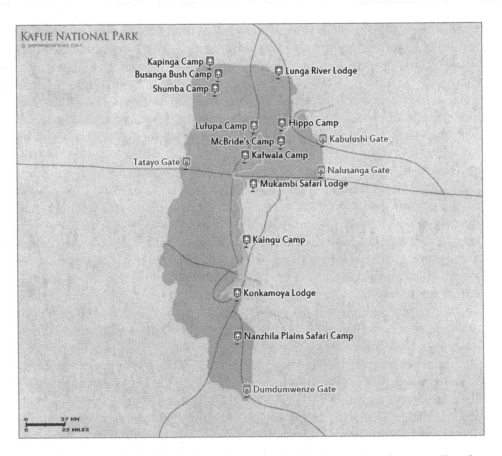

KAFUE NATIONAL PARK

Kapinga Camp
Busanga Bush Camp
Shumba Camp
Lunga River Lodge
Lufupa Camp
Hippo Camp
McBride's Camp
Kabulushi Gate
Kafwala Camp
Tatayo Gate
Nalusanga Gate
Mukambi Safari Lodge
Kaingu Camp
Konkamoya Lodge
Nanzhila Plains Safari Camp
Dumdumwenze Gate

37 KM
23 MILES

as University roommates where both were studying for degrees, "at the world renowned 'Durrell Institute of Conservation Ecology' – University of Kent UK. During that time Phil and Tyrone hatched the idea of establishing an ethical safari business, whose goal would be to utilise expert local knowledge, provide employment for the local people and adhere to strong ecological and conservationist values, principles which continue to underpin Jeffery & McKeith Safaris. Today, Musekese [near Hippo Camp] & Ntemwa [in the northern Busanga Plain] camps are globally recognised for their quality safari experience and the incredible passion and extreme dedication of J&M's promotion and conservation of the wildlife of the Kafue. Currently, Phil and Tyrone are working hard to promote 'Musekese Conservation' whilst maintaining the global reputation that Jeffery & McKeith Safaris and its two camps, Musekese and Ntemwa, have established."[48]

All of the Camps were superb and their owners showed us extraordinary hospitality. The trip was most memorable, visiting a place where I earned my spurs for the first time in wildlife conservation and community relations. Everything privately owned or outside the Park was well devel-

48   https://www.jefferymckeith.com/your-hosts

oped but inside the Park things have fallen apart; the roads, my former house, Ngoma Lodge and the shocking drop in large mammal numbers from poaching and too much burning, no doubt to encourage the larger mammals as this management practice stimulated the growth of fresh grass which was very attractive to ungulates and other very edible species. From that point of view it was a depressing trip and clearly the Kafue National Park was now badly managed probably as a result of a lack of investment and the political shenanigans.

However *A Visitor's Guide to Kafue National Park, Zambia* by Peter Moss (Author) with John Hanks (Editor) was published in 2013 and I was asked to add a commendation: "At last we have an invaluable and long awaited guide to the Kafue National Park embedded in the heart of Africa, the centre of Zambia; rich in biodiversity, with an enviable list of flora and fauna and intimate, private Lodges and exquisite camps resting in unspoilt landscape. This compact book will be a friend to newcomers and a detailed reference for those who have visited the Park already. Anything you need to know is here. We hope that the guide will help you enjoy this vast, unspoilt wilderness so you can come away understanding its secrets and with a love of its tranquillity as we have."

It goes without saying that sustainable tourism is a major source of revenue from wildlife providing the locals can share the benefits and together with the owners protect and conserve the biodiversity, the source of their income. Peter Moss taught me so much in my first job since leaving academia, and about Central Africa.

We had planned a piece of work to examine where aid has not fulfilled the aspirations of both donors and recipients in Africa, and why the billions donated have had so little lasting effect, in contrast to the lasting success of some notable exceptions. With that in mind, three eminent wildlife authorities carried out surveys in eleven of these countries over 60 years ago to assess the status of these resources and to provide guidelines to governments and other related agencies for their optimum use, management and enhancement for long-term socio-economic development. Since the value of wild resources remains as high, if not higher, in their relevance to these societies today as they did previously, this project aimed to revisit the field route and works of Sir Julian Huxley, UNESCO 1960[49], Sir Frank Fraser Darling, OUP, 1960[50] and Prof. E.B. Worthington for the Nature Conservancy, HM Stationery Office, 1960[51], to record the varying levels of im-

---

49 Huxley, J. (1961) *The Conservation of wild life and natural habitats in Central and East Africa.* A report on a mission accomplished for UNESCO July–September 1960. Paul Dupont. Ns.61/D.31/A.
50 Darling, F.F. (1960) *Wild life in an African territory: A study made for the Game and Tsetse Control Department of Northern Rhodesia.* OUP.
51 Worthington, E.B. (1960) *The Wild Resources of East and Central Africa.* HMSO London.

pact, successes and failures in implementation of the earlier recommendations and to make scientific comparison of the present with the past. We never got round to it!

I owed him so much for being a staunch friend not only in Zambia but in later years around Asia where he worked as a consultant as I did part-time. I made sure he was remembered by drafting his obituary in *The Daily Telegraph*[52].

Colonial Office No. 352

52 Swingland, I. (2017) https://www.telegraph.co.uk/obituaries/2017/07/28/peter-moss-pioneer-ecosafari-obituary/

CHAPTER 7
Oxford and Aldabra Atoll 1974–1977

Leaving again

We landed in Oslo from Zambia via Nairobi and London and were picked up by her family chauffeur. Astrid and Sven Viig were most welcoming as were Berit's sister and husband. The parents lived at Ljan, south east of Oslo, and sometimes in a summer house in the southern islands of Jomfruland.

Once back in Norway in early 1974 we went cross-country skiing (langlauf) soon after arrival at Geilo in the Hardangervidda. It had become clear that Berit wanted to pursue her career as an organic chemist, stay close to her family in Norway, while I was determined to work on biodiversity and conservation worldwide. We returned to Oslo from skiing in separate cars and this culminated in spending 10 minutes with the Fylkesmannen or county governor of Oslo who had the power to formalise our divorce with the help of our lawyers. A civilised process since we had no argument, no shared assets and no children.

Divorcing was the right thing to do since neither Berit nor I would have been happy if one of us had to give up a lifelong passion and career for the sake of the other. Sven Viig, my former father-in-law, was good enough to compensate me for the extra cost of leaving Zambia much earlier than planned and organised a plane to take me home. Since it was Easter and Oslo airport, then Fornebu, was closed I ended up as the sole passenger on a jet to London. Berit and I had been married for 700 days.

Now what to do? No job, no money, no prospects, stuck! And I was living with my mother in her house in Totteridge which was far from ideal. I was at a loose end. I made a trip to Canada via Ann Arbor, Michigan where my cousins Michael and Helen Radock lived. He was Vice President for University Relations and Professor of Journalism for the University of Michigan from 1961–1981 and then advisor to the Mott Foundation at Flint.

I was interviewed by Schlumberger Limited, the world's largest oilfield services company, who wanted young men who would go anywhere and do anything.

"Have you ever bribed officials in any country to get your way?"

"Could you stripped down a Land Rover and put it back together so it worked?"

"Can you handle a gun? Have you ever shot anybody?"

I answered 'Yes' to all the questions although I had only worked on fairly basic Land Rovers unlike Peter Moss's vehicle in Zambia which he drove from England and was six cylinders and sophisticated. The pay was astronomical and they looked after their people very well but I was not a geologist and although I could probably have learnt what was necessary quite quickly I would have got used to the large pay packet and the constant global travelling that would have stymied any private life, and, as with Shell, feel trapped.

Zoology Department, Oxford University

Then I noticed an advert in a *Nature* for a job to work as a research assistant on giant tortoises based at Oxford University but under the Royal Society on the island of Aldabra Atoll, Indian Ocean. This suited me ideally as after all the past events and giving up a fascinating job in Zambia I needed something challenging, that took up all my energies and intellect, in some remote location so I could reconstitute myself.

I was interviewed at the Royal Society in Carlton House Terrace where, admitting my ignorance of reptiles, Angus Bellairs, who was a renowned herpetologist, physician, surgeon, veterinarian and had the chair in vertebrate anatomy at St Mary's Hospital Medical School, merely replied, "I'm sure you'll pick it up as you go along." Another, who was a parasitologist, asked about the molluscicide Frescon and I satisfied him with my knowledge.

I accepted the job as a Post-doctoral Research Assistant, University of Oxford, to work on the reproductive biology of the Aldabra giant tortoise with Dr Malcolm Coe in the Zoology Department and promptly left for Canberra to attend the 16th International Ornithological Congress, Canberra, Australia, 12–17 August 1974 knowing many members of the Oxford department were bound to be there as it housed the Edward Grey Institute of Field Ornithology.

I spent some time with a bunch of Commonwealth Scientific and Industrial Research Organisation (CSIRO) ecologists like Peter Fullagar who brought the Lord Howe Island Woodhen, a flightless rail very similar to the species on Aldabra, back from the brink of extinction. And R. Mykytowycz[53] who worked on rabbits especially myxomatosis at the historic Gungahlin Homestead which is home to ecosystems-focused research including the Australian National Wildlife Collection.

I stayed with Alan Newsome who worked on the red kangaroo (*Macropus rufus*) and the dingo (*Canis dingo*), two of Australia's iconic mammals. In doing so Alan became an icon himself since both species are highly politicised either for competing with grazing livestock or for killing them. By

---

53 Mykytowycz, R. (1953) An Attenuated Strain of the Myxomatosis Virus Recovered from the Field. *Nature* **172(4375)**: 448–449.

working on dingoes Alan was the focus of considerable hate mail especially after he confirmed that dingoes were capable of attacking small children at the Chamberlain Enquiry at Uluru (Ayers Rock)[54]. Seven children had been attacked by dingoes in the three months before baby Azaria Chamberlain's disappearance in August 1980.

I met Dr Christopher Perrins FRS at the Congress who was the director of the Edward Grey Institute (EGI) in the Zoology Department, a global centre of avian ecological research, formerly led by Dr David Lack FRS. Chris was able to give me some initial pointers for my eventual arrival at Oxford later that summer. The University of Oxford Zoology Department was world-famous with some outstanding intellects and accomplishments to boast of such as Mr Charles Elton FRS who founded the whole science of ecology and the Bureau of Animal Populations, the forerunner of the Animal Ecology Research Group (AERG) where I was to work.

Dr Malcolm Coe was a member of this Group and an experienced field ecologist in contrast to many who did limited fieldwork or used mathematical insights into the voguish but useful genre of the day; evolutionary ecology. He served with the Royal Air Force 1950–1955. Malcolm was born in 1930 in Leyton, London, a few miles from where I lived in the Mile End Road, and was awarded the Royal Geographical Society Busk medal 1988 as well as the Gold Medal of the Zoological Society Southern Africa, 1989, and is now an Emeritus Fellow of St Peters College, Oxford University since 1995. He loved smoking cheroots and the strip light above his desk was light brown from condensed smoke. His long love affair with Africa included elephant dung, dung beetles, and field research; a traditional ecologist, affable and approachable.

Although I had fascinating conversations with the likes of Richard Dawkins, who was writing 'Selfish Gene' at the time, and John Krebs, who was to lead the new Food Standards Agency, design a badger project focused on bovine tuberculosis resulting in a cull, and tit research (like Perrins who wrote a book called 'British Tits' which sold well) and become a Lord and Master of Jesus College, I was busy preparing for my eventual departure from England for the next two years by Christmas 1974.

My room was next to Charles Elton's who came in every Thursday. He was once asked in front of me by some innocent student why he didn't have a DPhil. Charles accepted the question quite openly and said, "In my day, one didn't need one." Elton was tutored as a student by Julian Huxley. Dr John Phillipson was Elton's replacement and appointed Reader in the AERG from Durham University. He was known for the Phillipson microbomb calorimeter used to understand ecosystem energetics.

Professor John Pringle was an insect physiologist and head of Zoology

54 https://trove.nla.gov.au/newspaper/article/118270851

having worked on radar during World War II. He was a somewhat stiff and dry character who never acknowledged people in passing them in a corridor (earning him the nickname of 'Laughing John') and had a fetish about administrative tidiness and wanted order which was not the natural state of the AERG! Dr Mick Southern was a doyen of the AERG and had been working on the small mammal populations of Wytham Woods for decades. Wytham Woods are one of the most researched areas of woodland in the world being the focus of most field research in the Zoology Department. The Edward Grey Institute worked on tits for an enormous length of time in the same wood. Many other characters stick in the memory such as Professor George Varley, head of the Hope Department of Entomology which survived until Varley retired. He was often to be seen cycling up the road to Summertown, in the north of Oxford, with a basket full of College claret. I also lived in Summertown and I remember one occasion when he was wobbling on his bike and I was able to save him and the precious wine.

There were many research students pursuing their doctorates who have become lifelong friends. Mark Stanley-Price was studying Coke's hartebeest and friends with Linda Partridge. They first befriended me when I joined the Department and showed me around. When the lift doors opened there was a fairly aged skeletal character in slippers holding a lighted candle on a saucer and when he saw Linda he spat out

"Urgh! Women!"

"Who was that?", I asked Linda who was laughing

"Oh, Henry. He's the man who founded ecological genetics. E.B. Ford."

When I returned from Aldabra two years later my room was next to his! He was famous for his eccentricities such as calling all dogs cats, or was it the other way around, and walking into a lecture to exclaim, "There is no-one here! I am just off to Honolulu anyway," ignoring a theatre full of female students. He was also found in Wytham Woods with his candle spotted by badger watchers but no badgers. I met Miriam Rothschild once near Oundle. She was an expert on fleas, a conservationist and a friend of Ford who made an exception in her case, as a female, as he was avidly against women becoming Fellows of All Souls College.

Mark went on to research the potential for domesticating the fringe-eared Oryx in Kenya, from there he moved to the Sultanate of Oman to design and manage the pioneering effort to reintroduce the Arabian Oryx to the wild, the first case of a species being returned to the wild when there were none remaining anywhere else in the wild. Then he ran the African Wildlife Foundation in Nairobi, and subsequently directed the Durrell Wildlife Conservation Trust in Jersey. He then joined David Macdonald's Wildlife Conservation Research Unit (WildCRU) at Oxford. I caught up with Mark in Kenya where he married Karen then working with Richard Leakey in the Coryndon Museum now the National Museum, Nairobi where she showed me the ancient hominid skulls that he and his father had discovered housed in a very secure, safe-like room. Dame Linda Partridge FRS is now a high-powered geneticist, who studies the biology and genetics of ageing and age-related diseases.

Chris Richards was also in a neighbouring room studying small mammals for a DPhil and has become a lifelong friend currently a farmer but also an international chair of major companies such as Arysta Life Science Corporation. His college, St John's, had excellent squash courts underground and on one occasion I can remember that he broke his leg and the ambulance men and I had enormous difficulty getting him up the only exit, a spiral staircase! He is now a trustee of the Wallacea Trust[55], which I chaired.

David Macdonald was working on fox ecology when I was there and was hardly ever seen as he spent most nights awake. Robin Buxton was working on termites, having left Cambridge with a canoeing Blue, given to a person who has represented Cambridge University at a particular sport in a match against Oxford University, and has been involved in my Institute (DICE, which I founded in 1989) for many years; even his son chose DICE to pursue his doctorate. Robin's substantial accomplishments in conservation are outstanding as was his stepfather's, Sir Martin Wood's, in establishing the first substantial commercial spin-out company from the University of Oxford, Oxford Scientific Instruments.

I met Steve Cobb in Nairobi who put me up for a night in a sleeping bag and sometime during the night I woke as the bag seemed to have developed a life of its own. I then found I couldn't escape the bag as some bright spark had tied up the neck around me so I was cocooned and trapped with a little tough wriggly animal which had sharp tasks. I bear the scars today of the baby warthog Steve had introduced me to but I hold him in some regard as he founded The Environment and Development Group, an environmental consultancy in Oxford, which was a constructive haven for all the research capabilities and experience of former research assistants.

British Promise

Three months after I arrived in Oxford I was on my way to Aldabra Atoll. The brand new oil tanker British Promise, built by Rozenburg 1974 and owned by BP[56], was provided courtesy of Frank Judd (now Baron Judd),

---

55 http://wallaceatrust.org/people/
56 Sanandaj, Flag: Iran, Owner: National Iranian Tanker Co., ex: British Promise – 1982 Built: 1974 DWT: 253,836, Status: 19/03/1988 set on fire by Iraqi aircraft whilst at Kharg Island (all 29 crew lost). Later Scrapped (DLR 1994/05) http://www.aukevisser.nl/supertankers/part-1/id107.htm

Under-Secretary of State for the Navy and I boarded at Ras-al-Kaimah in the Gulf. It was quite a climb up the rope ladder as the freeboard was 99 feet unloaded. I was greeted by ' Black Jack' the captain who said, "Where's the professor?", expecting an old man since "I came from The Royal Society" he told me later.

The tanker then loaded with crude oil at Kharg Island and as I was devoid of anything to do became a deckhand for 10 days to fend off the stultifying boredom of floating around on this big bag of oil. Pushbikes were needed to circumnavigate the deck and it took at least half an hour to make one circuit. At the bottom of the bow there was a large bulbous structure which charged through the waters of the Red Sea and disturbed thousands of sea snakes basking on the surface.

The ship could carry 250,000 tons of oil, was 1200 feet long with a draft (minimum depth of water a ship can safely navigate) of about 200 feet unloaded and nearly 300 feet loaded. It was capable of 16 knots and was highly automated. There was no wheel just a small knob which directed the ship although the autopilot was normally in charge.

I boarded her about Christmas Day 1974 and we had numerous dinners and lunches over the Christmas and New Year period. On New Year's Day I stood to give a toast only to be pulled down by the First Mate who said, "In the merchant Marine we don't stand". He was an unusual character constantly dreaming of the 60 foot, Bermudan rigged, cruising yacht he intended to build when back on shore leave which was three months away.

Most officers and crew did three months on and three months off. It was one of the strangest jobs since nothing happened from day-to-day and riveting boredom was the daily diet but this could all change in a second should there be a collision, a pirate's attack or fire all of which could destroy the entire ship and 20 crew. They were aware of the possibility of pirate activity although in 1974 it wasn't particularly active and I never saw any provision to fend off a boarding party or arms to defend themselves.

Maybe because there was little to occupy the mind from day-to-day, the First Mate had become a charismatic Christian and was dying to get me on my knees committing my life to God. There were times on Aldabra when I nearly did get on my knees with the ever present dangers on the Atoll, the dangerous marine life and the strange behaviour of a few exacerbated by the isolation.

The television in both the officer's mess and the crew's were exclusively fed by VHS video cassettes mostly of Benny Hill comedy shows and other such light entertainment. Everything was kept very shipshape, no rubbish, no rust, nothing that would detract from keeping everyone's spirits up and provide a source of danger such as waste or discarded oil cans. The paperback library was immense, stocked every trip by the crew leaving behind their personal collection with racy titles that fired the imagination if nothing else!

British Promise (courtesy Auke Visser www.aukevisser.nl)

The British Promise tragically came to her end 14 years after I was an honorary member of the crew when Iraqi jet fighters using Exocet missiles destroyed her at Kharg Island as she was loading with the loss of the entire, mainly Norwegian, crew. By that time she was called Sanandaj and owned by the National Iranian Tanker Co for six years. She was scrapped six years later.

Aldabra – the island that wants to kill you[57]

She took me from the Persian Gulf to Aldabra Atoll by January 2nd 1975 and it was quite difficult to disembark from a ship seemingly bigger than the island and having to maintain a minimum speed or 'way' of 7 knots to steer herself without hitting undersea coral having an enormous draft when fully loaded. A speed which the Station diesel launch picking me up could hardly match so my trunk was thrown overboard and I jumped onto the launch roof as by now the tanker's freeboard was only a few feet unlike

---

57 Photographing Giant Tortoises on an Island That Wants to Kill You. https://www.nationalgeographic.com/photography/proof/2014/10/22/photographing-giant-tortoises-on-an-island-that-wants-to-kill-you/

British Promise being manoeuvred towards a loading terminal at Kharg Island Iran 1974

when loading in the Gulf!

I spent two years on Aldabra Atoll as Visiting Scientist, Royal Society Research Station, Aldabra Atoll, British Indian Ocean Territory (BIOT) and then Republic of the Seychelles, and had the second best time of my life studying giant tortoises, their behaviour, and their secrets such as environmental sex determination, frequency dependent selection, and other unknown scientific discoveries. The Atoll is the largest raised coral reef in the world with an elevation of 8 metres (26 ft); and the second-largest Atoll in the world after Kiritimati Atoll. The Royal Society Research Station was built by the Royal Engineers some years before and was reasonably civilised with our only source of freshwater created by using cloche-like tanks which collected the freshwater evaporating inside the glass from the power of the sun. The evaporated water collected in channels which fed underground cisterns. Until, that is, the second Station director filled the cisterns with seawater endangering our survival!

The coral Atoll is composed of fossilised coral, thus porous and completely saturated with sea water. Any rain falling on the above-water rim quickly percolates through the surface sand and encounters the salt water underneath. Aldabra Atoll is of sufficient width to minimise tidal fluctuations in the aquifer, and the rainfall (in excess of 102.5 inches/260 cm per year on average) is sufficient in amount and periodicity for the fresh water to form a series of convex, freshwater, Ghyben-Herzberg lenses floating on the heavier salt water in the saturated sediments. When a Ghyben-Herzberg lens is fully formed, its floating nature will push a freshwater head above mean sea level forming pools or Bassins. There are five or so Bassins in eastern Grande Terre (see Figure 1) and two wells, as well as two Bassins on Picard, one of which is known as the upside-down jellyfish pool.

At spring tides freshwater percolated up through the coral surface, and when it rains, collecting in the small depressions in the substrate, but these were far too shallow for tortoises to drink from with their mouths which is why Aldabran giant tortoises can drink through their nose as the freshwater algae found in their nasal cavities and direct observation confirmed.

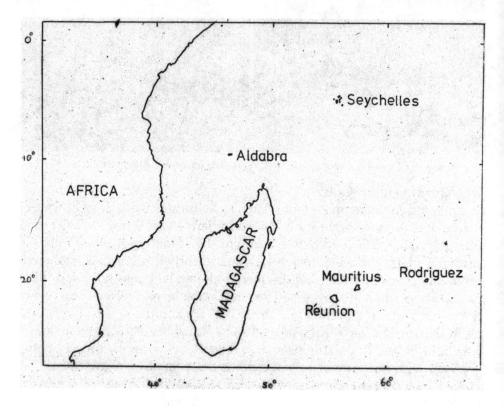

The Seychellois were mainly labourers and boatmen and lived in their own accommodation a few hundred yards away from the main Station. Harry Charles and Bernard Legae worked closely with me on my research and saved my life on two occasions at least. They became intimate and utterly trustworthy friends who were utterly practical about the business of surviving on this remote island where there were no emergency or rescue services. The lagoon was especially dangerous as nearly every shark species from black-tipped, white-tipped, hammerhead and tiger all of which were a nuisance when the tide was down and we had to push the dories standing waist deep! Great white sharks were available mainly outside the lagoon.

After so long on the Atoll I got used to the presence of sharks whatever I was doing in the sea but I had to be alert all the time whether diving or merely standing in the sea. Very large sharks because of their shape, being dorso-ventrally flattened, can swim in very shallow water enabling them to feed on the many species of rays that lie on the bottom of the lagoon.

Sailing from the research Station on Picard to my field site on Malabar, Anse Malabar, was relatively easy as we went round the outside of the Atoll even though it had inherent dangers with the currents and the open sea so we had to take extraordinary precautions, but travelling to my most easterly site on Grande Terre, Cinq Cases, involved a 20 mile trip through the lagoon. This required careful study of the tide tables so that we left with a fully loaded dory with Harry Charles at the helm and Bernard and I sitting up front so we could dash across the lagoon starting at high tide at Picard and hoping to arrive at Bras Takamaka, the landing point for Cinq Cases (Five Huts), before we ran out of water and the boat's outboard would start hitting coral heads in the lagoon which could scupper our return let alone getting to our destination. It only needed the pin securing the propeller to the driveshaft to be broken without a spare to hand and we were marooned! No walkie-talkie or mobile telephones!

On many occasions after a long trip across the lagoon we ran out of water and either had to use long poles to punt ourselves the remaining distance or get out and push. The trouble was that it was especially difficult to keep an eye out for sharks when pushing the boat as the water in Bras Takamaka was cloudy from the mangrove mud while at the other end of the lagoon near the Station the water was crystal clear but with the sun shining it was like a mirror and Polaroid sunglasses were only partially successful cutting through this glare. Sharks are cowards at least those that we came across on the Atoll. One hefty prod with a stick or a smack on the snout normally deterred most of them but it was the small juvenile blacktips that were a nuisance, nipping around the place and one's ankles, and the big adult blacktips and of course the tiger sharks that were frighteningly dangerous.

On one particular occasion we were pushing the boat back to the Station with about half a mile to go and while irritated by the little blacktips nipping my ankles I could see this pressure wave in the water coming towards us about 50 yards away. This bump in the water was caused by a very large shark speeding our way. Very fast. As we made haste to get into the boat, helped by Harry, the tiger shark was almost on us, attracted by my blood, and being one of the most dangerous sharks in the world it was no surprise when it decided to grab us once on board. With its head now out of the water and half on board Harry and I grabbed pangas and stabbed it in the eyes which had the desired effect and indeed caused other sharks to start chasing it because of the blood trail in the water.

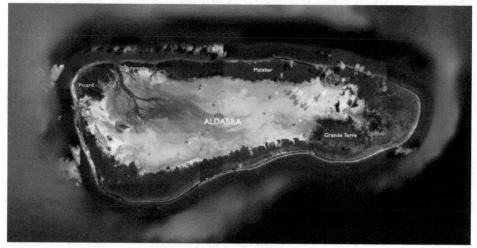

Aldabra Atoll (Courtesy © Google Maps)

Living and Working on the Atoll

I had two main research sites one in the northern island at Anse Malabar and the other at Cinq Cases on Grande Terre, in the extreme east (see Atoll map p.117, *Phil.Trans.R.Soc.Lond.B* 286). Fred Topliffe, the director during my first tour, was anxious about me using the landing beach halfway along the northern side of Malabar that could only be approached by sailing outside the Atoll so he wanted me always to take two boats (a dory and the large

Bernard, me, nephew Brian, Harry, Inesse Houreau. Aldabra 1976

Black-tipped reef sharks (*Carcharhinus melanopterus*) Photo: Jon Rawlinson (licensed under the Creative Commons Attribution 2.0 Generic license)

aluminium 'bumboat') and two engines just in case. There were very strong currents around the Atoll and should an Evinrude engine fail one could end up disappearing forever. Anse Malabar was a very small beach in the middle of Malabar or Middle Island on the open sea side. It had very dense vegetation whereas Cinq Cases ('five huts') was a large open area on the extreme south-east coast of Grande Terre that needed a high-speed dash, planning (hydrodynamic lift) if possible, lifting the hull onto the surface avoiding the coral heads at high tide, to get from the Station in the west right across the lagoon to the extreme east before the spring high tide disappeared otherwise the engine would hit coral heads and the pin securing the screw to the driveshaft would constantly need replacing. The 'high-speed dash 'was not often possible for our extended trips into the field with all the supplies we took with us so we had to resort to using a large dory negotiating round coral heads which needed either polarising sunglasses or the practised eye of the Seychellois.

By the time we could set off from the Station in the west the tide was already going down in the east and we often had to pole or push the boat the last half mile waist deep in water struggling through the mangrove-lined creek. Having arrived at Bras Takamaka, we tied up the boat exhausted. We had backpack frames to cart all our rations, emergency water in the dry season, tents and scientific gear another few miles across the island to Cinq Cases on the coast. Like Anse Malabar, there was a hut with some crudely fashioned bunks and drums which stored rainwater from the roof lightly shaded by one of the few remaining large shade trees, a *Guettarda* with very large leaves used by very large numbers of tortoises to shade midday. I left the hut to the guys who would sleep their and sleep on the bunks. There was a kitchen of sorts, actually just a bench, and we always carried paraffin stoves. Primus stoves which needed methylated spirits to get them started. Whenever we went into the field every month for several weeks Harry would prepare the boat the engines and the fuel, I would prepare the plastic backpacks full of food, matches, paraffin, and everything else we would need including a first aid kit, and Bernard would take care of everything else. And, of course, if anything was missing or went wrong it was my fault!

The boats we normally used, other than an old wooden launch called Myfanwy by David Griffin, an administrator at The Royal Society, but dubbed 'My Fanny' by us, were double skinned fibreglass dories recommended by the Royal Navy. Over time unfortunately the outer skin leaked from being dragged over coral heads and water got between the two hulls making them water sodden and fairly useless. The traditional boat of the Seychelles was the wooden pirogue which was 'sharp' at both ends and therefore dealt with approaching the beach and the surf behind much better than modern blunt-sterned boats. All of the outboard engines were 35hp Evinrude and one soon learnt how to manage them when out in the field as one's life depended on it. The smaller dory was called 'Katiti', the Seychellois name for the endemic kestrel, a small craft, with one person for short field trips could get up enough speed to plane, lifting it out of the water and avoiding the dangerous coral heads, and get across the lagoon before the tide went out when going from the Station to the other end of the Atoll. Looking at the tide tables, the weather and the condition of the Moon became a vital part of survival on Aldabra. My field trips to Cinq Cases were entirely governed by the little book of tide tables, unlike those to Anse Malabar.

Once at the Station I ate whatever was going like everybody else but I can remember a contentious issue was how much chilli should be in the meals which in one form or another dominate Seychellois cuisine. Out in the field a staple and recurrent diet was curried baked beans and tinned bacon for 2 years relieved on occasion by a dish called *chatini requin* made from dried shark meat which Harry and Bernard brought with them. Just boil the shark meat for a day and then fry with fried onion and papaya juice mixed with rice. For salad there were a number of plants available especially *Portulaca* which we doused in papaya juice which was also useful to tenderise tuna and other meats which could be consumed raw. A recurrent standby was bread lathered with peanut butter and Marmite.

To relieve the tedium of eating the best fish in the world and coconuts,

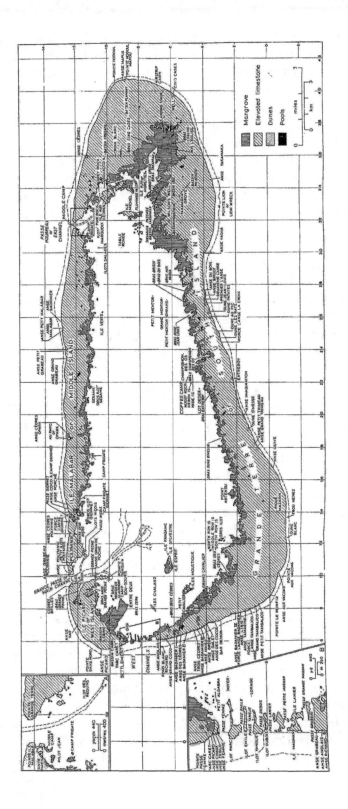

Harry, Bernard and I chased feral goats across the razor sharp coral on Grande Terre using rocks to stun one for a fantastic curry. Ben Gunn had nothing on me! The rubber black sandals we all used were made by Bata and a godsend but fall over and you'd be sliced up quite badly. We always carried a first-aid kit. We always favoured females as they tasted better but if we were unlucky and got a male Harry would castrate them and tie them up for a week before we slaughtered them. By selecting females we were accelerating a reduction in the introduced goat population which were affecting the vegetation as much as they do in the Galápagos. When a female came into season they attracted the robust attention of many males which sometimes ended in the death of the female. By reducing the number of females we made that possibility more of a certainty.

We were resupplied every six months or so by Nordvaer, a supply ship, which came with 45 gallon oil drums of diesel for the Station generators which had to be pushed up the beach, petrol for the outboards, scientific supplies, and personal mail together with cornflakes, Russian tinned salmon, Lea & Perrins Worcestershire sauce, Marmite and other such delights organised by Len Mole (ex British Antarctic Survey) and David Griffin at the Royal Society who looked after our needs on a daily basis. This munificence was unnecessary as it was quite possible to be completely self sufficient on the Atoll as there was sufficient food available from the sea and the goats released by the Arab slave traders for precisely this purpose of self-sufficiency, a herd they could cull when passing, and enough vegetation to vary the diet including chillies and papayas growing nearby the Station. But five vital elements would have been missing, diesel for electricity, petrol for the boats, rice, and, of course, Marmite and Lea & Perrins Worcestershire sauce which have been a staple diet for me over 70 years.

On one occasion the Seychelles Prime Minister France-Albert René, a former lawyer turned up, before he became President for 27 years a year later, and demanded several hundred mature tortoises be loaded on Nordvaer, our supply ship that visited about three times a year. I had to make instant decisions so that he took only the more abundant immature animals to impact the population least. It was never clear where the tortoises went but the market price of an adult giant tortoise was considerable.

The Seychellois who worked with me on the Atoll were very industrious in a whole variety of ways. They liked to fish and were always drying their catches and sharks' jaws which they shipped back to Mahé for their families whenever the supply ship Nordvaer came, collecting coconut palm sap to make their alcoholic drink, calou and carving intriguing puzzles made from wood that clicks together as a cube. Mazarin was the head labourer named after a dockside crane hook which hit him on the head and there was a carpenter called George who could fix whatever was required

Aldabra lagoon with dory Katiti; the Aldabran kestrel

as well as carve those cubes.

The dried sharks' jaws were a great money spinner and at the end of my time on Aldabra Harry, Bernard and I went to a small island Grand Mentor in the middle of the lagoon for two nights and fished for shark non-stop. We were using the aluminium 'bum' boat, as it was called, which was a somewhat sizeable and unwieldy beast but in 48 hours we filled it to the gunwales with sharks. One was a tiger shark that we measured at 16 feet whose dried jaw could be dropped over a standing man without the teeth touching his skin!

Harry Charles particularly liked whisky and after an extended session of drinking 'calou', fermented coconut sap extracted from the trees around the Station in the same way as sap is collected from rubber trees, down in his own house, he would walk through the Coconut Grove to the Station leaning to starboard at a dangerous angle wearing an orange builders hat to prevent being knocked out by the tree trunks, and top up with some Scotch I gave him and Bernard after a hard and extended field trip with me

The land or coconut crabs (*Birgus latro*), the largest in the world weighing 4 to 5 kg, were useful in opening cans and bottles in the field if one forgot the can opener with their enormously powerful claws. I was always forgetting a can opener when packing for the field and these overlarge hermit crabs were excellent and produced a very neat V-cut with their claw, great for knocking up a Bloody Mary with Royal Society tomato juice and Worcestershire sauce. A drinks kit was an essential part of field equipment but the crabs liked Worcestershire sauce as much as me and on two occasions they snapped off the neck of the bottle! On many occasions' research visitors asleep at night in their tent found a curious land crab on their chests, inches away from their face, woken by the crabs' antennae tapping their cheeks. After they stopped screaming it was difficult to get them back to sleep especially after watching me use a panga to ward off the marauding crabs with no effect whatsoever.

The crab came in two different colour forms, red and blue. The red forms were much commoner and seemed to dominate the blue form on every occasion. The females would retain their fertilised eggs under their tails and then later in the year they would go down to the sea and taking care not to be washed away since the adults were not marine animals, waggle their tail releasing all the eggs. As in Zambia the toilets were constructed by digging a large hole lined with 45 gallon oil drums with the bottom and the top knocked out. A small wooden shack was put on top with some sort of signalling device when in use. Once again visitors, especially female visitors, could be heard screaming when using these facilities as the land crabs enjoyed using them themselves and often were found in burrows near the top where they had torn an entrance through the rusty oil drums into the sandy substrate. Their long antennae could be felt brushing one's rear end as one relieved oneself!

Other animals had curious dietary habits such as the feral rats which ate the soap, often seen wandering around inside the huts and Station occasionally foaming at the mouth; again a means of terrifying visitors. After two years my aim with a flying panga slicing a rat in two as it scurried

Mazarin, Andrew, Bernard and Harry Charles gathering hundreds of tortoises demanded by the Seychelles Prime Minister France-Albert René

along the wall was pretty accurate. We had phenomenal parties fuelled by Tiger beer and whisky which was less than a £1 a bottle as we were our own Customs Officers, and indeed at our own jurisdiction under the British Indian Ocean Territory (BIOT) before the Republic of the Seychelles absorbed most of BIOT. On one occasion a researcher studying the flightless rail was strumming his guitar, leaning against the wall of his room, well lubricated, and as he slid down the wall the very large hooks used for fishing got embedded in his rear end. Although fairly nifty with my dissection kit, since part of my job involved dissecting giant tortoises which I hated, I was asked whether I could help which I was happy to do but the researcher in question wasn't keen on the idea. I was able to help Fred Topliffe and provide him with a simple means of extraction by using novocaine to deaden the area and pushing the hook so that the barbed head could be cut off and the shank pulled out backwards. Operations on humans involving the kitchen table, anaesthetics and sterilised dissection kits with guidance from a doctor on the wireless were not unknown.

Aldabra was extremely dangerous with razor sharp coral, very poisonous fish like the stonefish, man-eating sharks, fierce currents, vast flows of water in and out of the central lagoon through the three channels (Grande Pass, Passe Houreau and West Channels by the Station), and the inevitable interpersonal politics in such a small group that didn't choose to be with each other; half of them didn't want to be there, not having found a job in the UK, and the others did, most of them scientists.

The outstanding individuals were the Station director and his wife during the first year that I was there, Fred Topliffe and Lorise his wife, who behaved impeccably and very helpful. Apart from the director there was a Scottish mechanic to ensure that the generator, the outboard engines, the dories, and all the necessary equipment was serviced and worked. There were also meteorologists (3 in succession) who every few hours had to report by radio the readings which were used internationally. The radio was our only means of communication with the outside world as we had no roads, no cars, no computers, no Internet, no cell phones or mobiles, in fact nothing except the basic facilities and buildings built by the Royal Engineers of which one (Derek) were still there as engineer when I first arrived, a jocular and philosophical old hand. The cook was a Seychellois and of course was brilliant with fish and rice, trying to ignore the pleas from some visitors and short term staff for insipid curries.

Several scientists who were resident with me such as Bob Pryce-Jones and Malcolm Potts together with some visiting scientists, who only stayed for short periods of time, left a mark on me. Bob today is the Curator of Ornithology, Natural History Museum based in Tring Hertfordshire. Malcolm Potts became the founder and director of the Virginia Tech Center

Coconut crabs *Birgus latro*: checking a nesting giant tortoise at night, a blue variant while we were inspecting nests, a female with an egg cluster under her tail and releasing them when a wave breaks

for Genomics and then joined Qatar University in 2006 as Director of the State's initiative – 'Qatar Biofuel'.

Visiting scientists came from around the world such as Prof. Rudolf Reinboth from Gutenberg, who wanted to do some sort of research on the Atoll on sex change in fishes, sent a radio message transcribed as saying that he needed "Five little boys?" Of course this set off a tirade of puns and jocularity, centred on the use of such boys. It is often said that Americans and the British are divided by a common language based on the different usage of words let alone their spelling. He obviously meant buoys; a word with distinct pronunciation differences between both countries. Another was Dr Dr Heijo Schmidt from Heidelberg who was a world authority on deep sea invertebrates and so he joined me on field trips to both my field site so he could make deep dives at night and photograph the extraordinarily large invertebrates that came out and rolled around the seabed or swam. Heijo, equipped with two tanks and a large underwater camera with enormous flash equipment, would tip over the side of the boat, over-weighted so he sank quickly and reached a hundred metres and then resurfaced after 20 minutes or so when I fished him out of the ocean. I found the whole experience frightening as it was often pitch black in open sea with strong currents and only me and Harry making sure we found him and fished him out. He was a tough guy! What would happen if we couldn't find him! Apparently another German custom in academia is the repetitive mention of degrees i.e. Prof. Dr Dr or Dr Dr.

The main pastime at the Station was trawling using leather gloves, large hooks and thick lines for caranx, tuna, diable du voile or sailfish, and marlin or fishing from a Stationary boat we caught grouper, barracuda, and many species of shark.

Close to the Atoll and inside the lagoon the skittish blacktip reef shark were common and very localised, normally remaining in an area of a few square kilometres, while nipping at my legs when pushing boats having run out of water, and sicklefin lemon shark (shy, sedate shark). The tiger shark (second only to the great white in recorded attacks on humans[58]) is a solitary, normally nocturnal hunter I found in the lagoon, but offshore hammerheads swam in schools during the day becoming solitary hunters at night. Hammerheads gave me the willies as they had a habit of looking round the corners and circling coral heads behind which I would be hiding from a school while diving.

The aggressive oceanic white tip shark was hardly ever seen although I caught a 200lb specimen in Grande Passe which took 5 hours to land with six-inch hook and chain trace connected to 100 lb nylon. I saw great white sharks on several occasions. Once I was swimming in the open sea off Malabar Island and found I was in the midst of a huge herd of manta rays and I counted 112. Manta rays are very large and harmless but still sent a tingle down my spine as they resemble all those mainly evil movie characters like Dracula. Rays are common in the lagoon and I made a letter opener from the poisonous spine of a whiptail stingray barb, the kind that killed Steve Irwin, an Australian television personality, who specialised in making a genre of wildlife programmes, so common these days, that spectacularly interfered with wild animals. The rays' dried tail is very rough and was used years ago as a whip in Seychelles' prisons. The British, like the French before them, saw Seychelles as a useful place to exile troublesome political prisoners

There were other fish like the stonefish, the most venomous fish known, which were dangerous as they would lie camouflaged on the reef flat. The poisonous spine would drive into your foot, even through flip-flops, and was potentially lethal which is why we always wore the thick rubber black sandals to protect ourselves especially from the razor sharp fossilised coral of the Atoll.

Stonefish were not the only dangers as lionfish were also a problem but very dramatic in their appearance and easily spotted. They have a habit of suddenly reversing if threatened as their poison was located in venomous fin rays and blow jets of water while approaching small prey, apparently

---

58 Knickle, C. *Tiger Shark Biological Profile*. Florida Museum of Natural History Ichthyology Department.

to disorient them. We all wore those sandals when in the water to protect us from these fish hiding on the reef flat, the area between the beach and the coral reef before it plunged into the extreme depths of the Indian Ocean. Pufferfish were only dangerous if eaten. The source of tetrodotoxin in puffers has been a matter of debate[59], but it is increasingly accepted that bacteria in the fish's intestinal tract are the source[60].

Cone snails were also dangerous to the uninitiated and those who weren't zoologists since the poison is injected into a human hand through the side of the snail and not the ends as most people imagine. They are very pretty and people like to collect them which is forbidden on Aldabra. The larger species contain one of the most virulent natural poisons known and people are often caught unawares. Cone snails have transformed their radula into a kind of gun that shoots small glassy, poison harpoons. The harpoons are excreted with enough force to penetrate a diver's wetsuit. The venom contains an analgesic so the victim feels almost no pain. A single creature can carry enough poison to kill a dozen people. The poison is potent and fast-acting nerve agents for which there is no known antidote or antivenin.

Death can occur in less than 30 minutes with cone snails; for comparison with other toxins (LD_{50}=lethal dose, which is defined as the amount in milligrams needed to kill 50 percent of the animals tested):

1. anthrax (0.0002);
2. geographic cone snail (0.004);
3. textrodoxotine in the blue ring octopus and puffer fish (0.008);
4. inland taipan snake (0.025);
5. eastern brown snake (0.036);
6. Dubois's sea snake (0.044);
7. coastal taipan snake (0.105);
8. beaked sea snake (0.113);
9. western tiger snake (0.194);
10. mainland tiger snake (0.214);
11. common death adder (0.500).

The taipan snake is endemic to Australasia while the sea snakes were those I watched from British Promise on the way to the Atoll. Gaboon viper, so easy to step on early in the morning in Zambia when they are not warmed

59   Lehman, E.M. (2006) Egg Toxicity and Egg Predation in Rough-Skinned Newts (Doctoral dissertation). Proquest Dissertations and Theses database. UMI No: 3229594. pp. 32–33.

60   Shibamoto, T. & Bjeldanes, L. (2009) Introduction to Food Toxicology (2nd ed.). Amsterdam: Academic Press/Elsevier. p. 105. ISBN 978-0-12-374286-5.

up, has a lethal dose of about 0.400–0.700mg but it's both neurotoxic (necrotising (death of tissue)) and haemorrhagic, and produces the largest amounts of venom of all poisonous snakes.

I had arrived on Aldabra in early January and left on 5 July 1975, returning for my second tour in late September 1975 until I finally returned to England in November 1976 with my girlfriend for the past year who had arrived on Aldabra with her sister and brother-in-law while I was away in Oxford. She was research assistant to Ross Robertson from the Smithsonian Tropical Research Institute in Barro Colorado, Panama working on surgeon fish (*Acanthurus* spp.) behaviour which involved hours of floating with a snorkel watching what individuals did and being vulnerable to randy male green turtles that would creep up behind unsuspecting female researchers.

She and I were irresistibly drawn to each other and at the end of our time on Aldabra we walked right around the Atoll on foot including the Passes to say 'Goodbye' to Aldabra. It was a *tour de force* carrying all our food and water, and having to watch the tides carefully so at each pass we had to walk a long way into the lagoon at very low spring tides to circumvent the very deep channels created by the rushing lagoon water at low and high tides. Not many people performed this dangerous exercise although David Stoddart, the Royal Society Aldabra co-ordinator, and Len Mole, the Royal Society administrator, made a point of taking it on whenever they visited.

Aldabra again 1990

Some years later on 14th May 1990 I returned to Aldabra with George Zug, Curator of Herpetology, National Museum of Natural History, Smithsonian and five others (Jerry Louton entomologist, Chris Glasby worms, Diane Valsamis entomology, Belinda Alvarez echinoderms and Linda Ward worms) on an expedition where he and I worked on giant tortoises' ecology. The plan was to write a definitive scientific and detailed book together on the Aldabra species, much of which had never been published, but to our everlasting regret my other commitments got in the way.

We met in Paris at the Charles de Gaulle airport and flew on to the Seychelles where Brian Kensley met us. He was a research Zoologist at the Department of Invertebrate Zoology, National Museum of Natural History, Smithsonian. His primary area of study was systematics of decapod and isopod crustaceans including Aldabra. He had made all our travel arrangements, provide a boat and loaded necessary supplies for the month long trip. The next day we had lunch at the Pirates Arms pub in Mahé where we met Philip Marzocchi, the skipper of 'El Gringo', a 65-foot Bermudan rigged yacht, that was to sail us the 700 miles to Aldabra Atoll. We left at

5 PM with an unseasonal westerly wind which was blowing quite hard. What we did not know and weren't told was that a cyclone called Ikonjo was bearing down on the Seychelles right across our route to Aldabra.

Nicknamed 'Ikonjo' it was blowing a hundred kilometres an hour and nearly sunk our yacht before we had got very far. All of the Smithsonian team were below decks suffering from extreme seasickness, and no doubt very frightened, whereas I was in the peak bunk and having experienced this before on Aldabra and, being of a somewhat phlegmatic disposition, which some of my friends and lovers would dispute, I read a small book by Machiavelli called 'The Prince' which is the best treatise on how to manage people that I'm aware of. But not under those circumstances!

We only just made it to Desroches 150 miles away by midday the following day 16th after our self-steering gear had broken. George, a mild and educated man, was spitting bricks about setting off when others knew we would be heading straight into a cyclone including the skipper. By the next day 17th the wind had increased to 130 km an hour with very high seas and although some rooms were provided for us in this luxury resort with gold taps, coconut palms were being uprooted and crashing straight through the individual chalets.

The failure of the steering gear was actually a godsend as the skipper would have ploughed on to Aldabra in a cyclone which was the worst in 16 years. Four days after we set out on the 19th we were still sleeping in the Desroches Hotel and I found a cosy corner in the hotel corridor which I felt had a bit more brickwork around it to avoid being smashed by falling palms. Late in its duration, Ikonjo became a rare storm to affect the nation of Seychelles. It passed nearest to Desroches Island, where it destroyed much of the island's hotel. On the primary island of Mahé, Ikonjo produced strong winds reaching 83 km/h (52 mph) at Seychelles International Airport, strong enough to knock over several trees. Nationwide, the storm caused $1.5 million (1990 USD) in damage and two injuries. A ship passing through the centre of Ikonjo reported wind gusts of 148 km/h (92 mph)[61].

At around midday on the 19th George had got the Smithsonian to organise an Otter plane which had taken off but turned back halfway because of bad weather. The next day the Otter arrived early afternoon and within 75 minutes we were back in Mahé. This plane is the quintessential explorer's aircraft being extremely rugged under any conditions. The de Havilland Canada DHC-3 Otter is a single-engined, high-wing, propeller-driven, short take-off and landing aircraft developed by de Havilland Canada.

Once back in Mahé we went to the fishing harbour to see if the boat was back and grab our gear. We put up at the Harbour View Guest house and

---

61   Tropical Depression Ikonjo, 11–21 May 1990. National Climatic Data Center (Report). Global tropical/extratropical cyclone climatic atlas. 1996. Retrieved 2015-01-20.

Ian Swingland, Aldabra (Malcolm Potts)

thanked God we were still alive.

We sent a message to Carl Gans, the famous herpetologist who died in 2018, and resolved my baby son being overdue in Ann Arbor in 1987 by recommending Fiona had a Chinese meal (it worked), "Tropical depression Ikonjo was endangering lives on board yacht bound for Aldabra. To save our souls consigned your MS to waves and was thus saved. God Save America. I and G." Betty Beckett MRCVS, a naturalist who inspired me for many years with her enthusiasm for the islands, Ron Nussbaum of Michigan University, Katy Beaver and Lindsay Chong-seng, all Seychelles ecologists, had dinner with us the day after we got back to celebrate survival. We sent the Otter back to get the rest of the team and had another celebration as the first wasn't enough!

Kantilal Jivan Shah owned the main general store in the centre of Mahé, and was a significant amateur naturalist. He was tremendously helpful and even the slightness thing was no problem and could be found somewhere among the mountains of items stacked to the ceiling whether shorts, knives, hooks, pure alcohol, formaldehyde, and most important of all his encyclopaedic knowledge of Seychelles natural history. His son Nirmal Jivan Shah (Nimo to his friends) is the leading conservationist of the Seychelles and founder of Nature Seychelles having been Director of Conservation in the Department of Environment for the government. He told me that giant tortoises could be bought from the government. On the 24th May we had another shot at getting to Aldabra after spending time with Nimo and Guy Lionnet, who has contributed much to conservation in Seychelles as chairman of many conservation agencies including the Seychelles Islands Foundation, and Willy Andre, a pioneer of nature conservation for more than four decades, who were critical of the cliquishness and territoriality of the Oxbridge set over Aldabra.

Three days later we arrived on the Atoll at 6pm. Harry Charles was the first to greet me as I fell into the bumboat after dark. My old companion and life saver from the two years I spent on the island almost 15 years before hugged me and laughed. The research Station on Picard was very run down with pigs and chickens running around. The following day, 29th, we left Picard and sailed to Passe Houreau where we stopped using four anchors because of the extreme currents and had a fish curry lunch conjured up by Harry, my old friend Bernard Legae and a young man called François. After exploring Malabar we set sail again the following day on a

Cyclone Ikonjo over 'El Gringo' 15th May 1990

rising tide to reach the Cinq Cases anchorage (Bras Cinq Cases) amongst the mangroves five hours later as we had to stop twice to wait for more water. We walk for an hour and a quarter and arrived at the Cinq Cases hut to find the main shade tree, a Guettarda, was dead and many dead tortoises mostly females. Spotting some goats Bernard and François went shooting off and came back with a female after two hours which was soon turned into a curry as usual.

Various journalists joined us but we carried on our work regardless conducting the transect survey work up to Point Houdoul and inland as I did all those years ago which essentially confirmed my observations in the papers I published showing that the tortoises found on the coast 15 years ago still frequented the area and those that frequented inland areas were still there. The interesting observation was that nearly all those animals found on the coast were females no doubt attracted by the additional food supply that helped reproduction even if the danger was a lack of shade which can kill. One female we examined during post-mortem showed no pre-ovulatory or post ovulatory follicles, very little fat, goats' droppings in the gut, and we concluded from examining the scutes that she had died of old age.

On 3 June we walked to Point Houdoul Bassin, a great site for fossilised shark's teeth, and then via Bassin Flamant to Grande Bassin and back to camp. We saw many tortoises, few of them marked with discs, goats and also coccids and rust infections of much of the vegetation. I left Cinq Cases the last time 4 June 1990 and walked to Bras Cinq Cases, passing many tortoises drinking through their noses from the shallow depressions in the coral full of the night's rainwater. We waited eight hours for there to be sufficient water to float the boat and we just got off and managed to get to the lip of Passe Houreau and plopped into the channel. The following day we sailed to

DUPLEX CALL
FIRST IDENTITY

XDD 19 1437Z

1664101 DESR X
2316 SEYCS SZ

TO   : DESROCHES HOTEL   TLX 1664101 DESR X
         ATTN: LIZZIE POTTER - HOTEL MANAGER

FM   : BON ESPOIR   TLX 2316 SEYCS SZ

SUBJECT: LATEST INFO. ON TROPICAL DEPRESSION 'IKONJO'

    QUOTE
:1 LATEST POSITION OF MODERATE TROPICAL DEPRESSION 'IKONJO'
    AT 1700HRS 06.7S 53.2E. BECAUSE IT IS GRADUALLY MOVING TOWARDS
    THE NORTH ALTHOUGH NOW IT IS WEAKENING, IT WILL BE PASSING
    ABOUT 200 TO 300 K.M OFF DESROCHES; HENCE IT WILL BE NORMAL THAT
    DESROCHES WILL BE EXPERIENCING WIND AT 100 K.M PER HOUR (50KNOTS)

:2 HEAVING RAIN WILL BE ACCOMPANYING AND ROUGH SEAS WILL EXISTS.

:3 BY TOMORROW 20TH TROPICAL DEPRESSION 'IKONJO' WILL CONTINUE
    MOVING NORTHWEST AND WEAKENING IN MOVEMENT AND BY TUESDAY 22ND
    MAY IT WILL DISSIPATE.

    UNQUOTE

WE HOPE SITUATION WILL IMPROVE TOMORROW. ANYWAY IF W. SCHULTZ IS
    TRYING TO RE-ORGANISE THE ANTENNA SYSTEM FOR THE H.F RADIO, HE
    SHOULD NOT HESITATE TO CALLS ON 7696KHZ FOR ANY NEW DEVELOPMENT
    OTHERWISE PLEASE BE IN CONTACT BY SATELLITE.

    BEST REGARDS,

    BON ESPOIR

Anse Malabar my other principal site where we concentrated on the main nesting areas and measured the temperature profile as well as the eggs. Yet again there was no statistical difference from those data collected a decade and a half before.

While enjoying the company of some of my closest friends like George and Harry and Bernard while working on the ecology and behaviour of giant tortoises as I used to, I was thinking about the future of the Tortoise Specialist Group of IUCN[62] which Sir Peter Scott had encouraged me to create 10 years before and had combined with the Freshwater Turtle Specialist Group. I had decided to retire as chairman on the occasion of the General Assembly IUCN in Perth, Western Australia at the end of the year. I had just directed and hosted the enormous First World Congress of Herpetology at my Institute the year before, after five years hard work of planning and organisation, but the question was who should I recommend to replace me? I suggested Ed Moll, the first Chair for the IUCN Freshwater Turtle Specialist Group, to head the combined Tortoise and Freshwater Turtle Specialist Group.

It's always interesting to me how people behave and certainly my education started in earnest observing the interpersonal politics that were rife at Oxford, the pinnacle of the art after 700 years of practice. One thing has become clear during my life is that all the people who want promotion, preferment and privilege are just the people that shouldn't have it, and all the people who should be in those positions don't want it.

On June 7 expecting 'El Gringo' at Anse Malabar we gave up hope until 16:30hrs when a single 40 hp boat arrived and got us back to the Station by sundown. The US Embassy had been in touch to say a tropical depression, another cyclone, was 900 miles south south-east of Mahé and heading our way. George and I spent the next three days collecting location data of marked tortoises over the previous years, visiting the upside-down jellyfish pool and any other data lodged in the Aldabra library.

I left Aldabra 08:30 on 11 June 1994 for the very last time with Harry Charles ferrying us to 'El Gringo' because the bumboat engine didn't work. I'm not good with 'goodbyes' and so a quick hug with Harry and I was gone. Harry died a few years later when under a general anaesthetic at a dentist's in Mahé. So we returned to the Harbour View Guesthouse in Mahé run by the Collie family on the 14th and started making plans for future research on Aldabra and its fauna with the Smithsonian and the British Deputy High Commissioner Robert Jenner as well as Nimo and all my other friends in the Seychelles.

While George and his wife Pat have remained close friends for over

---

62 https://portals.iucn.org/library/sites/library/files/documents/IUCN%20Tortoises%20and%20turtles_no.%204_Sept%201989.pdf

three decades I still hanker after writing a book together since what I read about giant tortoises especially the Aldabra species is amateur and wrong; for example, the Wikipedia entry is clearly written by somebody who knows nothing about the ecology and behaviour of the species and boldly states that the Aldabran "tortoise has two main varieties of shells", resembling I presume the Galápagos species dome shaped and saddleback carapaces, "burrows underground" for shade, and "the neck of the Aldabra giant tortoise is very long", but like so much in Wikipedia is sometimes inaccurate. There are some minor differences in shell shape, burrowing underground is impossible through rock-hard fossilised coral and their necks are not "very long" whatever that means. It has not being corrected by the anonymous editors who protest their religion is accuracy and stand guard over it.

CHAPTER 8
Giant tortoise ecology and behaviour

Giant tortoise history in the Seychelles

On 4 April 1893 the Administrator of Aldabra wrote to the Governor of Mauritius and refers to Lord Ripon's letter giving an extract of Dr A. Gunther's letter in *The Times* of 11th January 1893. He refers to Mr Spurs, the leasee of Aldabra, giving strictest instructions to his labour not to kill giant tortoises. He mentions that the greatest enemy are the rats that kill the eggs (they aren't as the mucus and urine-soaked earth after nesting bakes rock-hard which only the land crabs can excavate). He also mentions that Dr Abbott (Smithsonian Institute) visited Aldabra for four months. "I will issue instructions that a number of tortoises will be brought to Curieuse Island at first opportunity."

M.J. Nicoll[63] describes giant tortoises breeding freely at Government House, Mahé while unpublished documents on the history of the Seychelles Islands before 1810 by A.A. Fauvel[64] refers to Jean-Baptiste Malavois' report in 1787 (pp.278–286) on the wholesale destruction and the concomitant safeguards he proposes since 6–8000 giant tortoises are on the Seychelles but 13,000 giant tortoises have been taken by boats in the last four years. On 26 July 1909 the Seychelles Governor wrote to the Secretary of State for the Colonies that A. d'Emmery de Charnoy, the then leasee of Aldabra, "reports that stocks of giant tortoises on Aldabra are in danger of extinction because cranes [i.e. *Aldabra ibis*] are preying on the young but there was no imminent danger because of Government House's herd. Mr J. Standley Gardiner of Caius College Cambridge and his colleague Mr Fryer could advise on this. Numbers could be placed on Astove, Curieuse, Felicité and Long island where there is enough food. Felicité already has a herd".

On 20 August 1909 the Governor writes again to the Secretary of State saying that he had received the Secretary of State's dispatch number 65 of 21 July containing correspondence with Mr Standley Gardiner re: tortoises in Aldabra group of islands.

> I have reached the conclusion by conversations with local experts that the population is safe from depredation on Aldabra because of their wild state [i.e. remote]. Damage to young by rats considerable but by herons (florentins) is not. The adult perish by falling into pits. The maximum number will be limited by the food supply. Ultimately the race will die out in a wild state at Aldabra, as they have died out in other islands where remains of

63 Nicoll, M.J. (1908) *Three voyages of a Naturalist*. Witherby & Co. 246pp.
64 https://dl.wdl.org/2396/service/2396.pdf

them have been discovered in a wild state.

He goes on to observe that,

it's not worth transferring Aldabra animals to other islands as this is not effectual in protecting them. The race will not die out. Apart from Government house, whose herd is recorded in a studbook, several other large herds in private hands will be well looked after as long as they have market value for sale to zoos. I consider there is no necessity to remove the Aldabra herds as they are as safe there as anywhere. I shall place on record that in the event of any revision in the lease of the Aldabra group of islands, the leasee shall be bound to present yearly to the Governor of Seychelles an adult pair of land tortoises for preservation at government house. There are specimens of **Testudo daudinii** *(Gunther) in the herd at Government House corresponding to drawings and descriptions in Dr Gunther's monograph 1876. Possible that these are survivors of Mahé breed.*

He writes again 1st June 1910 with notes on the breeding of tortoises at Government House Mahé:

…in June 1904 there were 42 tortoises at Government House and 17 young hatched in 1902 in 1903. Most of the herd was from Val des Prés from an old Mahé family; the animals were transferred to Curieuse Island and then back to Government House in 1902. Plus there is a large male 'Gordon' presented by Gen Gordon in 1881 – carapace 4 foot 9 ½ inches plastron 3'9". *Undoubtedly* **Testudo elephantine** *plus 'Spurs' presented by Mr Spurs (Europa Island) carapace 4'5" plastron 3'7". Grown slowly in breadth since 1904 but not length. Probably* **Testudo daudini**. *(A Testudo elephantine died in Colombo aged hundred and 55 years.) Females in her the largest 3'8" carapace and 2'8" plastron not grown since 1907. Breeding season January to April. Females carry eggs for 10 weeks. Eggs in nests 9 to 25 weeks. There may be two nests per female per year. Young hatched in 120 230 days. Half the eggs at Government House infertile. In droughts few young emerge not being able to work their way up. At four years old carapace 1'6" – 1'10". At 25 years old full grown. Number of young 1904 – 1908 is 168. Rat predation is bad until shell hardens. On Aldabra young are killed by cranes, rats and wildcats. Some specimens were sent by Adml Sir John Durnford to Groote Schuur Pretoria and London Zoo. Four adult females and 18 adult males and 27 young was sent to Long Island.*[65]

Giant tortoises are genetically similar and the multiple shapes are primarily induced by the food available to them. On some Galápagos Islands the rain falls mainly on one side of the mountainous volcanic peaks and so dome shaped animals are to be found where it rains most (grazers) and saddleback tortoises (browsers) are found where it doesn't, in the drier area on the other side of the peak, so shell shapes on one island are determined by food availability or primary production and they interbreed!

---

65   Gunther, A. (1878) *Gigantic Land Tortoises*. British Museum.

F abulous tales and stories surround the giant tortoises of the Seychelles. Some tortoises have become famous characters and entered the annals of history.

Until the advent of Man the giant tortoises was found in many Western Indian Ocean islands, especially Seychelles, Mauritius and Rodrigues. Wild populations everywhere have now become extinct except on Aldabra Atoll. Like the Dodo and the Giant Elephant Bird of Madagascar, they have fallen prey to Man's greed. Early accounts of exploration and settlements of the Seychelles comment on the very larger numbers of tortoises found on these islands and how they were easy prey to sailors and settlers. The quality of the meat and live transportation at sea made them very popular. The first recorded mention of their existence in the Seychelles is in the Journal of John Jourdain who was on board the *Ascention* which drifted to the Seychelles on January 16th 1609. They did not know where they were, found no trace of human inhabitants but saw large numbers of tortoises. John Jourdain noted in his Journal: *"The boat returned and brought as many land tortelles as they could well carrie. The tortelles were good meat as good as fresh meat; but after two or three meales our men would not eat them, because they did looke so, ugly before they were boyled".*

The next mention of Seychelles tortoises is after a gap of a century and half (1742) when Lazare Picault on his voyage of discovery found the islands covered with the giants. Every successive expedition and passing ship took as many tortoises as they could. The hardy tortoises were the best source of fresh meat in the days when there was no refrigeration.

When Chevalier Marion du Fresne's expedition visited the islands in 1766, they took back to Isle de France (Maruritius) five giant tortoises. One of these was still living at the beginning of the 20th Century. In 1901 one Dr. Gadour reported that though this tortoise had become blind it was otherwise of regular habits and in good health. Its shell length was reportedly over a yard. Another tortoise was presented by Sir John Colville, Governor of Mauritius, to the London Zoological Society in 1833. It was still living in 1895. Another giant was found in the Barracks at Port Louis when the city was taken by the British in 1810. Tortoises were so numerous and liked that we find in a letter by Brayer du Barre, dated 1795 that

M de la Corriere, Commander of the Kings vessel *Mascarin*, called at Seychelles and exchanged fowl for tortoises.

So many ships were taking tortoises that the situation alarmed de Malavois, one of the best administrators of the Seychelles colonial period. He wrote a very long report to the Governor of Isle de France, impressing upon him the need for protecting these animals. He gave detailed statistics of the numbers of tortoises left in Seychelles. This led to the first conservation regulations.

Many tortoises were brought to Mauritius by the Maurels, Langlois and other 'Grand Blancs' when they packed up and left the Seychelles when slaves were emancipated. Jean Francois Hodoul, well known Corsair who settled in the Seychelles at the turn of the 19th century and who became the most prominent and affluent personage of those days, is said to have done a roaring trade by supplying ships with tortoises from Aldabra. The price: 3 Piastres each!

Long lived giants

Admiral Sir Henry Keppler (1809-1909) in his book "A Sailors life under Four Sovereigns", mentions a huge tortoise in the grounds of Government House at Port Louis in Mauritius: "It could move with six men on its back three aside, standing on the edge of its shell holding hands across." Regarding this very same tortoise. Colonel Fredrich Fair from 1916 to 1923 wrote: *"The tortoise that R.A. Battery brought from the Seychelles in 1766 and mentioned in 1828 by Henry Keppler, died at Fort George in 1918 after falling twelve feet and breaking its neck. The Battery notebook suggested that it had committed suicide on hearing that Fort George was to be manned by the local Volunteer Force:"*

Fredrick J. Mourat of the Bengal Medical Staff in his "Rough Notes of a Trip to Reunion, Mauritius and Ceylon with Remarks on their eligibility as Sanatorium for Indian Invalids" published in 1852 mentions seeing at Reduit (Governors residence in Mauritius) *"A huge venerable antidiluvian tortoise, a type of solar steadiness and deliberation, sadly opposed to the mercurial activity of this age of electricity, steam and progress."*

Love sick tortoise

Some years ago the Governor of St. Helena was said to be looking for a mate for Jonathan, an ancient Seychelles tortoise which had taken to disrupting croquet games by sitting on the croquet balls. The prospective mate had to be about 140 years old with a keen sense of humour. Jonathan had pushed his first mate over a cliff in the 1850's.

What happened to Gordon?

Gordon, a giant tortoise presented in 1881 to Government House in Seychelles died in the 1920's. He was supposedly 200 years old. His carapace measured six and a half feet. Having the freedom of Government House grounds, old Gordon like Jonathan, was reported to have often upset games of croquet.

Conservation

In 1874 Charles Darwin, alarmed at the extermination of the tortoises of Aldabra, started a petition with Hooker and others for the protection of the remaining population. In the 1890's when Mr. Spurs was the lessee of Aldabra, the Seychelles Administrator, R. Griffiths, visited the Atoll and recommended immediate protection for the tortoises. However it was not only in 1900 to 1904 that any legal provision was made in the lease of Aldabra for their protection. Lord Rothschild made these tortoises into almost a cult. He took a great interest in their protection and in his museum at Tring in England he had several giants from Aldabra, one weighing over 550 lbs and estimated to be centuries old. Another specimen brought to Lord Rothschild in 1897 was 40 inches in length and 32 inches over the curve of the back.

Tortoise Farms

At the turn of the century, many land owners had tortoise farms. There was one at the old Government House aswell. It was not an uncommon sight to see tortoises tethered by the leg and exposed for sale at the market. In nearly all the farms the tortoises bore a number painted in white on the shell. Many farm owners kept a record of their stocks, while at the old Government House a complete register was kept with dates of hatching and so forth. Until recently, a tradition in Seychelles was to give a tortoise to a newly born female child and to slaughter it when she got married.

George and Esmeralda

Today the most famous tortoise in the world is Esmeralda on Bird Island. Esmeralda recently broke the record for the heaviest tortoise in the world. As with all famous personalities numerous yarns have been told about Esmeralda over the years.

Another famous tortoise is George on Cousin. The story goes that George, a usually docile creature, became quite aggressive only once when it snapped at the hand of Archbishop Makarios who was visiting Cousin!

Kantilal Jivan Shah wrote in 1990; The Seychelles giant tortoises. Note and Anecdotes. *Seychelles Today* 7, January 1990

I discovered on Aldabra that some tortoises migrated and others didn't and there were slight differences in shape between them. Moreover they do not borrow underground simply because it's a coral island with very little soil covering the surface and only deeper in some pockets favoured as nesting sites. The neck is shorter than most Galápagos island races, not longer, and these races are now described as species by taxonomists who have run riot over the naming of giant tortoises describing races as species and renaming them all in different Latin binomials. The International Committee on

Ian astride a giant tortoise, Aldabra, 1976

Zoological Nomenclature has had to adjudicate over many years about the Aldabra species with taxonomists fighting like cats to change the names but losing to the moderate ecologists. Taxonomists use morphology as their trade, and doubtful historical information about provenance, which is most misleading when it comes to giant tortoises, ignoring the genetic fact that there are no differences between these various so-called species, and overlooks the 'plasticity 'of the shell which can be made any shape in captivity by differing food regimes. There are even tortoises in the main granitic Seychelles which have been given Latin names and breeding colonies created. All of these animals originally came from Aldabra Atoll.

Albert Gunther of the British Museum, who later moved to the Natural History Museum of London, enlisted Charles Darwin and other famous scientists to help him to conserve the Aldabran giant tortoises working with the government of Mauritius to establish a preserve at the end of the 19th century and they wrote a letter in 1874 publicising their concerns.

London, April 1874.

(Signed by)

Jos. D. HOOKER, P. R. S.

H. B. FRERE, P. R. G. S. & R. A. S.

Charles DARWIN, T. R. S.

Richard OWEN.

John KIRK, F. L. S., H. M. Political Agent
and Consul General.

Alfred NEWTON, M.A., F. R, S, V. P. Z. S.

Zoological Department, April 20th 1874.

— 107 —

3. No means being taken for their protection they have become extinct in nearly all these islands, and Aldabra is now the only locality where the last remains of this animal form are known to exist in a state of nature.

4. We have been informed that the Government of Mauritius have granted a concession of Aldabra to parties who intend to cut the timber on this island. If this project be carried out, or if otherwise the island be occupied, it is to be feared, nay certain, that all the Tortoises remaining in this limited area will be destroyed by the workmen employed.

5. We would, therefore, earnestly submit it to the consideration of Your Excellency whether it would not be practicable that the Government of Mauritius should cause as many of these animals as possible to he collected before the wood cutting parties or others land with the view of their being transferred to the Mauritius or the Seychelle Islands, where they might be deposited in some enclosed ground or park belonging to the Government, and protected as property of the Colony.

6. In support of the statements above made and the plan now submitted to the Mauritius Government the following passages may be quoted from Grant's " History of Mauritius." (1801, 4) :

I have done so many things for illogical and irrational reasons but one thing I did do was join the Athenaeum Club in Pall Mall in 2004 because of Darwin. Sir Charles Darwin used the Athenaeum to study in 1838. In one letter, dated August 9, he said: "I go and dine at the Athenaeum like a gentleman, or rather like a lord, for I am sure that the first evening I sat in that great drawing-room on the sofa by myself, I felt just like a duke. I am full of admiration for the Athenaeum, one meets so many people there that one likes to see ... Your helping me into the Athenaeum has not been thrown away, and I enjoy it the more because I fully expected to detest it." I joined it with the same trepidation, with a reputation as the most elite and upper cut Club in London, but I found it a haven of reason, civility and intelligence, with good bedrooms and excellent full English breakfast that keeps me going all day! It welcomed women while others were still barring them and everyone there treats you as an individual. Best of all it has the same dramatic painting of Darwin in a black cloak in the Morning Room that hangs in the Boardroom, Zoology Department, Oxford.

Giant tortoise, slaves and politics

Giant tortoises are capable of surviving for very long periods of time without food or water and can be easily stored upside down in the holds of ships. In the absence of refrigeration it is just about the only animal that could provide fresh meat in days gone by with little attention as live animals require food and fresh water needed for the crew.

Two hundred and fifty years ago the inhabitants of the Western Indian Ocean especially the Seychelles were actively involved in transporting enslaved Africans to Île de France (region around Paris) and Bourbon (Réunion). Because of the importance of slave ships' cargoes they carried tortoises as a convenient and healthy source of food. Seychellois tortoises were imported into Mauritius and Réunion as an additional commercial venture. Much has been written about the trade and politics affecting tortoises and I am indebted to Peter Nicholls' PhD thesis (University of Kent 2018) for some insights[66].

Slavers habitually broke their journeys at the Seychelles and indeed there is clear evidence of visits to Aldabra. Diving at Passe Houreau at the eastern end of the atoll I discovered bi-convex round discs of a heavy stone like granite which I've been told we used as ballast by traders and slavers in their ships. Slave ships would restock with tortoises and goats which they had probably released on the island to breed and provide future supplies together with wood, jettisoning the ballast stones to compensate. No

66   Nicholls, P.A. (2018) 'The Door to the Coast of Africa': The Seychelles in the Mascarene Slave Trade, 1770–1830. Doctor of Philosophy (PhD) thesis, University of Kent. https://kar.kent.ac.uk/67029/1/232Peter%20Nicholls%20PhD%20thesis%20The%20Door%20to%20the%20Coast%20of%20Africa%20The%20Seychelles%20in%20t.pdf

distinctive ballast stones were found in the other two Passes of Grande Passe and West Channels near the research station.

In 1777 Captain Chateauxneuf of the Aventurier, sailed from Île de France to the Quirimbas with slaves and was instructed by the voyage's financiers to purchase tortoises and bring them back to Île de France in the event of a refreshment stop in the Seychelles becoming necessary[67].

While tortoises exported to the main Mascarene Islands (Réunion, Mauritius, and Rodrigues) were only a small proportion of those consumed by passing ships, tortoises were a significant source of income for slavers and especially Seychellois settlers. Slavers landed on the archipelago's outlying islands where hunting was forbidden such as Aldabra to harvest tortoises for free supported by settlers who competed with each other to provide slavers with supplies of the tortoises which they had secretly acquired[68]. In 1780 Commandant Gillot accused the settlers of conspiring with the slavers in selling large numbers of tortoises and tried to stop the wholesale destruction of tortoise populations. The Aventurier's expenses show how cheaply services could be obtained in the Seychelles at the time of Gillot's tenure.

Lieutenant Charles Routier de Romainville was sent from Paris in 1778 to try and halt the devastating tortoise trade and had two small ships on patrol around the uninhabited islands[69]. Only eight families lived in the Seychelles at the time of Malavois's arrival in 1787 and they could not grow enough food to satisfy the needs of passing ships and so the population of the Seychelles needed to expand, thwarting any English intentions of colonising the Western Indian Ocean who already controlled Diego Garcia which became a United States Air force base in 1971 after Britain's initial attempt to develop Aldabra as the USAF base met a wall of resistance from conservationists[70] and the Royal Society. So Malavois led a significant expansion of agriculture on the islands and offered free plots of Crown land to attract planters from union and although the market for produce was smaller, slaves were cheaper. Although the planter's industry in cash crops such as indigo and cotton improved the economics of the Seychelles, it still provided too little money to pay for the government to protect the islands against slavers who were encouraged by the increasing supply of food. This increasing economic progress in freshwater, tortoises, turtles and spices, and the Revolution in France, increased the Seychelles' demand for autonomy.

The indiscriminate culling of tortoises decreased as a result of Malavois's conservationist measures but continued to be used by slavers as an

---

67   MNA OB29/24, and Allen, European Slave Trading, p. 96.
68   MNA TB7, Gillot to Souillac, 8 May 1787.
69   Scarr, Seychelles since 1770, p. 9; McAteer, Rivals in Eden, pp. 85–86.
70   Beamish, T. (1970) Aldabra Alone. George Allen & Unwin.

important source of food until about 1800 by which time the numbers had declined dramatically[71]. The profitable relationship between settlers and slavers, where the French government administration was too weak to intervene, helped to damage the ecological balance of many of the outlying islands but contributed to the growth of the Mascarenes' East African slave trade.

The British frigate *Orpheus*, commanded by Captain Henry Newcome, arrived at Mahé on 16 May 1794. Terms of capitulation were drawn up and the next day Seychelles was surrendered to Britain. Independence was granted in 1976 and a year later a coup d'état by France Albert René ousted the first president of the republic, James Mancham. In 1965, the United Kingdom split the Chagos Archipelago from Mauritius and the islands of Aldabra, Farquhar and Desroches from the Seychelles to form the British Indian Ocean Territory (BIOT). The purpose was to allow the construction of military facilities for the mutual benefit of the United Kingdom and the United States. The islands were formally established as an overseas territory of the United Kingdom on 8 November 1965[72]. On 23 June 1976, Aldabra, Farquhar and Desroches were returned to Seychelles as a result of its attaining independence. Subsequently, BIOT has consisted only of the six main island groups comprising the Chagos Archipelago.

Giant tortoise ecology and behaviour

I spent two years on Aldabra Atoll from January 1975–November 1976 with a short break in the middle. I quickly accustomed to the physical effort needed to do my research and to the social customs and behaviour of the people working on the atoll.

I redesigned my approach to understanding their ecology and behaviour, distinct from the original research proposal which required killing many tortoises instead of the very few I eventually did dissect. Not only did I hate the idea of slaughtering so many animals but believed that the data from transects (surveys), nest and eggs would provide all the data needed to understand much of their ecology. So I collected data using transects, noting which tortoises were seen (many were individually marked with titanium discs embedded in their carapace by a previous researcher David Bourn), their measurements, their activity, and because I had two separate populations to observe, one on the northern densely wooded island of Malabar with large animals and the other on the more open environment of Grande Terre, in the extreme east, composed of mangrove swamp near the lagoon then open woodland with 'tortoises turf' and the

71 Lionnet, The Seychelles, p. 130.
72 United States Dept. of State. Office of the Geographer (1968). Commonwealth of Nations. US Government Printing Office. p.15. Retrieved 7 November 2013.

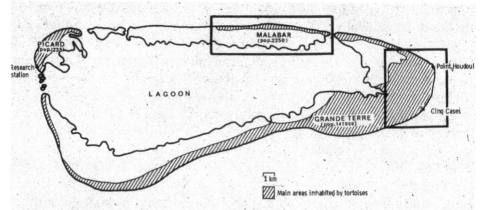

Aldabra Atoll, Indian Ocean, showing the sampling sites. The hatched area is frequented by giant tortoises and the remainder shows the extent of dense inland *Pemphis* scrub

Carrying giant tortoises was an occupational hazard as they often relieved themselves which is why I never did put them on my shoulder like the Seychellois! Royal Society Aldabra Research Station Aldabra 1974

coastal grasslands that had very little shade.

Out in the field I started work at first light walking set transects and using a tape recorder recorded every tortoise that I came across within 50 feet, took note of their disc number if they had one, measured their third dorsal scute and took note of their sex. This was later transcribed from the tape when I got back to the station in the air-conditioned library into formatted sheets and later when back in Oxford these data were input into a mainframe computer and using SPSS as I had with my rook research in Edinburgh carried out analysis to find out what these amazing animals were up to and what life history strategies they were employing.

The Aldabra giant tortoise nares are the most forward part of their head enabling them to drink from a teaspoon as I have demonstrated. This surprised Nick Arnold, Curator of Herpetology, Natural History Museum London as he had seen the algae in nasal chamber of skeletal specimens but didn't have an explanation until I told him (see p129)[73]. He subsequently discovered a flap-like ridge that contains cavernous tissue projecting from the median wall. This may be capable of closing of the olfactory area in life. Alice 'Bunty' Grandison was also a Curator in the same department and helped me understand more about the soft tissue and organs of tortoises but these conversations were often held on the fire escape stairway outside the building as Bunty was a chain smoker and many of the specimens were in pure alcohol.

I was particularly interested in the reproductive behaviour of the animals in these two distinct populations so I invested enormous amount of time to see which females were nesting where and what happened to their individual eggs even though I was told by everybody that finding nests was very difficult if not impossible. With Harry Charles and Bernard Legae we were able to find hundreds of nests and I weighed and measured all the eggs, putting them back in exactly the same position in the nest, while monitoring nest temperature throughout incubation.

The most exciting conclusions that came from all this work[74] in the

73 Arnold, E.N. (1979) Indian ocean giant tortoises: their systematics and island adaptations. *Phil. Trans. Roy. Soc. Lond. B* **286:** 127–145.

74 Swingland, I.R. (1977) Reproductive effort and life history strategy of the Aldabran giant tortoise. *Nature* **269:** 402–404.

Swingland, I.R. & Coe, M. (1978) The natural regulation of giant tortoise populations on Aldabra Atoll. Reproduction. *J. Zool. Lond.* **186:** 285–309.

Swingland, I.R. & Lessells, C.M. (1979) The natural regulation of giant tortoise populations on Aldabra Atoll: movement polymorphism, reproductive success and mortality. *J. Anim. Ecol.* **48:** 639–654.

Swingland, I.R. & Coe, M. (1979) The natural regulation of giant tortoise populations on Aldabra Atoll. Recruitment. *Phil. Trans. Roy. Soc. Lond. B* **286:** 177–188.

Coe, M.J., Bourn, D. & Swingland, I.R. (1979) The biomass, production and carrying capacity of giant tortoises on Aldabra. *Phil. Trans. Roy. Soc. Lond. B* **286:** 163–176.

Swingland, I.R. & Frazier, J. (1980) The conflict between feeding and overheating in Aldabran giant tortoises. In *Telemetry and Radio Tracking*. Amlaner, C.J. & Macdonald, D.W. (eds) Oxford: Pergamon.

Swingland, I.R. & Gould, M. (1980) The tortoise and the goat: interactions on Aldabra Island. *Biol. Cons.* **17:** 267–279.

Swingland, I.R., North, P. & Parker, M. (1981) What determines individual movement patterns in tortoises? *Amphibia & Reptilia* **47:** 13–14.

Greenwood, P.J. & Swingland, I.R. (1983) Animal movement: approaches, adaptations and constraints. In *The Ecology of Animal Movement*. Swingland, I.R. & Greenwood, P.J. (eds) Oxford: Oxford University Press.

Swingland, I.R. (1983) Intraspecific differences in movement. In *The Ecology of Animal Movement*. Swingland, I.R. & Greenwood, P.J. (eds) Oxford: Oxford University Press.

Swingland, I.R. (1984) International Symposium on Tortoises. Amphibia-Reptilia 5:1–80.

Coe, M. & Swingland, I.R. (1984) Giant tortoises. In *Biogeography and Ecology of the Seychelle Islands*. Stoddart, D. (ed.) Nederlands: Junk.

Stubbs, D. & Swingland, I.R. (1986) Recent developments in the conservation of Testudo hermanni in France. In *Studies in Herpetology*. Rocek, Z. (ed.).

Swingland, I.R. & Stubbs, D. (1986) Movement patterns in Testudo hermanni and implica-

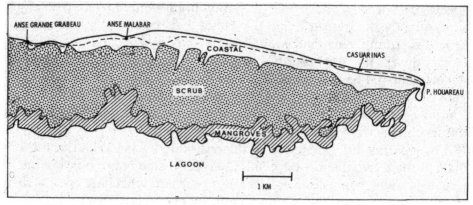

Malabar showing the camp site at Anse Malabar and the transect route (dotted line)

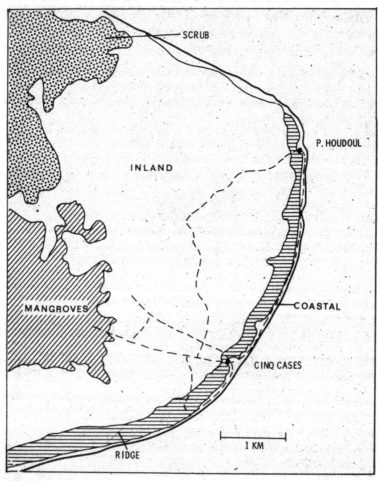

Eastern Grande Terre showing the camp at Cinq Cases and the transect route (dotted line)

Tortoise drinking through its nose from a shallow pool after rain

Harry Charles, Bernard Legae watching me record
hatchlings and eggs on my tape recorder

tions for management. In *Studies in Herpetology*. Rocek, Z. (ed.).

Swingland, I.R. (1989) *Tortoise and Freshwater Turtle Action Plan*. Gland and Cambridge: IUCN.

Swingland, I.R. (1989) Geochelone gigantea. In *The Conservation Biology of Tortoises*. Swingland, I.R. & Klemens, M. (eds) Gland and Cambridge: IUCN.

Swingland, I.R. & Klemens, M. (1989) *The Conservation Biology of Tortoises*. Gland and Cam-

toughest environment I've ever had to work in are:

Frequency dependent selection

Imagine two populations of birds, one are fishers and the other pirates. Every day the fishers go out to catch prey and as they return the pirates dive-bomb them stealing the fish. As the pirates become more successful, causing the fishers to starve, the fishers' population goes down with the failure of breeding success. Meanwhile the pirates have a problem. Without the fishers the pirates have no food and they also suffer with a lack of breeding success. For both populations to survive an equitable balance has to be struck so that there are enough fishers for their chicks to flourish and not too many pirates that they 'shoot themselves in the foot'. The frigate birds on Aldabra would be gliding up high near the coast on the winds that cooled the atoll and as the red footed boobies came back laden with fish, dive-bomb them. To escape the boobies drop their fish catch for the frigates to scoop up from the sea surface.

This is frequency dependent selection where there was a balance of 80% fishers and 20% pirates.

By surveying the movement of marked giant tortoises in two island populations (Malabar, Grande Terre) I demonstrated that in one population, on Grande Terre, some of the tortoises migrate to the coast during the rainy season although many stay inland where there is more shade so vital to tortoises' survival as they can overheat if they can't find shelter at midday.

Death is much higher on the coast than it is inland; due to the lack of shade on the coast many tortoises die from heat exposure. The coastal vegetation is quicker to respond to the beginning of the rains than the 'tortoise turf'[75] found inland. 'Tortoise turf' is a complex assemblage of plants that resembles a well manicured putting green. So while migrant tortoises gain

bridge: IUCN.

Swingland, I.R. (1989) Geochelone elephantopus. In *The Conservation Biology of Tortoises*. Swingland, I.R. & Klemens, M. (eds) Gland and Cambridge: IUCN.

Swingland, I.R., Adams, J. & Greenwood, P.J. (1990) Environmental sex determination. In *Living in a Patchy Environment*. Shorrocks, B. & Swingland, I.R. (eds) Oxford: Oxford University Press.

Mittermeier, R., Carr, J., Swingland, I.R., Werner, T.B. & Mast, R. (1992) Conservation of Amphibians and Reptiles. In *Herpetology: current research on amphibians and reptiles*. Adler, K. (ed.).

Balmer, O., Ciofi, C., Galbraith, D.A., Swingland, I.R., Zug, G. & Caccone, A. (2011) Population genetic structure of Aldabra giant tortoise. *Journal of Heredity* **102**(1): 29–37.

75   Grubb, P. (1971) The Growth, Ecology and Population Structure of Giant Tortoises on Aldabra. *Phil. Trans. Roy. Soc. Lond. B* **260**: 327–372; Hnatiuk, R.J. & Merton, L.F.H. (1979) *Vegetation of Aldabra, a Reassessment*. Atoll Research Bulletin No. 239, The Smithsonian Institution.

from the higher productivity of the coastal vegetation at the beginning of the rains they are faced with the problem of overheating if they can't find shade within a reasonable distance of the food.

The ponderous pace of a giant tortoise even at full speed meant that animals could not venture further than about 600 yards from shade and to maximise time spent feeding they would stay out on the range all night. Meanwhile those individuals that stayed inland where there was abundant shade had to survive on more meagre rations which were slower to grow once the rains came but the benefit was lower mortality.

The reproductive output of migrant females that frequented the coast is higher than those that remained inland i.e. they laid more eggs than the non-migrants. By tracking the movement pattern of the individual marked tortoises we could show that the population consisted of migrants and non-migrants. We argued that migrant and non-migrant individuals persist together in the population because they receive approximately equal pay-offs; although coastal individuals risk a greater probability of death their migration allowed them to achieve a higher reproductive success mediated by the greater primary productivity of coastal vegetation.

The costs and benefits of migration will be frequency dependent, so the equilibrium ratio of migrants to non-migrants should be stable. In other words, if too many tortoises migrated there wouldn't be enough space under the few shade trees to accommodate them at midday and they would overheat and die. Whereas those staying inland, the non-migrants, would survive on more meagre rations but with much less chance of dying with considerably more shade available. They would live longer even though they produced fewer offspring per year.

My data of the resighting frequencies of tortoises on the coast in different wet seasons suggested that migrant tortoises go to the coast in a relatively high proportion of years and that there are some 'inland' tortoises that never go to the coast. We also observed a marked difference in shape where those that migrated were longer and narrower than those that frequented inland areas.

Environmental sex determination

During the two years I spent living on the Atoll I spent a lot of my time finding nests, measuring the eggs and replacing them exactly where they were, and measuring the temperature. I also recorded where precisely each individual female nested and tracked the progress of each nest and what hatchlings emerged. This information provided a rich insight into the games the giant tortoises were playing.

Firstly, the giant tortoises of Grande Terre produced far smaller eggs and fewer than those on Malabar. Indeed the clutches on Malabar with large eggs and many of them frequently caused the top eggs to be broken

Tortoises grazing in the late evening on the coastal grasslands in eastern Grande Terre at Cinq Cases close to one of the few Guettarda shade trees

Grazing tortoises in the late afternoon on coastal grasslands of Grande Terre looking towards Cing Cases hut, just visible to the left of the Guettarda shade trees and my tent to the right

as a female covered her efforts after laying. Finding nests on Grande Terre was much more difficult than on Malabar because the nests were more dispersed as there were no favoured sites in particular. Whereas there were few available nesting sites on Malabar with sufficient depth of soil where the sun could penetrate the dense vegetation as the whole island was fos-

Tortoises shading at midday, piled high, under the few much-used shade trees on the coast of Grande Terre

silised coral with a few pockets where the soil accumulated. These sites were frequented by the land crab *Birgus latro* and the two colour forms could often be seen to compete while excavating tortoise nests, the reds dominating the blues.

A female giant tortoise would approach the nesting sites carefully sniffing the ground either to determine whether others had nested there all to assess the temperature. They then dug the nest just like a marine turtle with their back legs using each one alternately and holding the excavated earth on their foot using their claws. The female would urinate as she commenced digging the hole which stabilised the sides and allowed the soil to adhere to her feet. After laying she would cover over the hole smearing the urine-soaked soil over a wide area confusing nest predators. The urine is laden with mucus which dries to a fairly hard cake.

I discovered environmental sex determination in giant tortoises by mistake in 1975 as did Claude Pieau, unbeknownst to me until years later, at the Institut Jacques Monod (Paris, France) with the European pond turtle, *Emys obicularis*[76] at the same time as I was on Aldabra. Environmental sex determination is where some environmental parameter influences the sex during embryonic development; in the case of giant tortoises it's temperature.

---

76   Pieau, C. (1974a) Sur la différenciation sexuelle chez des embryons d'Emys orbicularis L. (Chélonien) issus d'oeufs incubés dans le sol au cours de l'été 1973. *Bull. Soc. Zool. Fr.* **99**: 363–376; Pieau, C. (1974b) Différenciation du sexe en fonction de la température chez les embryons d'Emys orbicularis L. (Chélonien); effets des hormones sexuelles. *Ann. Embryol. Morphog.* **7**: 365–394; Pieau, C. (1976) Donnkes rkcentes sur la differenciation sexuelle en fonction de la tempkrature chez les embryons d'Emys orbicularis L. (ChClonien). *Bull. Soc. Zool. Fr.* **101 (Supp1.4)**: 46–53.

A marked giant tortoise with a titanium disc walks along a pathway from inland to the coastal grasslands of Grande Terre

I was aided in my research by an extraordinary discovery which allowed me to discern the sex of young hatchlings without sacrificing them. A scale near the base of the tail enabled me to count the scales from there to the tail tip and since all hatchling's scales were of equal size, and males have vastly longer tails than females when adult, it was possible to identify what sex they were. It required a magnifying glass, considerable patience and for the hatchling to be still!

My intensive study indicated the nesting behaviour of individual female giant tortoises may involve choice. On one of the several isolated islands which form the Atoll (Malabar), the few available nesting areas are small and discreet with very different temperature characteristics. In two of these areas, one generally warmer than the other (by 3°C), most of the nearby females would nest several times during each year. Manipulation of the temperature characteristics of the areas induced individual females to vary the nesting pattern and it was also observed that although nests were not unisexual, being large (with a temperature gradient from top to bottom 3°C) and relatively thermally stable from day to day, there were statistically significant differences in the sex ratios between nests. The sex of eggs also differed according to their position within the nest with males more likely to emerge from the bottom of the nest.

In the warmer of two areas so many females nested that many of the nests were excavated by subsequent nesting visitors; the end of each nesting season the same number of viable nests were left intact. Moreover, apart from local temperature differences within the areas, the seasonal ambient temperature rises during the incubatory period. Early nests (colder) produced more males whereas late nests (warmer) gave more females; early nests took longer to hatch than late nests. Although late nests were more likely to remain intact, 80% of the nests were made in the first half of the nesting period before the weather started warming.

By nesting early, mothers increase the proportion of sons that will hatch and decrease the chance that the nest will survive the incubation period; by nesting later, the sex ratio will be increasingly biased towards daughters and the nest is more likely to survive. Females may nest several times within a season but there is insufficient data indicating whether some females are laying more nests either early or late.

Individual females returned to the same nesting areas within and between seasons. Preliminary data also suggests that individuals nested within the same temperature range on each occasion (i.e. warm or cool) which differed between individuals.

Larger females laid more large eggs than smaller females and tended to be the later nesters. Larger eggs give rise to larger hatchlings and ultimately larger adults; and larger females lay heavier clutches than smaller females. This tends to indicate that mothers which lay large eggs are selecting daughter-producing sites (and vice versa). A further study on a European species of tortoise (*Testudo hermanni*), which lay small nests of few eggs which are all of one sex, tends to support the evidence from Aldabra that individual females choose a specific nesting temperature.

I do not believe environmental sex determination is anything other than an ancient characteristic and has not evolved. In other words, I do not believe that female Aldabra giant tortoises choose which sex of offspring to produce by their nesting behaviour. When sex depends on environment rather than genotype, the sex expressed under relatively unfavourable conditions will be more abundant[77]. This result refers to numbers of males and females in the population. By contrast, no clear prediction can be made about the allocation of resources to the two sexes.

Hot babes and cool dudes!

Harry Charles making a tortoise long-stretch

Long stretch and the flightless rail

A peculiar posture that both sexes of giant tortoise demonstrated was to stretch up as far as they could on their legs and stretch out their necks. I called this the long-stretch posture and it can easily be elicited by humans tickling the inside of their back legs.

Whenever a flight-

77 Frank, S.A. & Swingland, I.R. (1988) Sex ratio under conditional sex expression. *J. Theor. Biol.* **135**: 415–418.

less white-throated rail or Cuvier's rail approached a tortoise, especially if they started pecking, it would stretch up and the rail will inspect every inch of the body presumably for ectoparasites. Most of the time rails were searching for other food which included tortoise hatchlings, rotten eggs we excavated or anything else. They were quite fearless as with all animals on Aldabra except perhaps the goats. The difference being we chased the goats for food but not the others.

I was elected as the youngest member of the Zoological Club founded in 1822, a dining club following meetings and lectures of the Zoological Society of London, but it ceased to exist in the 1990s after interfering busybodies fetched the ire of the Society.

CHAPTER 9
Back in Oxford 1977–1979

After a brief sojourn in London I went to Oxford to start writing up the scientific papers from two years field work on Aldabra Atoll. In March 1977 I gave a paper at the Royal Society during a symposium on the terrestrial ecology of Aldabra. My paper concerned the natural regulation of giant tortoise populations on the Atoll and concentrated on recruitment. It was extremely well received and I was delighted that David Stoddart, who was the chief lynchpin of the Aldabra program at the Royal Society, but based at Cambridge, was very complimentary. I was disappointed that Miss Mary Geddie, who inspired me with her lessons on natural history at my prep school, didn't come.

```
From:  Sir David Martin, C.B.E.
```

The Royal Society
6 Carlton House Terrace, London, SW1Y 5AG
Telephone 01-839 5561   Telex 917876
```
              (ext. 277)
                92/PBC
           3 November  1976
```

```
Dear Dr Swingland,

        I am desired by the Officers and Council
of the Royal Society to send you this official
invitation to present a paper at the discussion
meeting on 'The terrestrial ecology of Aldabra'
organized by Dr D. R. Stoddart and Professor T. S.
Westoll, F.R.S., to take place here on Wednesday
and Thursday 16 and 17 March 1977.
```

USA

My girlfriend from Aldabra sent me a telegram in January 1977 and stayed in Cambridge with her brother-in-law and sister. We occasionally saw each other although I had little accommodation in Oxford and little income. The relationship between her and me was clearly diverging especially after I made a two-month trip in late 1977 across the States when she joined me in California and we visited her hometown of Modesto taking a wolfhound with us as a present for her mother.

It was a fascinating trip since we explored California from the top to the bottom by car but it was clear she was wedded to the States, and more especially to living on a tropical island, whereas I had no idea where I was headed, what I wanted to do and thought it unfair to her to restrict her dreams.

I knew that I was not keen on the idea of pursuing my life or career in the United States even though I had been going to Ann Arbor (University of Michigan) for many years which is an oasis in the middle of the Rust Belt, 30 miles due west of Detroit. I was in admiration of what I could see being achieved but I could not embrace the thought of living in the USA. During one of my visits I stayed with my great uncle John Hower who lived in Erie, Pennsylvania. While there he introduced me to a garage owner who showed me my great grandmother's tomb on the Scottish side of my family which immigrated to the United States for a few decades before returning. John's daughter Helen Radock often hosted me in their large Ann Arbor house in woodlands.

I toured the United States giving seminars in all the major universities in 1977; at the department of Ecology & Evolutionary Biology and Society of Fellows at Rackham Graduate School at the University of Michigan (Ann Arbor), Michigan State University (East Lansing), Humboldt State University (Arcata), Washington State University (Pullman), University of California at Davis and at Berkeley, Hawaii, UCLA Radiation Laboratory, San Diego State University, Stanford (Paul Ehrlich, Jon Roughgarden, Hal Mooney), then dropped down to Costa Rica for a couple of days (Guanacaste), Duke, Duke Prosimian Center, National Museum of Natural History, and finally a Seminar with Dillon Ripley, Secretary of the Smithsonian, Washington DC. This garnered me various sobriquets such as Distinguished Guest, Society of Fellows, University of Michigan; Distinguished Lecturer, The Smithsonian Institution; and Distinguished Lecturer, Duke.

This seminar tour gave me enormous insights into the nature of American higher education and how staff were hired, tenure being a key goal of many but given to few, particularly in the best institutions regardless of research record. Little did I guess that I would be back in Ann Arbor for a sabbatical year working at the Museum of Zoology and Department of Biology 10 years later? The University of Michigan is one of the top 10 universities in the United States, judged by its academic standards, with an enormous endowment, although not recognised as Ivy League since technically it's the agricultural College of the State of Michigan. A very tough 'school' as I found out much later!

I went to Costa Rica after sustaining a parachute fracture in my right heel when I jumped over a small wall in the Stanford University car park rushing to give a lecture for Paul Ehrlich and discovering the other side was 10 feet! Going south my plane stopped at Tegucigalpa, the capital city of Honduras, and as we took off I could hear machine-gun fire. When we landed in San Jose, Costa Rica several of our tyres were flat. I went straight for treatment on arrival to a man who used some kind of probe that he moved across my heel heating it up and making it feel a lot better.

I joined my friends Peter Moss (my Zambian friend) and David Lloyd (a wild friend who helped establish Kasanka National Park, Zambia) who together with Irvin J. Wilhite, who served in the North Dakota State Senate, were proposing the establishment of a privately owned conservation park close to Guanacaste National Park in the north. It seemed to me a bit of a pipe dream and of course with Messrs Lloyd and Moss we ended up one night in cramped accommodation with two single bunks and a double bed. We had by this time got a very attractive American assistant whose job was unclear, or where she emerged from, but chose the double bed while the two men quickly grabbed the only bunks leaving me no choice. Of course during the night I prevaricated but was egged on by all three! The following day we flew to Limon then north by car to La Perla, presumably another possible site. Nothing transpired from these Expeditions but it did implant the idea of the private sector being a major player in biodiversity conservation.

Indeed Guanacaste National Park had been supported by Daniel Janzen from the University of Pennsylvania who raised funds by 'selling' patches of a square yard to thousands of people using the slogan, 'use it or lose it', referring to the conservation of biodiversity.

The last seminar at the Smithsonian had to be a *tour de force* as, although I didn't want a job there, I wanted to put on a good show. The huge audience was well over 1000 and I was introduced by the head of molluscs in rhyming couplets and then there was a deathly silence as a man of imposing stature came slowly down the auditorium preceded by a dog that cocked its leg on the rostrum and urinated. Dillon Ripley was probably the most respected and best-known Secretary of the Smithsonian in the last century. Established by a gift from an Englishman called Smithson, who never visited the United States, it was the pre-eminent research institution and Dillon Ripley was also a great fan of the work done on Aldabra Atoll and cooperated with the Royal Society to support it. He and I had lunch at the Smithsonian 151 Rhode Island Ave. NW where I met the owners of National Geographic and the Rockefellers. I didn't realise that the Smithsonian Secretary is the only unelected member of the United States Cabinet. My late afternoon seminar went well covering environmental sex determination, frequency dependent selection, population dynamics, and egg-size strategy used by females. Clearly the earlier anointing of the rostrum bode well, as I received an ovation at the end; quite extraordinary and something that hasn't happened too often in my life.

Prof. Janet Kear of Sir Peter Scott's Wildfowl and Wetlands Trust at Slimbridge became a great friend when we were both involved in Gerald Durrell's zoo in Jersey. She once confided in me that, "scientific research, and an ovation, far exceeds sex". She was without doubt one of the few trailblazers for women in science especially ecology. Thank goodness I've had the pleasure of knowing many who have made major contributions.

Back in Oxford after this extended trip to the States I carried on during 1978 finishing the publications, trying to find a job and living off the dole. I was attracted to continuing my work with animals although not in Oxbridge which is a magnet to many young scientists who could not imagine working anywhere else. I also became disaffected from this somewhat elite form of higher education and although I am completely apolitical the concept of continuing education, which had its bedrock in socialist politics, attracted me. One hundred and forty years ago, a movement called 'Oxford Extension' began at Oxford University – an initiative that sprang from general educational reforms in the mid-Victorian era, and from a growing national sense of social awareness. A handful of dedicated Oxford tutors who felt that educational opportunity was essential to the nation's welfare and future set about collaborating with ordinary citizens to design a format of education that served their needs; and it's the story of adult education (éducation permanente) evolving as successive generations of students, from 1878 to the present day, participated in ever-growing numbers.

To make ends meet I acted as College Tutor at St Peter's Hall, St Catherine's, Magdalen, and Lady Margaret Hall. The latter had a remarkable ground floor lavatory for men only since it was a college for women at that time. The jokes on the walls were classic and clever, as were the students. I can remember one LMH student that for some reason I had to visit as a moral tutor and she slammed the door once I was inside. I explained to her that the rules were: "You have to have a book between the door and the doorjamb when entertaining a man alone", at which point she said, "That's easy!", and promptly slammed the door again, this time with a book of matches in place. She became President of her country.

Royal Geographical Society Gunong Mulu Expedition

Another Expedition that I went on in 1978 was to join the Royal Geographical Society's Expedition in Mulu Sarawak Borneo, one of the largest scientific Expeditions from the United Kingdom ever undertaken. I researched the resource division in sympatric species of flying dragons *Draco* spp., the question being why two species of the same genus could live in the same place at the same time. I was supported by the National Geographic Society, and later worked on the sustainable management plan for Gunong

Mulu National Park, Sarawak to obtain World Heritage Status. Frogs, snakes and lizards all glide in Mulu probably because living in the canopy getting from one tree to another is easier if you glide across than go all the way down, across the ground and all the way up; less danger from predators, quicker and makes them more interesting to study.

I took off in an RAF VC-10 from Brize Norton in March. To get there we had to travel with the help of British Armed Forces specifically the 7th and 10th Gurkha Rifles who accommodated me at Gun Hill Barracks Hong Kong and later in Borneo in Bandar Seri Begawan.

Wallace's flying frog (*Rhacophorus nigropalmatus*) and similar species composed of five human females

I was accompanied by my roommate from the Zoology Department at Oxford, Ilkka Hanski, who had a scholarship for Finns from Queens College doing a DPhil involving meta-populations. Ilkka lived life to the full and we often ended up in the Turf Inn in central Oxford and helped each other home. He had long blonde hair which the authorities in Borneo took exception to. They insisted he shorten it and he insisted there was no way that was going to happen. The compromise was to tie his hair up in a sort of short pigtail. Ilkka became one of the world's top ecologists and evolutionary biologists, widely respected as an expert both in the academic community and among the general public. Like me he was committed to biodiversity conservation and believed that ecologists should not restrict themselves to producing scientific information but participate in the conservation processes using the information produced. I talked to him on the phone from Stockholm in 2012 when I was a member of the Swedish Research Council (Vetenskapsrådet), Linnaeus Midterm Evaluation. He died a few years later in 2016 at 63 years old which was a tragedy for such a dynamic and productive person probably the most famous evolutionary ecologist Finland has ever produced.

The Expedition was led by Robin Hanbury-Tenison who was in the rafters of the longhouse when I arrived at the headquarters, making noises not dissimilar to an orang-utan, and was greeted by Nigel Winser who effectively ran the show, the nuts and bolts. Both Robin and Nigel have become lifelong friends working together on many initiatives and projects over the last 42 years.

The most startling was the invitation during the Expedition was to a Berawan wedding in a longhouse some distance away from our headquarters and we set off in late afternoon in large dugouts. We had to negotiate rapids en route and a rotten tree stuck at an angle caused us to capsize. Andy Eavis, one of the world's greatest speleologists, was thrown into the water with me and was more concerned at the loss of his camera than the fact that he couldn't swim. While helping him, I reflected on the fact that he had discovered with his companions one of the largest cave systems in the world in Mulu which requires squeezing through completely dark, tight passages, inundated with running water, miles underground; an experience that I never want to have. This would traumatise me which explains his nonchalance at nearly drowning. So I was not surprised that he won the Merdeka Prize from Malaysia for his cave survey and the discovery of the Sarawak Chamber.

The people who were on the Expedition either for the entire year, or who made brief trips of only a month or so, have become the Who's Who of modern field ecology. Those that stood out to me were Mark Collins studying the termites, Jeremy Holloway discovering lots of new species

of moths, John Proctor science director whose daughter proudly produced a roundworm which I pickled for her, David McDonald chasing civets at night since David has always been a nocturnal animal, and John Ogle a very fine English GP who treated my many cuts and abrasions which wouldn't heal in the humidity.

Gathorne, Lord Medway, now Dato Sri Gathorne, Earl of Cranbrook, help me enormously before I joined the Expedition as he was an extremely experienced Southeast Asian zoologist who not only knew Malaysia and Borneo well but was an excellent field zoologist. This has been recognised by the Malaysian state and many others. I've had the privilege of co-supervising with Gathorne a very able young man of Chinese extraction from Sarawak, Lim Chan Koon, who studied every aspect of the ecology, genetics and sociology surrounding cave swiftlets for a doctorate at DICE. Cave swiftlet's nests are used in bird's nest soup and for other purposes, and fetch enormous prices to the extent that some caves are protected by the local people using automatic weapons. Gathorne's son Jason joined DICE for a short period but now invests his time in art and design associated with both Malaysia and Suffolk where he lives. When I had to suddenly retire from DICE through ill-health in 1999 Gathorne was my surprise guest who my colleagues kept hidden until the last moment.

The Berawan wedding itself was remarkable. As we arrived we were each required to drink from a straw in a large jar containing very strong liquor called borak made from fermented rice similar to the hooch made from coconut palm sap on Aldabra. We had to keep sucking until the person minding the jar said some indicator suggested we had had our tot. How he made that judgement who knows but the party went with a swing with much traditional dancing by a single man holding a panga to music played by inhabitants. A very slow and balletic performance so elegant in the hands of the locals and so comic performed by us. Jeremy Holloway performance was startling and dramatic, and in one striking moment he plunged the room into darkness capturing the only light bulb with his butterfly net in place of a panga. As the evening wore on my recollection of events became very hazy but I woke up with two beautiful young girls each side of me and wondering what had happened. I needed to relieve myself and negotiating my way along the longhouse to the river fell through the floor into it a midden. This caused huge hilarity especially from the young girls as I washed myself off in the river. The nature of the local people, both the more sophisticated and worldly Berawan and the very gentle and unsophisticated Penan, was one of exceptional happiness and contentment, not unlike those in similar remote places I have lived, untouched by the ugliness and aggression of modern urban behaviour.

When the BBC discovered my curious way of capturing flying lizards

(*Draco* spp.) they wanted to film the whole process. I needed to mark lizards and work out how several not-dissimilar species could occupy the same habitat, indeed why there were more than one species in the forest. Unga Paren, a Penan, was helping me alongside Sawing, a young Berawan. To catch the lizards the Penan simply reversed the poisonous dart in the blowpipe so that the pithy stopper at the end came out first and hit the flying lizard on the head temporally knocking it out.

Unga Paren. Mulu 1978

Nyapun using blowpipe with a bamboo quiver of poison darts of different strengths, some barbed others not. A Penan's objective was to use whichever dart insured the prey did not become hyperactive and flee too far. With some monkeys, hit by a dart, they didn't move and after 20 minutes they dropped out of the tree dead

The beautifully made hardwood blowpipes of the Penan had perfectly true bores and were deadly accurate. I would collect the lizard from the forest floor and mark them with a unique identification using Tipp-Ex Correction Fluid so it was easy to identify individuals from a distance. Barry Paine, the BBC director, filmed the whole process.

Unga went on later to be one of the prominent Penan who stood up against forestry company's destruction of his home[78]. He talked to me a lot about Penan ways. He couldn't see why Westerners like us had too many possessions, too much money and filled our

BBC filming 'Mysteries of the Green Mountain' with Hugh Maynard (cameraman), me and Barry Paine

stomachs with too much food – and then wanted more! He didn't blame us as Malaysian and Sarawakian politicians were just as greedy and behind the destruction of much of the forests in Sarawak[79].

Barry and his film crew found themselves in an extraordinary world of limestone pinnacles, secret rivers, huge caves and different kinds of tropical forest. Importantly, Barry had the Expedition scientists to help and advise him – leading to novel sequences that might otherwise have been missed. His film was in the BBC series *The World About Us* and called 'Mysteries of the Green Mountain'. Some of us, the scientists and naturalists, on

78 https://www.youtube.com/watch?reload=9&v=mMHKf-oRb68
79 Exposed by Clare Rewcastle Brown in many articles, books and speeches e.g. *The Sarawak Report: The Inside Story of the 1MDB Exposé*. 2018.

that Expedition went on to form the Rainforest Club of which Barry was a proud member and later President.

Twenty years later (1999) Robin Hanbury-Tenison and I returned to make a film for Channel 4 Productions about the changes that had happened dubbed `The Lost World of the Penan'. We revisited the area with a film crew and Louella and Merlin, Robin's wife and second son, to record our reactions, those of the local people, the changes in biodiversity and local people's living conditions over the last two decades, and what happened to us over a two-week period. The film was screened worldwide February 1999.

The film concludes with a late evening conversation with Robin who having co-founded *Survival International* was used to defending tribes against the worst excesses of the modern world by protest and legal means. On the other hand, I defended a different approach when it came to forest conservation. It centred on having a constructive conversation or argument with the destroyers of the environment who trash indigenous people's lives by providing effective incentives to make them desist. When we returned to the UK, fired up by the destruction we had seen, we formed a partnership that created a company called Sustainable Forestry Management (SFM) to use private sector approaches to conserve forests and improve the standard of living of those who were dependent on them. This was the heart of Sustainable Forestry Management's approach.

The forests around Mulu had been destroyed right up to the boundary of the park and sometimes beyond. A new longhouse had been constructed where Penan were encouraged to move in but many were reluctant such as Nyapun, an amazing man who saved Robin's life during the Expedition and is still alive as I write. Most die by 40 years old. A chapel had been built and a school but it was clear that the Penan were treated prejudicially and so

Capturing Carbon and Conserving Biodiversity: the Market Approach (2003) London: Earthscan. Cover: Mulu Rainforest

Robin and I set about helping them with writing books, pencils, erasers, anything that would help. When the Penan hurt themselves the local facilities treated them cursorily and if attending hospital they had no means of feeding themselves or any accommodation for the family. Here again Robin and I helped but it wasn't until I visited Mulu again in 2005 I was able see the forest, it's development as a tourist site with aerial walkways and routes laid our brilliantly by Brian and Sue Clark of Borsarmulu Park Management and the conditions in the local camp and longhouse. There were still-water pools under the longhouse which allowed mosquitoes to breed and the Penan knew it! So Tony Jack, a friend from Perth Australia, and I paid for the ground to be concreted.

Logging right up to the boundary of the Park. 2005

Years later, as a bit of light relief to divert me from this vexing problem of conserving forests and international politics, I helped develop the International Media and Environment Summit (IMES) in Kuching, Sarawak from 30 November – 2 December 2005 led by Alexander Thomson (News World International's MD). It brought together everybody from the news media including Reuters and *The Times* of London to Singapore newspapers, radio stations and in effect all the key players in Asian media with most of the major movers in the environment.

As a side trip Illka Gobius, who helped organise all the on-ground ar-

Nyapun and his blowpipe 1978 and meeting in 2005

rangements for the Summit, arranged the travel logistics for me when I invited my friends to the Royal Mulu Hotel owned by Robert Geneid. I invited Tony Jack (SFM Australasia), Clare Rewcastle Brown (journalist and co-organiser of IMES), Niu Zhiming (ADB China Environment) and Illka. We had a wonderful time not least because I was able to meet Nyapun again, a Penan that help us a lot on the Mulu Expedition years before; a wonderful break from 3rd to 5th December 2005.

While at the Summit, Reuters interviewed me about conserving forests and benefiting local communities, which was published December 22, 2005: *'Science and Economics Work Together Toward Environmental Improvement'*:

> *British biologist Ian Swingland took up the idea of trading commodities to fund afforestation programs after he witnessed the devastation caused by logging in the Malaysian rainforests of Borneo in 1998, two decades after his first visit there. Now his company has bought about 10,000 hectares (25,000 acres) of Kangaroo Island, Australia's third-largest island, to demonstrate that afforestation can offer a major investment opportunity through trading in carbon credits.*
>
> *"Conventional conservation is a disaster story," Swingland, the founder of Britain's Durrell Institute of Conservation and Ecology at the University of Kent, said in an interview."What isn't a disaster is where you make a business of it, and everybody's lives are improved by it, and we give them ownership of their own future." I'll let the full story speak for itself--but I like the last line: "If you don't even have incentives, how can you get people*

Tony Jack (SFM Australasia), Clare Rewcastle Brown (Journalist and co-organiser of IMES), Niu Zhiming (ADB China Environment) and Illka Gobius (PINPOINT PR, a PR consultancy and Verve MPR, a marketing consultancy). Four exceptional people in their very different talents

to look after the environment?"

Swingland lived alone for two years in the 1970s on the coral Atoll of Aldabra in the Indian Ocean. There he studied the giant tortoises, numbering around 154,000, the island's only other inhabitants.

Now his company has bought about 10,000 hectares (25,000 acres) of Kangaroo Island, Australia's third-largest island, to demonstrate that afforestation can offer a major investment opportunity through trading in carbon credits. "Conventional conservation is a disaster story," Swingland, the founder of Britain's Durrell Institute of Conservation and Ecology at the University of Kent, said in an interview. "What isn't a disaster is where you make a business of it, and everybody's lives are improved by it, and we give them ownership of their own future."

Kangaroo Island, off the state of South Australia, is home to two nature reserves with koala populations, but about 34,000 hectares (85,000 acres) of native bush land exists on privately held land.

Carbon trading is a key part of the European Union's strategy to cut emissions of heat-trapping gases under the Kyoto Protocol. The EU Emissions Trading Scheme, launched this year, covers 11,500 European manufacturing plants and power stations and lets companies that emit below their limits sell credits into the market where they trade as a commodity. Under the scheme, 230 million tons of carbon dioxide, which is blamed for global warming, has been traded. Industry groups forecast the value of business this year at $5.3 billion.

A major initiative in trading of emission credits is the Clean Development Mechanism that gives companies credits for funding environmentally friendly projects in developing nations.

"A WIN-WIN SITUATION"

Other scientists welcomed Swingland's initiative at the meeting in Sarawak, one of the two Malaysian states on the island of Borneo, which teems with luxuriant plant and animal life. "I think it's a win-win situation," said Mick Poole, former chief of Australia's CSIRO Center for Environment and Life Sciences and an expert on how climate change affects farming. "Not only do you put in trees, it has other benefits, such as improving soil salinity, and the watershed, and so on."

New South Wales is the only Australian state where carbon is traded, said Noel Ryan, a climate change analyst with the Wilderness Society. But other states and national territories are in talks to establish a national emissions trading system. "There's a lot of opposition from the federal government at the moment, but everybody expects that there will be carbon trading everywhere in the future," Ryan said. Analysts say Australia's federal government, which is not a signatory to the Kyoto Protocol, believes that putting caps on emissions of gases would hurt industry, and curb job growth.

Sir Peter Crane, director of the Royal Botanic Gardens at Kew [who I had invited as a guest along with Sir Crispin Tickell, a self-taught environmentalist], said, "It's quite likely that you have a lot more biomass locked up in lowland forests; I could believe certain types of forests in the tropics, not all forests, but certain types of forests."

Malaysian officials are examining carbon trading regimes across the world to understand how they could benefit. Sarawak forestry official Cheong Ek Choon said the state was studying different nations' schemes but had made no decision. "Some types of plantations qualify, some don't," he said. "At least now there is some monetary value being placed on trees."

Chief Minister Mahmud Taib[80], First Minister of Sarawak, said it was a tough balancing act to weigh Sarawak's development needs against conservation aims, and only the prospect of concrete benefits would spur people to protect the environment. "As you know, this carbon sink scheme has never taken off the ground very much," he said. "If you don't even have incentives, how can you get people to look after the environment?"

Evolutionary Ecology

In the five years I was at Oxford the hot topic amongst those who worked on animal behaviour was evolutionary ecology which is a field within both ecology and evolution that examines how interactions between and within species evolve. Most of the key characters involved in the development

80 https://en.wikipedia.org/wiki/Clare_Rewcastle_Brown; Clare Rewcastle Brown (2018) *The Sarawak Report: The Inside Story of the 1MDB Exposé.* Lost World Press.

of evolutionary ecology worked in the Zoology Department. Many were working on theoretical approaches in evolutionary ecology. This branch of ecology enabled us to predict what animals and humans might do in the future and helped in conserving the world's biodiversity. Intelligence about what motivates animals and humans is a key management tool.

We need to know that if we, or another animal, does X then Y will probably happen. Several watershed events in the study of social behaviour mainly took place in the 1960s and 70s but it all started in 1930 with *The Genetical Theory of Natural Selection*[81], Ronald Fisher's fundamental theorem of natural selection; an idea about genetic variance in population genetics developed by the statistician and evolutionary biologist. "The rate of increase in (Darwinian) fitness of any organism at any time is equal to its genetic variance in fitness at that time." Fisher outlined eleven concepts including *'Fisherian runaway'* explaining how the desire for a phenotypic trait in one sex combined with the trait in the other sex (for example a red deer's horns) creates a runaway development of that trait, larger horns more offspring[82], and *'sexy son hypothesis'* which explains why females choose promiscuous, unreliable fathers for their children in the hope of having similar sexy sons who give them lots of grandchildren. He laid the basis of evolutionary ecology.

Second was the challenge to David Lack, head of the Edward Grey Institute in the Zoology Department, by Aberdeen University zoologist Vero Wynne-Edwards, who's controversial *Animal Dispersion in Relation to Social Behaviour* (1962)[83] proposed a pervasive role for group selection, allowing sacrificial behaviour for the good of the group or species. Largely discounted by most who believed that such altruism should rarely evolve, most elegantly put down later by Richard Dawkins in *The Selfish Gene* (1976)[84], or *The Immortal Gene* as he would now prefer to call it 40 years later, expounding the simple truth that the more individuals are related to each other, the more they behave selflessly with each other. David's son Peter was doing a DPhil while I was there on the birds in Tsavo National Park, Kenya where I visited him and later helped him alongside others with his thesis.

Third was British evolutionary biologist W.D. Hamilton's proposal in 1964[85] that kin selection plays a role in the evolution of altruism, coopera-

81   Fisher, R.A. (2013) *The Genetical Theory of Natural Selection*. Paperback, HardPress, 304pp.
82   http://rumdeer.biology.ed.ac.uk/evolution-and-genetics
83   Wynne-Edwards, V.C. (1962) *Animal Dispersion in Relation to Social Behaviour*. Oliver and Boyd, London, 653pp.
84   Dawkins, R. (1976) *The Selfish Gene*. Oxford University Press, 224pp.
85   Hamilton, W.D. (1964) The Genetical Evolution of Social Behaviour. *Journal of Theoretical Biology* **7(1)**: 1–16; The Genetical Evolution of Social Behaviour. II. *Journal of Theoretical Biology* **7(1)**: 17–52.

tion, and sociality. Kin selection is based on the concept of inclusive fitness, which is made up of individual survival and reproduction (direct fitness) and any impact that an individual has on the survival and reproduction of relatives (indirect fitness). The elements of kin selection lead directly to the concept, now known as Hamilton's Rule, which states that aid-giving behaviour can evolve when the indirect fitness benefits of helping relatives compensate the aid giver for any losses in personal reproduction incurred by helping.

I was once having a beer in a pub with John Maynard Smith from Sussex University who asked me, "How many siblings would you be prepared to die for?" The underlying basis of the question, since he was a brilliant mathematician and ecologist, was how many of my siblings would together have my entire gene complement. It was a play on J.B.S. Haldane famously joking that he would willingly die for two brothers or eight cousins and who set out the mathematics of kin selection in 1931[86]. Since brothers' genetic complement will in part duplicate each other it is likely that to ensure JBS's full gene complement was passed on he would have to save slightly more than two brothers.

Fourth in the theory of evolution and natural selection, the Price Equation (1970-1972) describes how a trait or gene changes in frequency over time. The equation gives a mathematical description of evolution and natural selection. It provides a way to understand the effects that gene transmission and natural selection have on the proportion of genes within each new generation of a population. The Price Equation was derived by George R. Price[87], working in London to re-derive W.D. Hamilton's work on kin selection. The Price Equation also has applications in economics.

The fifth major advance in social behaviour during this era was the sweeping summary and prospectus of the field provided by Harvard biologist E.O. Wilson with *Sociobiology: the New Synthesis* (1975)[88], which laid the cornerstone for the modern interdisciplinary study of animal behaviour. His final chapter, attempting to understand the evolution of human social behaviour using adaptationist principles, ignited such an intense debate led by Stephen Jay Gould, also at Harvard, that the very word sociobiology, until that time used synonymously with animal social behaviour, is now usually restricted to the application of such principles to human behaviour. Although some people remain disturbed by the idea of applying sociobiological principles to human behaviour (specifically

---

86 Haldane, J.B. (1931) Mathematical Darwinism: A discussion of the genetical theory of natural selection. *The Eugenics Review* **23(2)**: 115–117.

87 Price, G.R. (1972) Fisher's 'fundamental theorem' made clear. *Annals of Human Genetics* **36(2)**: 129–140.

88 Wilson, E.O. (1975) *Sociobiology: The New Synthesis*. Harvard University Press, 697pp.

genetic determinants of human behaviour[89]), the approach has flourished and provided insights into human behaviour that could not have come to light with alternative, non-evolutionary worldviews.

A major exponent of this view was Stephen Jay Gould who championed biological constraints as well as other non-selectionist forces in evolution. He considered many functions to be unintended side consequence of natural selection such as the higher functions of the human brain, female orgasms (see below), thus undermining an essential premise of human sociobiology. E.O. Wilson introduced his analysis of animal behaviour (including human behaviour) based on a sociobiological framework that suggested that many social behaviours have a strong evolutionary basis. Gould and others criticised Wilson's notion of a "deterministic view of human society and human action", but Gould capitulated[90] by writing in 1980: "Sociobiologists have broadened their range of selective stories by invoking concepts of inclusive fitness and kin selection to solve (successfully I think) the vexatious problem of altruism—previously the greatest stumbling block to a Darwinian theory of social behaviour. Here sociobiology has had and will continue to have success. And here I wish it well. For it represents an extension of basic Darwinism to a realm where it should apply."

Gould and Richard Lewontin suggested that any biological feature of an organism that arises as a necessary side consequence of other features may not be directly selected for by natural selection. Proposed examples in the context of evolutionary biology include the "masculinised genitalia in female hyenas, exaptive use of an umbilicus as a brooding chamber by snails, the shoulder hump of the giant Irish deer, and several key features of human mentality". An illustrative example is Elisabeth Lloyd's case study suggesting that the female orgasm is a by-product of shared developmental pathways. Her study of evolution and orgasm strongly rejects the claim that orgasm in women serves an evolutionary purpose and is just a by-product of the role that male orgasm plays in reproduction and the sharing of early embryonic tissue by the male and female genitalia.

Gould favoured the argument that evolution has no inherent drive towards long-term 'progress', and was merely directed towards diversification. The conflicts between Richard Dawkins and Gould centred on their disagreements over theoretical issues, including the prominence of gene selection in evolution. Dawkins argues that natural selection is best understood as competition among genes, while Gould advocated multi-level selection, which includes selection amongst genes, nucleic acid sequenc-

---

89 May, R.M. (1976) Sociobiology: a new synthesis and an old quarrel. *Nature* **260(5550):** 390–391.

90 Gould, S.J. (1980b) Sociobiology and the theory of natural selection. In *Sociobiology: Beyond Nature/Nurture?* Barlow, G.W. & Silverberg, J. (eds) Boulder, CO: Westview Press.

es, cell lineages, organisms, demes, species, and clades. Richard Dawkins approved of Gould's general argument but was insistent that evolution was indispensably progressive. He also devoted entire chapters to critiquing Gould's account of evolution in his books *The Blind Watchmaker* and *Unweaving the Rainbow*[91], as did Daniel Dennett in his 1995 book *Darwin's Dangerous Idea*[92].

John Maynard Smith and myself just before delivering
the DICE Annual Lecture, University of Kent

John Maynard Smith was among Gould's strongest critics. Maynard Smith thought that Gould misjudged the vital role of adaptation in biology, and was critical of Gould's acceptance of species selection as a major component of biological evolution. Maynard Smith wrote that Gould, "is giving non-biologists a largely false picture of the state of evolutionary theory", which gave some inherent dissenters like creationists the false argument that Darwinian explanations had been proven to be unscientific.

The Darwin Wars, as they were dubbed, is beautifully and accurately told in *The Darwin Wars: How Stupid Genes Became Selfish Gods*, by Andrew Brown published by Simon & Schuster 1999.

91   Dawkins, R. (1986) *The Blind Watchmaker: Why the Evidence of Evolution Reveals a Universe without Design.* Norton & Company, Inc.; Dawkins, R. (1998) *Unweaving the Rainbow.* Houghton Mifflin.
92   Dennett, D. (1995) *Darwin's Dangerous Idea: Evolution and the Meanings of Life.* Simon & Schuster, 586pp.

People

One of the people that I often had lunch with in Halifax House, designed as a hostel, club and social centre for postgraduates and senior members of the University without college affiliations, right next door to the Zoology Department (Tinbergen Building), was Dorothy Hodgkin[93] who probably worked somewhere in the vast concrete edifice which used to house both zoology and psychology[94] until closed because of asbestos in 2017. She was a woman of some years and not infrequently she had carpet slippers on. She was delightful company, not at all pretentious, but had an 'evil' and hilarious take on life and people, and I didn't find out until years later that she had the Nobel Prize.

Another was Wilma Crowther, an Oxford Zoology don, who worked on gundis or comb rats, a group of small, stocky rodents found in Africa. A very remarkable woman with whom Kate Lessells, my girlfriend, and I got along with extremely well but she did have the most amazing dress sense quite different to anyone else. Peter Brunet was another kindly don whose daughter married Guy Weston who figured much later in my life when I dallied with the private sector as an instrument for conservation in Sustainable Forestry Management Ltd.

During my last year at Oxford, without an income, I took on any task that might lift my bank balance from rock bottom. I acted as a Consultant for the Government of the Republic of the Seychelles, Royal Society, and the Seychelles Island Foundation in the matter of their application for World Heritage status for Aldabra Atoll as I did later for Mulu, Sarawak.

I was also involved with Peter Moss[95], again who by this time had left Zambia and was in Wales at the Coedmor Estate owned by David Lloyd[96], developing the Cardigan Wildlife Park which is now called the Teifi Marshes Nature Reserve, part of Afon Teifi Site of Special Scientific Interest and Special Area of Conservation[97]. The reserve also forms part of the Coedmor National Nature Reserve. We also developed a consultancy initiative as well as a travel agency pioneering eco-safaris called Ecoconsult and Ecosafaris (now The Ultimate Travel Co.) respectively.

Father's plan for Aldabra as a USAF base

I hadn't seen my father since the divorce with my mother in the High Court 1972

---

93   Dorothy Mary Crowfoot Hodgkin OM FRS HonFRSC was a British chemist who developed protein crystallography, for which she won the Nobel Prize in Chemistry in 1964.

94   Closed 6 February 2017 as although it won prizes as a concrete structure it contained asbestos.

95   https://www.telegraph.co.uk/obituaries/2017/07/28/peter-moss-pioneer-ecosafari-obituary/

96   https://www.telegraph.co.uk/news/obituaries/8334051/David-Lloyd.html

97   http://jncc.defra.gov.uk/protectedsites/sacselection/sac.asp?EUCode=UK0012670

when I came down from Edinburgh, 6 years before, as a possible witness in the proceedings since in those days there had to be 'cause'; who did what to whom and when. My mother who was being difficult as usual and seemed to have little legal support. She needed my comfort while feeling sorry for my dad. At least he had the support of his brother Owen who was a QC. Six months after I got back from Aldabra I asked my father to lunch in June 1978 at the London Zoo where there was a Fellow's Restaurant which was infrequently used.

When he walked in he said, "It's so nice to see you. Where have you been for the last six years?" And I explained, "I've been running a national park in central Africa and then went to Oxford spending two years living on Aldabra Atoll."

Welsh Black Cattle ③

The meadows on the South of the railway track receive the freshwater run-off from the high land around. On these meadows you can see plants like Yellow Flag, Meadowsweet, rushes and damp meadow grasses that are intolerant of salt water and therefore do not grow on the river side of the track. It is probable that from the time that man first kept cattle in this area, these naturally fertilized meadows were known to be rich grazing, possibly the finest natural pastures in the whole of Pembrokeshire. The Welsh Black Cattle which may be in the meadow today, with their wide sweeping horns, are the traditional breed of this area. They are hardy beef cattle and milkers, so that they were useful as allrounders on farms of small acreages and were more frequently seen in West Wales in the past than they are in the more specialised farming of today.

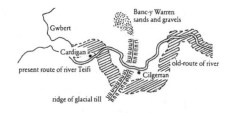

The wide valley which you are looking across was once the bed of the river Teifi, but when the Irish sea ice pushed its way up the valley 12-20,000 years ago, it formed a dam so that the river started to cut its present course north of Cilgerran, shaping the rocky gorge ahead. Today the Piliau stream meanders across the old river bed to join the river at the town entrance to the Wildlife Park.

A page from the Cardigan Wildlife Park brochure at Coedmor 1978. We bought young Welsh black cattle to manage the marsh as they could handle both the wet and the weather. The bull grew into a champion that paid for replacing the very expensive oak flood gates from the marsh into the Teifi River at low tide

My God! In the mid 60s I was planning to make that place a USAF base in the Indian Ocean. The plan was to have the runway on the largest island [Grande Terre], blow up the seabird colonies that would cause airstrikes – what are they called boobies and frigate bird? – and then use a controlled atomic explosion in the lagoon for instant deep water harbour for Jet A1 fuel tankers near Passe Hulot.

Passe Houreau Dad. It's the nearest to Grande Terre. Hulot is a character played by French comic Jacques Tati.

But the Royal Society and many others made a big fuss about its importance for animals and plants and things like that – and even a book ('Aldabra Alone'[98]) was published against what the Ministry of Defence was planning. Actually it was Prime Minister Wilson devaluing the pound which protected Aldabra as we could not afford to build a military base for the US.

So what did you do?

We acquired Diego Garcia, to the north and much nearer the Middle East, preferred by USAF, but the difficulty was we did not own the Chagos Archipelago. So we bought Diego Garcia for £3 million from Mauritius, moved the few remaining inhabitants to the Seychelles, other islands in the archipelago or Mauritius and in exchange we got Polaris missiles at half price.[99]

Didn't the inhabitants of Diego Garcia kick up a fuss?

Of course we expected that. Diego Garcia is the only inhabited island of the remaining British Indian Ocean Territory (BIOT) which Aldabra was part of until the Seychelles took over. The Chagossians – about 1500 – have taken their complaint to the House of Lords quite recently.

It was quite an emotional lunch to our surprise and we never lost contact thereafter although it took some management on my part to maintain a relationship with both my mother and my father without either getting upset or meeting! He was frightened of her and she despised him.

Today the Chagossians are still pursuing their grievance even though their former home is now destroyed by military activity, most especially leakage of jet fuel which travels for miles through the coral. Nevertheless the case continues[100]. My father retired from his career as D MOD PE, otherwise Director, Procurement Executive, Ministry of Defence, in 1982. To personally remember my father 'saving' Aldabra Atoll I instituted a prize at DICE for the best MSc where a student went from the bottom to the top of the class called the Maurice Swingland Prize. I was told King Fahd of Saudi Arabia was in tears saying goodbye to dad when he retired as he had set-up the Al-Yamamah arms deal worth £85billion to the UK (£305billion today) which was finally signed 3 years after his retirement.

98   Beamish, T. (1970) *Aldabra Alone*. Allen & Unwin, 224pp.
99   http://news.bbc.co.uk/go/em/fr/-/1/hi/uk_politics/1005064.stm
100 In September 2018, the International Court of Justice in The Hague, plans to hear arguments in a case regarding whether Britain violated Mauritian sovereignty when it took possession of the islands for its own purposes.

I was offered a Bowra Fellowship at Wadham College, University of Oxford after an interview with Stuart Hampshire but was persuaded to turn it down by a Fellow who had another young candidate who needed the funds and, "I was obviously destined for a great future after the Royal Society event." It was not difficult to turn it down since I did not have this obsession that life couldn't continue outside Oxbridge.

Adieu Oxford

In my last few years, after returning from Aldabra, I lived with Kate Lessells in 25 Summertown House where we kept harvest mice in a specially designed tall aquarium made by the AERG technician with growing wheat and babysat 'four downy vandals 'or Canada geese chicks. We occasionally had a few meals at Quat' Saisons, a very plain restaurant with gingham tablecloths and very good food cooked by Raymond Blanc, with whom I stay in contact even now.

Kate is a lovely and very intelligent woman who passionately cared about animals, a refreshing change from many zoologists' attitudes that treat them as a means to an end. Kate Lessells graduated from the University of Oxford in 1976, and continued there in the Edward Grey Institute of Field Ornithology as a PhD student working on '*Some causes and consequences of family size in the Canada Goose Branta canadensis*' (PhD thesis, 1982) while continuing to work on the mating system of Kentish plovers with my help in the Camargue for four months each year. We were stationed at the Tour du Valat, part of Luc Hoffmann's home, with many research workers including John Krebs (bee-eaters) and Mark Avery (bats).

Kate and I took a memorable canoe trip down the nearby Ardèche with two other zoologists, Mike Hassell and Vicky Taylor, which involved negotiating rapids. We took on a lot of water and had to get the water out of the two-person canoes. The banks were littered with hundreds of naked bodies sunbathing from the naturist campsite in the Ardèche Gorges which meant negotiating carefully between their legs carrying a sodden canoe, and tentatively tipping the cold water out. Tricky! Mike and Vicky married in 1982.

Kate got back from a trip to Canada working on Canada geese from May to July 1979 where I remember she had an altercation with a polar bear. I was in the Galápagos. She then competed for a prize Fellowship at Christ Church, Merton and Magdalen Colleges which required her to present her PhD thesis after only two months of starting it! I acted as her personal assistant and I remember sequentially stamping the page numbers on three copies of what she envisaged. She chose Magdalen. Soon after she invited me to join her at the Judge Randolph dinner, a rare and lavish event, with many courses and progressions from one room to another. I can remem-

Kate Lessells and I were tackling the Ardèche Gorges 1982

ber arriving at the College and the other Fellows assumed I was the new fellow until Kate joined me putting on a gown at which point there was surprise, a woman no less!

At one point I left the throng for a smoke and found myself in a corridor alone with another. We started chatting and I soon realised I was talking to A.J.P. Taylor who was well known through his ITV television programs about the Second World War. He did them straight to camera, live and without an autocue, and outraged many by, in their view, demeaning the high calling of Oxbridge academia by becoming a television personality. Today most academics crave to reach such a large audience with their thoughts and views while Alan Taylor was so popular he had to give his University lectures at 8:30 a.m. to avoid the room becoming over-crowded; watched by millions because of his stunning clarity and accessible descriptions and analyses of the major events in modern history. He asked me not what I did but, "Why are you here?", and I explained that my girlfriend had just won this Fellowship to which he said, "It doesn't count for much. What matters is that you know yourself you're worthwhile and have something to say that is valuable. Don't be put off by the labels and appurtenances that others crave. Are you any good?" I mumbled some inadequate rejoinder and he came back, "Just believe in yourself and make sure you're the best!" I didn't know when we were talking that in 1964 Oxford University refused to renew his term as lecturer in the aftermath of the controversy occasioned by his TV programme *The Origins of the Second World War*.

While casting around in 1979 for a job John Ashworth, who I knew from my application to Essex University where he specialised in slime moulds, wrote me a handwritten, long letter with career advice from the Cabinet Office where he was on the Central Policy Review Staff as Chief Scientist. John Black, head of the Department of Forestry and Natural Resources, Edinburgh University where I did my PhD, was by now principal of Bedford College, University of London and he also did his best to help. My publisher Bruce Wilcock at OUP was writing to the Royal Society about the book on the entire ecology of the Aldabra giant tortoises which received enthusiastic support and was still on my mind years later when George Zug and I went to Aldabra on a Smithsonian Expedition in 1990.

I also joined Kate at the Magdalen College Christmas party. Dudley Moore, a former organ scholar at the College, was playing the grand piano after the choristers had sung while the rest of us were milling around and deep into the toasting and mince pies. A beautiful California blonde was draped over him and the Steinway while he played both popular music and JS Bach. He died in tragic circumstances with brain disease almost alone in 2002. A man was sitting in an armchair facing the roaring fire who had the largest head of any human I have met. He was Robert Maxwell, born Ján Ludvík Hyman Binyamin Hoch, a Czechoslovakian, to a poor, Yiddish-speaking orthodox Jewish family. He lived at Headington Hall above the city, which was in fact the largest council house in England and now inhabited by Oxford Brookes University, while he had become a press baron who defrauded his worker's pension fund. He also died in tragic circumstances when he fell off his yacht 'Lady Ghislaine' at night.

After a two-year interlude as a post-doc in Prof. Mike Hassell's group at Imperial College, working on the dynamics of patchy insect populations in the Silwood Park laboratory, Kate spent 9 years as a lecturer in the Department of Animal and Plant Sciences at the University of Sheffield, where she worked on the social behaviour of European Bee-eaters and life-history evolution of laboratory populations of bruchid beetles. Our interests, careers and geography eventually split us apart.

She was one of the very brightest people I have known at solving problems, although she admitted herself she wasn't quite as sharp as me in thinking of the critical questions. She has been at the Department of Animal Population Biology at the Netherlands Institute of Ecology since 1993, where her work centres on the evolution of life histories and parental investment, in particular the effects of evolutionary conflicts of interest including sexual conflict and parent-offspring conflict, using a combination of field experiments and theoretical models.

Moving on

Apart from scheduled lectures, the traditional form of teaching at Oxford was the tutorial system where a student was expected to fulfil written assignments for discussion. This one-on-one form of tutoring alongside lectures is the norm in Oxbridge but I was increasingly interested in enabling anyone of any age to be accepted by University without sparkling GCSE/A level results or any at all.

I've always been somewhat prejudiced against exams as a means of estimating a student's potential since many flower when they get to university like me, having always been quite bad at exams (like me), and prefer some form of continuous assessment. It's an attitude – 'helping the underdog' – I conveyed for twenty years at Kent University, and when establishing DICE in 1989, and ever since with my charities like Earthwatch and Wallacea. The brightest at Oxford could teach me, while the dumbest still found a place there; Oxford has average undergraduates, the same as any other good university, but the extremes were far more pronounced than anywhere else. This set the seeds of my helping to change the way we did things nationally and internationally in teaching and research to suit ordinary folk like you and me.

The Zoology Department was generous to all those research workers whose posts had concluded and were looking around for the next thing by providing temporary accommodation and other facilities. Malcolm Coe took me to an Oxford ceremony called Encaenia in the Sheldonian Theatre in 1979 which needed *sub fusc*, one of those Oxford quirks, a white winged collar and bow tie all encased in my somewhat dour Edinburgh doctoral gown. Encaenia takes place on the Wednesday of the ninth week of Trinity Term, the third and final term of the academic year at the University of Oxford. Basil Blackwell (bookseller), Graham Greene (novelist), Alan Cotterell (atomic physicist), and J.Z. Young (neuro behaviourist) were amongst those that got honorary degrees.

Another diversion was that Oxford University Press (OUP) delegates agreed to publish my book on animal movement[101] with Paul Greenwood who was to be my best man at my wedding with Fiona in 1985.

The day I finally left the Zoology Department in 1979 T.R.E. ('Dick')

---

101 Swingland, I.R. & Greenwood, P.J. (1983) *The Ecology of Animal Movement*. Oxford: Oxford University Press. (First and second paperback editions published in 1984 and 1985.)

Back Row

Dr. N.B. Davies
Dr. E. Ilgren
Dr. E. Adamson
Mr. D. Rice
Dr. D. Mercola
Dr. R. Ker
Dr. I. Swingland
Dr. L. Lefebvre
Mr. A. Kacelnik
Mr. P. Trotman

6th Row

Mr. W. Pulford
Miss J. Burridge
Dr. S. Oatley
Dr. K. Wilson
Miss B. Dickie
Mr. P. Artymiuk
Mr. A. Allen
Dr. D. Thompson
Mr. N. Wood
* Mr. B. Watts
* Mr. B. Gaskell
Mrs. P. Searle
* Mr. M. Rayner
Mr. P. Bacon
Mr. P. Nuttall
Mr. A. Richford
Miss M. Norris

5th Row

Mrs. J. Loupekine
Mrs. J. Bell
Mrs. H.L. Winkelman
Mrs. J. Stowe
Miss S. Guerra
Dr. F. Sin
* Miss M. Lucas
* Mr. J. Tyler
* Miss S. Dow
* Mr. K. Britton
* Miss P. Regent
* Mr. C. Sayer
* Miss A. Milner
* Mr. T. Knight
* Miss A. Harris
* Mr. M. Ridley
* Mr. P. Yudelman

4th Row

Miss A. Filipowska
Miss S. Ayers
Dr. I. Sin
* Miss R. Hill
* Miss E. Robertson
* Miss J. Spicer
* Miss R. Binks
Mr. E. Varney
* Mr. R. Lee
* Mr. I. Williams
* Mr. M. Hamer
* Mr. T. Johnson
* Miss C. Frank
* Miss R. Bagguley
* Mr. D. Freeman
Mr. D. Rose
* Miss B. Randle

3rd Row

Dr. G.A.B. Shelton
Dr. C.D. Rodger
Miss B. Bullard
Miss M. Clarke
Dr. G. Rossaminth
Mr. P. Cage
Dr. R. Abbott
Mr. T. Hughes
Mr. C. Elliott
Mrs. J.M. Dunkley
Mrs. L. Wallan
Miss A. Wells
Mr. B. Sutton
Mr. R. Cassels
Mr. I. Archibald
Mr. E.A. Stura
Dr. M. Dawkins

2nd Row

Mrs. P. Little
Mrs. M. White
Mr. R. Buxton
Dr. S. Randolph
Mr. S. Head
Mr. K. Davies
Mr. A. di Mauro Jr.
Dr. J. Brockmann
Mr. S. Larkin.
Mr. T. Burk
Mr. C. Barnard
Mr. J. Erichsen
Mr. J. Heath
Dr. J. Liberti
Mr. K. Lewis
Dr. R. Sibly
Mr. J. Helliwell
Mr. A. Houston

Front Row

Dr. W. Crowther
Professor J. Skinner
Dr. P. Miller
Dr. H.C. Bennet-Clark
Dr. T.S. Kemp
Dr. A.E. Needham
Dr. W. Holmes

Professor J.W.S. Pringle
Professor D.C. Phillips
Professor R.L. Gardner
Dr. P. Brunet
Dr. R. Dawkins
Dr. L.N. Johnson
Dr. C.M. Perrins

Zoology Department, University of Oxford 1978. I'm third from right back row. In *sub fusc* for Encaenia 1979

Southwood, the new Linacre Professor of Zoology and head of Department, was walking up the stairs with his boxes as I walked down with mine; the ultimate academic politician with whom I had a good working relationship for quite some years afterwards. Dick, or 'TREES' as he was nicknamed, was originally one of the Electors for the Chair and somehow they were unable to find a suitable candidate so he graciously resigned his Electorship, accepting their invitation! But he was always very pleasant and supportive of me. It's funny how nicknames are generally applied to those who are liked.

CHAPTER 10

Building magic castles at the University of Kent and worldwide 1979–1989

An opportunity arose to create the natural science programme in Continuing Education at the University of Kent. Kate and I went down to Canterbury 14 September 1979. We got the impression the evening before the interview that it was a wealthy city with the rings in Cousins, the jewellers beside the Cathedral, priced at over £30,000. I accepted the post at £4000 pa and started October 1, 1979.

The School of Continuing Education at the University of Kent was staffed mainly by middle-aged Oxford graduates since the provision was an implant of staff from the Oxford University Department for Continuing Education. It was firmly embedded in the traditional mould of evening classes throughout the county of Kent, titillating the senses and neurones of its denizens but not training them in a discipline. In setting about creating the natural science program, while I established many evening classes taught by an army of tutors, I added field courses and somewhat more taxing elements such as qualification courses (Diplomas and Masters) in my endeavour to get Continuing Education, *éducation permanente*, embedded in universities allowing people of any age or background to access degree courses.

This culminated in the national programme called Access which is primarily intended for people who have no previous experience of higher education. It allows anyone of any age without the traditional GCSEs to get a place at university. I played a part in establishing the Access program through local further education colleges and others in University Continuing Education.

In 1979 I kicked off my decade in Adult and Continuing Education with traditional evening classes all over Kent but this soon changed with courses at Wye College on countryside and land management jointly run with Bryn Green who had masterminded a very successful distance-learning MSc on the Environment. Wye was closed by its new owner Imperial College who wanted the land to sell to fill their empty coffers. Twenty years later, when Wye College had been emptied of everything it did, this MSc was still being managed there. Fiona, my wife, was part of the management team although Imperial College, where staff eschew teaching to pursue research and fame, had handed over the degree to the School of African and Oriental Studies (SOAS) and they eventually moved the team up to Russell Square, the death knell of Fi's involvement.

At the Commonwork Centre at Bore Place Farm I organised a large number of courses on animal noises, birds, 'The Compleat Naturalist', animal social behaviour, Kentish deer parks, orchids and fungi. The latter venue was owned by Neil and Jenifer Wates who became lifelong friends. After Neil fell off his horse and while repairing him the surgeons discovered cancer. Jenifer now lives in Oxfordshire but I befriended his younger brother Chris who's been a great pal ever since.

Bore Place farm in West Kent was a novel farm, where the waste from every process was the 'fuel' for another, for example, the cow dung generated electricity which powered the automatic dung scrapers in the yard and produced garden fertiliser, liquid manure and food for worms which could be freeze-dried and fed back to the cows as a protein supplement. Digging out the silage pits produced large quantities of clay which were moulded into Kent peg tiles, a rare commodity for the many Kent houses which needed them. The education centre in which I became involved had accommodation for a large number of people and all the facilities.

It was here at some event that Neil, Sir Colin Spedding and I dreamt up the idea of a think tank that would meet at weekends under Chatham House rules to discuss with ministers, farmers, land users and anybody else with expertise, different issues affecting the countryside. We founded an organisation called RURAL (Responsible Use of Resources in Agriculture and on the Land) which would focus on lower inputs (fertilisers and such like), maintaining financial margins, and support more conservation. We even invented the concept of `set-aside', which has subsequently been badly handled by bureaucrats as we predicted it would. It could only work with strong forward planning and sound ecological and fiscal management to allow farmers time to plan. Farmers needed to know way ahead of time what land of theirs the Department for Environment, Food and Rural Affairs (DEFRA) would designate as set-aside. We knew DEFRA would not be up to the task.

Les Mayons, Provence

When any project is funded by Government it should be designed to have a legacy, a self-proficient and self-funding future. So I started in France.

I received a research grant soon after arriving at Kent University of over £21,000 from the Natural Environment Research Council for a project 1980–83 on the ecology of the Mediterranean species of tortoises *Testudo hermanni* which was under threat based at the tiny village of Les Mayons, 40 miles north-west of St Tropez in the Massif des Maures. The village was surrounded by chestnut forests with quite a large population of Hermann's tortoise which I had found with the help of my French friends particularly Marc Cheylan (now at the Center for Functional and Evolutionary Ecology in Montpellier, part of the French National Center for Scientific Research) and David Stubbs my research assistant.

David managed to find accommodation for some time in the old chateau and adapted himself to life in that glorious region. The Common Agricultural Policy of the EU subsidises conservation by maintaining antediluvian ways of farming on the European continent prevalent around the village and Mediterranean countries. This means there are massive numbers of insects and other animals together with a stunning array of flowering plants which are missing in many other parts of Europe especially the north and the UK where farming has been virtually industrialised.

Life in Les Mayons, as a welcomed visitor, centred on the bar and on the gravel area further down the road where games of boules were played. It is an intense, emotional and simple game where the outcome was often random because of the uneven gravel surface. This caused more emotion but the bar was close at hand. Monsieur le Maire de Mayons helped us enormously so we could find somewhere to live and allow us to carry out the research unhindered. We lived part of the time in the Château des Mayons, an 18th-century house which was semi-ruined and unused but today houses the Maison de la Nature. We shopped in the local supermarket and did our own cooking which on one occasion caused a memorable faux pas. I accidentally tipped too much chilli into the curry I was making and David has always remarked that it showed how stubborn I was by eating it, as did he, showing he was not going to be bettered. The cost was extreme, needing large quantities of cheap 'vino collapse-oh' (a soubriquet invented in the Camargue) bought by the several litres in plastic bottles from Intermarché to put the fire out. The soubriquet for the wine was because the cheap plastic bottles crumpled up as we consumed the wine, needing to lie down in the hot sun!

Lying in the heart of Provence it was a land of pine trees, cork oaks and chestnut trees with the grandpere Chestnut Tree, planted in the Middle Ages, right in the middle of the village. It is a village created by former bousquetiers, people working in the forest. A number of producers make specialities based on honey and Châtaignes and Marrons, the sweet chestnuts of France, to recipes handed down from generation to generation. The tortoises lived in the forest and dug their nests in the open terraced fields where olives were grown. Herdsman with their sheep and goats used to wander through the area but in summer the village was always anxious about forest fires.

This culminated in the establishment of SOPTOM, Société d'Observation et Protection des Tortues du Maure and later Station d'Observation et de Protection des Tortues et de leurs Milieux, which established a Village des Tortues for tourists that provided a healthy income, and capitalised on en-

Les Mayons 1982

vironmental sex determination which I had discovered in giant tortoises on Aldabra. This was all established by Bernard Devaux, who worked at the Paris Bourse and on leaving vowed never again to (a) have a boss, (b) wear a watch, and (c) wear a tie. He did his national service as a tank driver in Algeria. When David met him and co-founded SOPTOM in 1984 he was doing a theatre production of Le Petit Prince. The Village des Tortues has now moved to its new headquarters at Carnoules and has gone on to become a worldwide conservation organisation concentrating on chelonia with its own glossy magazine La Tortue. David Stubbs went on to be instrumental in the environmental programs of the Olympics and is an international sustainability expert.

To start the Natural Science program I wanted something that would make a big splash so I put on a course concerning modern medicine 'Open Medicine' every Saturday at the University. The number that signed on needed a very large auditorium so we used the Senate building and amongst the lecturers were Sir Roy Calne (liver transplant surgeon who years later operated on Gerry Durrell), Dame Cecily Saunders (founder of the hospice movement) and Sir Godfrey Hounsfield (who invented x-ray computed tomography and won the 1979 Nobel Prize for Physiology or Medicine). There were courses on landscape and natural history with the University College of Swansea in the Gower Peninsula, a week-long Summer School on the 'Kent countryside in Trust' with many speakers, with Paul Greenwood of the University of Durham on the biology of islands involving a trip to the Farne Islands – and again with Paul, a great friend from my Oxford days, and Mike Walkey, who accepted me into QMUL (aka QMC) and taught me parasitology, took a large party to Mallorca,

Puerto Pollensa, for 10 days to study all aspects of the area's ecology for £235 including excursions, boat trips to outlying islands, travel and hotel accommodation.

Living on the University campus in Rutherford College as a deputy master, while I looked for a house to buy, effectively minding the 'shop 'at night, allowed me time to survey the biodiversity over its 300 acres and in 1984 I created a Kent University Nature Trail[102] with John Kesby, a social anthropologist and amateur botanist. John like me has worked in many parts of the world and published *Atlas of the Kent Flora* 1982.

My time as deputy master of Rutherford College only involved two emergencies, once when the fire alarms went off and everyone had to get out in their pyjamas (or less) and I was surrounded by many more women than men, and on another occasion a young man was arrested for drug offences and he was thrown in the back of a police van which seemed unnecessarily rough as he was semi-unconscious and this drew the ire of both myself and a lecturer in law.

A two-week trip studying the wildlife and archaeology of Greek Macedonia was followed by the establishment of a Diploma in Ecology to enable the large number of students which had touched my courses to pro-

Building a rook trap. School of Continuing Education, University of Kent 1980s

---

102 https://www.amazon.co.uk/Nature-Trail-Tour-Central-Campus/dp/B07PKJZ2Z3/ref=sr_1_1?dchild=1&qid=1592634923&refinements=p_27%3AJohn+Kesby+and+Ian+Swingland&s=books&sr=1-1

ceed much further. Of course, many said, "Oh, I don't think I can do this. I've forgotten how to learn." The facts however are that many people have qualified, some going further to an MSc, and indeed the original recruits from a Sevenoaks evening class had their last reunion in the Lake District in 2017, 30 years afterwards, all led by Terry Coulthard: "I would like you to know that when you let me come on the Ecology Diploma with my dodgy academic record it made a huge beneficial difference to my life."

Operation Drake – Seychelles and Galápagos

During this time I was asked to lead the Western Indian Ocean phase of Operation Drake, a round-the-world voyage with the participation of young people from many countries, having already joined it in the Galápagos a year before. The founding Vice Chancellor of the University of Kent, Geoffrey Templeman, refused to let me go during the summer vacation of 1980 as he did not consider fieldwork a necessary part of an academic's professional existence, "as all the disciplines currently represented at the University did not require fieldwork", being mainly arts and social sciences which were not quantitative, and of course the Biological Laboratory full of lab-based scientists. In other words, he thought I was having a free holiday while the University paid my salary!

The head of my School, Alec Barbrook – who was a political scientist, which has always seemed to me to be a contradiction in terms since studying what goes on politically is no science – hadn't a clue! It had to be explained to Templeman that he was wrong. Field research was very important in anthropology, ecology, and many other disciplines, and not just a ruse to skive off. A message was sent to him from quite high up, from the Patron's office that he should change his mind. The Patron was HRH the Prince of Wales who later described Operation Drake as like banging your head against a brick wall – *'jolly nice when it was all over'* at its conclusion at Tower Bridge some years later.

The voyage was centred on the brigantine *'Eye of the Wind'*, named after Sir Peter Scott's biography. She left Plymouth in October 1978 and returned to London two years later, in December 1980. Operation Drake was divided up into 9 ocean and 1 land based phases, each lasting about 3 months. On each phase, a number of Young Explorers, youngsters aged between seventeen and twenty-four, who were selected from countries all over the world, worked together on serious scientific exploration, research and community projects.

They were selected by novel means to determine their fortitude and intelligence by taking them to many venues including Porton Down, which my father knew well and was used later to ascertain whether badgers with tuberculosis do infect cattle which led to the Krebs Trial (named after John

Krebs who was at Oxford with me) to eradicate badgers in the hope of reducing bovine tuberculosis. The aspiring Young Explorers were given a sack and told that there was a small reticulated Python in a room and their job was to capture it and put it in the sack. What they weren't told was that the room was in complete darkness. Was there really a python in room or were we lying?

Before I led the Western Indian Ocean phase (VIII) in 1980 centred on the western area around the Seychelles and Amirantes, I visited the Galápagos in June 1979. Col. John Blashford Snell ('Blashers') was running Operation Drake from the Old War Office basement in Whitehall with Andrew Mitchell, a zoologist, as the scientific adviser.

In 1979 while I left for the Galápagos in May from RAF Brize Norton for seven weeks to join Operation Drake, Kate Lessells went off to join the Snow Goose team in Churchill Manitoba. During her stay in this very remote place with large populations of polar bears, one hungry individual tried to break into her cabin. Polar bear that is! Somehow or other Kate dissuaded the animal from continuing its break in. My trip to the archipelago was from London to the UK armed forces camp in Belize and then by commercial jet to San Jose, Panama, Quito and then Baltra, the Galápagos airport.

On the way back five weeks later Hurricane David had struck the Caribbean which required an enforced 48-hour stopover at the Belize camp, sharing a room with a plain clothed SAS soldier. He went for early morning runs with a heavy backpack in very high temperatures and humidity, never exchanged a word with anybody including me, and never took any meals. Harrier jump jets took off regularly to deter insurgents in the neighbouring country of Guatemala, which were threatening inroads into Belize, by hovering at low altitude over the forests which put them off.

After visiting the tortoises reserve I talked to José (Pepe) Villa, a Galápagos National Park Service guard, and then went to Buccaneer Bay, Sullivan Bay, and to José Cocha's camp on the top of Santiago island, for several days. Cocha headed the goat eradication team but the number of goats sometime made the rifles so hot work stopped. The Charles Darwin Research Station (CDRS) hired Miguel Castro, an Ecuadorian resident of the Galápagos, to do much of the fieldwork. Castro would go out with local fishers who dropped him on different islands as they worked. As Villa explained[103],

> Miguel Castro is probably the most important person speaking about the tortoises of the Galápagos. He took us to the field. We were visiting all the islands with Miguel. We went to see the situation with Miguel. He trained

---

103   Hennessy, Elizabeth Ann (2014) *On the backs of tortoises: conserving evolution in the Galápagos Islands.* University of North Carolina PhD thesis.

us in field work… The tortoises were our main focus. I was living on James [Santiago] for 5 months, behind the tortoises. The same of the volcanoes on Isabela, I was living on each of them. We were trying to have the first map of where they are, what are they doing? What were the trails they were following? Where are the nesting zones? How successful is the hatching of these animals? What are the difficulties, the enemies they have? Rats in some places, pigs in some places.

So when I got back to the main port, Puerto Ayora, I talked to Bob Tomkins and Barbara Best who were working on Hawaiian petrel, Fausto Cepeda (director), Bob and Elizabeth Tindle (flamingos and cormorants), Howard Snell (land iguanas), and Miguel Cifuentes (interpretation centre) and had dinner with Miguel Castro. Villa and Castro were among several people who collected basic information about tortoise reproduction and ecology. The work was often harrowingly difficult as the men spent months at a time living on remote islands. As Villa recounted, "the conditions were very bad, we didn't have any equipment, we didn't have any communication. Sometimes we didn't even know when we were going to come back". Sounds like my experience on Aldabra where the conditions were pretty much the same although, in contrast, for all the extreme difficulties, it was exciting and most satisfying.

Pepe Villa had a party at his house followed by one at the Tindle's where Miguel Castro dropped in. Through all this socialising and work at the research station it was a pleasure to meet Sylvia Harcourt (now Sylvia Harcourt-Carrasco) whose brother I had met on a number of occasions with his wife Kelly Stewart, a gorilla ecologist, who tragically accidentally lost a lot of her PhD field data in a fire but clearly had the resolve of her father James Stewart, a famous Hollywood actor, and finished the degree.

The nearest ecologist to me in my work on giant tortoises was a young American ecologist, Craig MacFarland, who began a long career in the Galápagos in 1968. After studying tortoises and later directing the Charles Darwin Research Station (1974–1978), he became president of the Charles Darwin Foundation for the Galápagos Islands (1985–1996). I talked to him by ham radio link with the help of Forrest Nelson at Hotel Galápagos in Puerto Ayora and visited Craig at his home in Turrialba in Costa Rica on my return. Working closely with Castro, MacFarland spent two years living in the field collecting this information as part of his dissertation research. When MacFarland started out in the field, he had planned to do 'pure' ecological research comparing two sample populations, but soon realised these studies were not working well both because of the difficulty of fieldwork and because conservation concerns were more pressing. He told Elizabeth Hennessy, a doctoral student from North Carolina, in 2012 that instead of his original plans,

I thought — I want to do core things. I want to see as many of the populations as possible on all the different islands… I mean, I wanted to do some of this ecological stuff, but I also want to begin to see what status are the different populations in? Which populations — some rough idea of how many there are, and, second, are they reproducing? If they're copulating and reproducing, are the babies — some reasonable percentage surviving? I know the majority die because that is a normal thing when anything is produced. Get some idea that there is survival so that when the older ones die the younger ones are building up. When I look at the populations I want to get some sense of full size adults — males and females and then juveniles and all the way down to young ones coming out of the nests. I want to find nests and see how they operate. So I said, I want to do some stuff on basic natural history: How does a population work and what does it do? Where do they nest? How do they make the nests? How long does it take from the time the females put the eggs in and create the nests? On different islands does it happen in different parts of the year or the same seasons? Does it take a longer period of time on a drier island or a higher island? Where do the ones on a higher island go to make their nests — do they go down to where there is more sun? Those kinds of questions.

Precisely the questions I answered with my work on Aldabra throughout 1975 and 1976. Craig was awarded a PhD from the University of Wisconsin-Madison for all his work on the ecology of the giant tortoises and his immense contribution to the conservation of the entire archipelago which had stalled him finishing his thesis.

Tortoises wallowing in Vulcan Alcedo, Galápagos. (Courtesy Craig MacFarland)

Galápagos

Giant tortoises are genetically quite similar and the multiple shapes are primarily induced by the food available to them. On some Galápagos Islands the rain falls mainly on one side of the mountainous volcanic peaks and so dome shaped animals are to be found where it rains most (grazers) and saddleback tortoises (browsers) are found where it doesn't, in the drier area on the other side of the peak, so shell shapes on one island are determined by food availability or primary production and they interbreed!

I discovered on Aldabra that some tortoises migrated and others didn't and there were slight differences in shape between them. Moreover they do not borrow underground (see Wikipedia) simply because it's a coral island with very little soil covering the surface and only deeper in some pockets favoured as nesting sites. The neck is shorter than most Galápagos island races, not longer, and these races are now described as species by taxonomists who have run riot over the naming of giant tortoises describing races as species and renaming them all in different Latin binomials. The International Committee on Zoological Nomenclature has had to adjudicate over many years about the Aldabra species with taxonomists fighting like cats to change the names but losing to the moderate ecologists. Taxonomists use morphology as their principal trade, and doubtful historical information about provenance, which is most misleading when it comes to giant tortoises, ignoring the genetic fact that there are no differences between these various so-called species, and overlooks the 'plasticity 'of the shell which can be made any shape in captivity by differing food regimes. There are even tortoises in the main granitic Seychelles which have been given Latin names and breeding colonies created. All of these animals originally came from Aldabra Atoll.

During this extended field trip to the Galápagos I was able to gather information on eggs, nesting sites, aerial photos, stunning photos given me by Craig and much other comparative information to my own work thanks to Operation Drake. I also learnt that it was Hungarian malacologist (snail ecologist) József Vágvölgyi who was having breakfast at CDRS and happened to mention he had seen a large tortoise on the island of Pinta on November 1, 1971. Unaware of the significance of this innocent observation he was soon challenged as tortoises were thought extinct on that particular island. But he had a photograph to prove it.

The animal became famous as Lonesome George and although many attempts were made to breed from him using animals from the Wolf Volcano region of Isabela Island they were unsuccessful and he died in 2012. As founder of the IUCN Tortoise Specialist Group suggestions were made by Duke University in the 1980s that we should use cloning techniques especially since I had discovered environmental sex determination in the

Aldabra species; in other words, I could produce girls from his genetic material. Lonesome George did an immense amount to publicise the conservation of this unique archipelago which has excited so many zoologists and evolutionary ecologists and, after some bitter in-fighting between the government and Galápagos, his stuffed body (courtesy of the American Museum of Natural History in New York City) returned home.

Nicholas Oliver Lawson, a Norwegian by birth, was acting governor when Charles Darwin visited the islands in September 1835. Darwin says in his diary: "An Englishman Mr Lawson is now acting as Governor. — By chance he came down to visit a Whaling Vessel & in the morning accompanied us to the Settlement." Lawson described having seen a reduction in the numbers and size of Galápagos tortoises taken for meat by the whalers. Just like the Arab traders who visited Aldabra and loaded giant tortoises which could survive long periods without water and food, chucking their ballast stones overboard, which resembled Olympic throwing discs (biconvex), and unloading goats as another source of meat for following trips.

In his zoological notes, Darwin recorded that, "It is said that slight variations in the form of the shell are constant according to the Island which

Giant tortoises and their island shell shapes

The distribution of the Galápagos giant tortoise species and their differing shell shapes which caught Darwin's eye when eating with Lawson, the acting Governor. In 2019, an elderly female specimen was discovered on Fernandina and other specimens may exist. (Published in *Operation Drake* (1981) Contributed by Ian Swingland.)

they inhabit — also the average largest size appears equally to vary according to the locality. — Mr Lawson states he can on seeing a tortoise pronounce with certainty from which island it has been brought." This was clearly demonstrated from the different carapace shapes hanging on the wall. Some animals are dome-shaped, feeding on growing grass with their head down, and others are saddle backed which are able to browse in xerophytic habitats on the overhanging vegetation and bushes as they can raise their heads quite high. This adaptation has not arisen on Aldabra where the three island populations are all dome-shaped. Attempts at browsing would be lethal on Aldabra, as tortoises can fall onto their backs irrecoverably and during copulation one pair fell over sideways into a hole in the fossilised coral. We found a couple in *flagrante delicto*, permanently conjoined; the male carapace is here with me in my study in England and the female probably in the American Virgin Islands.

Darwin was struck by these island specific carapace shapes and began to consider "such facts would undermine the stability of species", which was the current thinking at the time and ultimately led to his theory of natural selection backed up by the speciation he saw in the Galápagos finches.

Seychelles

A year later, in May and June 1980, I led the Western Indian Ocean phase of Operation Drake which was suddenly added onto the agenda as the Army officer in charge of organising the next phase in Oman had failed. I conjured up a schedule primarily using the workforce of the Young Explorers to search for, and find, the remaining specimens of some extremely rare plants, two 'extinct' species of balsam, a rare vine and the upside-down jellyfish tree with flowers so much like the upside-down jellyfish on Aldabra.

The rather small and insignificant vine *Toxocarpus schimperianus*, one of the rarest plants in the world is thought to have valuable pharmacological properties but is known only from 13 specimens on Curieuse and Mahé. Equipped with compasses maps and plant identification photographs groups of Young Explorers searched valleys and hillsides. We managed to double the number of known vine plants while fighting the 2 m high bracken on Mount Sebert and discovered another specimen of the jellyfish tree *Medusagyne oppositifolia*. Its total population is fewer than 30 plants scattered over three hilltops on Mahé Island in the Seychelles. On the island of Frigate, introduced giant tortoises were reduced in numbers, particularly females which were poached for meat, and we recorded 70 Seychelles magpie robin *Copsychus seychellarum*, a handsome bird with gleaming black plumage. The introduction of cats to the island had virtually eliminated them since they had a habit in the morning and evening of leaving the safety of the trees and hopping around buildings making them vulnerable to attack. On Praslin we saw the endemic black parrot *Coracopsis nigra* now confined to Coco De Mer palms in the Valley de Mai of which some 30 pairs remained.

The brigantine then sailed 200 km west to the African Banks. These two islets are famous for their seabird colonies which are harvested by the crateful in the cool season from the end of May to late July. Schooners ship the spotted eggs to the market in Mahé. The sooty tern *Sterna fuscata* were the most numerous of the eight species of tern which breed in the Seychelles and although a licence is required to export eggs from the islands many are poached. To get an estimate of the numbers we had the Young Explorers put the entire colony of three tern species into the air which was filmed and then analysed by a computer to assess numbers. Twenty five thousand was our estimate and although the egg trade is not significantly reducing the bird numbers as far as we know a new practice of killing adult birds for food may pose a far more serious threat in the future. Today it is estimated the population of all three species (sooty and black-naped terns and brown noddies) is now about 15,000 birds.

The African Banks are only a few metres high and often nearly inundated by high tides so we had to be cautious about how long we spent on land. Knowing the tide tables I managed to convince all the Young Explorers and everybody else that we needed to get back to the *'Eye of the Wind'*. It was almost dusk and somehow or other I convinced everyone to strip off and swim back. Nothing like social gatherings to binding people together when they have nothing to hide! Today the African Banks have almost disappeared as global warming causes seas to rise.

We had visited North Island, Praslin, Curieuse, St Anne, and other islands in the marine national park off Mahé, Frigate, and the African Banks, Darros and St Joseph in the Amirantes, and discovered the status of a number of rare plants and animals in the heavenly arena of the islands of the Seychelles, avoided any major disasters using the search-and-find capacity of the Young Explorers to full advantage.

Blashers asked me to take a lot of first day covers to the Seychelles with me to get them franked and contribute to the Operation's coffers. During the course of the voyage we ran into some rough weather during the night and I could hear Young Explorers were pushing something heavy around close to my bunk and giggling. I shouted at them which caused even more giggling. It turned out that the trunk with the first day covers was sliding across the floor and was on the brink of crushing me. An Army education officer was also attached and brought his wife. While in the capital of the Seychelles, Mahé, and resupplying the ship, the expedition was offered a free car there which this officer disappeared with! The ship had a small crew of Royal Naval officers with a very sophisticated telecommunications centre and the heaving and hauling and raising and lowering of the sails was done by the young people. They ranged from millionaires sons from California to down-and-out Borstal boys who needed a chance.

Before the *'Eye of the Wind'* came home Kate and I spent some time in September 1980 on the Scottish island of Rùm where Tim Clutton-Brock and Steve Alban had a long-term project on red deer. Steve is now in Aberdeen and Josephine Pemberton, my tutorial student at Oxford, who also worked with them, is now in my *alma mater* Edinburgh. They looked after us very well and we had an extremely interesting time in a project that produced many insights into evolutionary ecology.

When we returned the Operation Drake brigantine docked in December 1980 at St Katherine's Dock next to Tower Bridge which had to open to let it through. An exhibition had been mounted in a nearby hotel and HRH the Prince of Wales walk round on the 19th looking at what had been achieved under his patronage. Blashers had put me close to the sections concerning oceanic islands and there was an uninflated rubber dinghy on the floor beside me connected to a foot pump. He explained that Operation Drake was in the red and needed quite a lot of cash to balance the books. He asked me to have Prince Charles blow up the dinghy in less than a minute as the company who made it had promised a substantial cheque for a photograph.

After mimicking the noise giant tortoises make when copulating, and the way cone shells fire their extremely poisonous darts out the side not the ends, I invited His Royal Highness to tackle the dinghy. He looked at me twice (and has never forgotten me since) but gallantly tackled this challenge and succeeded in about 50 seconds. The manufacturers Redstart were delighted, Blashers was grinning and I realised the power of royalty.

Gerald Durrell

In 1981, nearly forty years ago, Gerald Durrell invited me to Jersey to talk about Madagascar because I had been heard talking about it in Cambridge as he was about to go on a filming expedition there. The irony is that I have never been to Madagascar but it was the beginning of a close friendship and cooperation for the next 14 years where I helped him with his dream and the international training centre, and helping to resolve, with Lee Durrell, Madagascar's problem with the avalanche of international scientific requests at the sixth World Conference on Breeding Endangered Species in Jersey 1992. We indulged in his fabulous curries having been born in India. He struggled against detractors and even went broke in 1960 raising loans using books he had not yet written as collateral. Like anyone, he was concerned with legacy and had the great good fortune to marry a young zoologist Lee McGeorge Wilson working on prosimian's vocalisation for her PhD whom he met at Duke University. Her tenacity has ensured his creation lives on and he had a staunch companion in Jeremy Mallinson, the co-founder of Jersey Zoo, who together created the Jersey Wildlife Preservation Trust now the Durrell organisation with Gerry.

Lee and Gerry Durrell next to me with Jeremy Mallinson at the back (in front of the door) to Les Augrès Manor with David Waugh to his right and John Hartley to his left. Kent University & JWPT course 1984

This friendship with Gerry was kicked off by working with David Waugh, the young director of their International Training Centre at Jersey Zoo, and creating not only further Continuing Education courses but also a Diploma in Endangered Species Management which Gerry dubbed the 'desman', a snouted and naked-tailed diving insectivore which he fell in love with in Russia.

Gerry came to Canterbury on a few occasions where his humour, humility and determination were exhibited in full like the numerous times I spent time with him in Jersey and in France where he came down to my tortoise project that still continues in Provence and has grown into SOP-TOM, a worldwide conservation organisation for tortoises and turtles. On one occasion he was bemoaning the absence of any place for visitors to his zoo when it rained as we looked out of the windows of his apartment on the first floor of Les Augrès Manor and watched people dashing for cover.

On my second pre-prandial Scotch I remarked:

> You need a 'pavilion' where perhaps people could see a short presentation
> about the zoo and its outreach programs of conservation which distinguishes
> what you have created from all other zoos. A kind of public relations Pavil-
> ion with your voice-over on the film which would excite people's enthusiasm
> for what you're doing and might even encourage them to donate.
>
> A kind of milking parlour, he rejoined.
>
> Yes but not so blunt. Perhaps you could also include some sort of demon-
> stration of your concerns to educate the public about conservation. Perhaps
> this pavilion could have a classroom running short courses for children from
> local schools?

By this time the bottle was empty so while he found another I had a
further thought. "How about not calling it the Public Relations Pavilion
but the initials PRP could stand for the Princess Royal Pavilion, after all
she is your patron?"

It took Gerry a very short time to raise the funds to build it and Buckingham Palace took months to agree the use of Princess Anne's formal name.
She is a remarkable woman and apart from her many other skills she is
one of the few that can give a very detailed long speech without any notes
whatsoever. The last time I met her was in Buckingham Palace's art gallery
at some event where she engaged me and Fiona and especially our children Kieran and Anna, who were very young at the time, with charm and
interest even leading them through the throng to show them a particular
famous oil painting. My children said she pointed to the extreme bottom
corner of this very large oil painting and said as a child she was bored and
scribbled in the corner. Whether that's true or not, I just don't know.

Komodo and the dragons

In July 1992 Ibnu Sutowo hosted my family for a short holiday in his
luxurious hotel at Nusa Dua in Bali. He flew us all out BA business class
and while my young family had fun I went to Komodo with his PA Endie
Singgih. We travelled by air and then by boat to Komodo Island where we
were accommodated in rough chalets on stilts to prevent Komodo dragons (*Varanus komodoensis*) from visiting uninvited. We arrived one evening
where I met Walter Auffenberg who had studied the species for years and
we had a jolly evening before retiring to our bedrooms.

Komodo dragons need to heat up before they become active and dangerous and so getting from the dining room to the chalets in the dark we
had to be accompanied as this very large lizard were still moving around.
Endie was quite frightened and indeed I could hear her praying as a Christian, on and off throughout the night, before we were taken early in the
morning, when it was still cool, up into the hills guarded by a group of men

with long sticks and knives. We were incarcerated in a strong enclosure as quite large groups of lizards began to warm up in the sun and take an interest, trying to push their way through the fence to get at their breakfast. Us! Getting back down to the camp at the seashore was a little tricky since by then, around midday, the sun was beating down and the animals were very active.

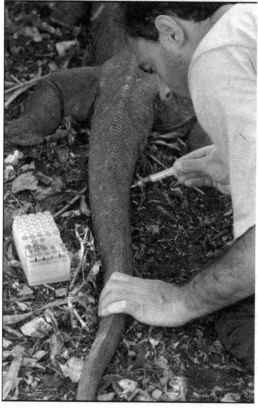

Going down the narrow paths one had to be careful since lizards would often wait in the undergrowth close by and would either try and bite you or bash you over the head or legs with their tails, a method perfected for their main prey Timor deer. So we ran at full tilt until we came across a few gathered on the path blocking our way. I was armed with one of these long sticks and so were the men but it was quite tricky for a bit as the large males weigh over a 100 kilos, are immensely strong and although we

To get a blood sample: first catch your dragon in a cage trap or noose, then restrain it (Credit: Nicolas Cegalerba) so Claudio can take his sample while making sure you avoid irate males which can run nearly as fast as a man

didn't know it at the time it's recently been discovered that they have two glands in the lower jaw which secrete several toxic proteins. One German lady, who was visiting at the same time, was bitten on her behind and died five days later since no antibiotic was successful as, at that time, it was believed that the dragon's mouth was just full of bacteria and not poisonous.

In the mid 1990s Claudio Ciofi, now a biologist at the University of Florence, arrived in Indonesia to complete a PhD in dragon genetics[104]. He was my postgraduate student at DICE and given the choice of working on tortoises in southern France or the dragons he had no hesitation! In 1999 he won the Whitley Award[105].

Inception

The evening classes continued all over the county, where my programme was running courses in every venue, provided an education in human behaviour. Extremely tiring and I often felt so exhausted that I was once pulled over by the Kent police in case I was drunk as it was always at

104   Ciofi, C., Beaumont, M.A., Swingland, I.R. & Bruford, M.W. (1999) Genetic divergence and units for conservation in the Komodo dragon *Varanus komodoensis*. *Proc. Roy. Soc. Lond. B.* **266(1435):** 2269.

105   The Whitley Awards, often known as the 'Green Oscars', are held annually by the Whitley Fund for Nature to recognise and celebrate effective grassroots conservation leaders across the Global South.

night, of course, but quite soon the word was out and my car (a red Golf GTI) and me were left alone. All because the police felt I was performing a service for the public good.

Running the entire Natural Science program in Continuing Education from the University of Kent and participating in many of the courses, giving lectures at night, during weekends and sometimes away for weeks, in other words working anti-social hours is an exhausting business but did leave me free during the daytime to plan everything but also think of the future.

In 1985, having collaborated with many others in different disciplines on campus but with the common bond of an interest in ecology, the environment and biodiversity, I formed a loose association called the Ecology Research Group which was the grit from which the pearl of my Institute (DICE) grew 4 years later.

I got married on 16 August 1985 to Fiona Lawson whom I met in Faversham as she was my dentist. On my first consultation, when saying thank you as I left, she said, "No, thank you!", which made me curious. She nodded to the Castellini dental chair and I noticed that it had no right arm enabling patients to get in and out easily. Then I twigged! I had gripped both arms of the chair with a firm grip, but what was I holding in my right hand!

Wildlife conservation needed a better multidisciplinary approach, continuity and excellent training both for inexperienced people as well as those much more experienced individuals in some sort of in-service program. I also knew I was being squeezed dry like a 'sponge' in continuing education without any topping up that one gets from research, interacting with people in pertinent disciplines, instead spending all my time in the company of colleagues in the arts and qualitative social sciences, areas rife with opinion but little rigorous analysis. There was no grist to my mill. No libation to fill my 'sponge'. I was dying intellectually. While I did not conceive of creating a multidisciplinary research and training Institute in 1985 I certainly began to become involved in a lot of other institutions, NGOs and many other outfits especially charities to get a feel of what was going on and what was missing.

During the early part of the 1980s I was also a Governor of The Powell Cotton Museum, Quex Park, Kent, which houses the largest collection of African zoological and ethnobiological material in Europe. The founder of the museum had two daughters and a son, Christopher Powell Cotton. None married although all were very accomplished. Christopher himself won the Military Cross and was exercised about the inheritance and maintaining the museum, the collection and the estate.

I met a lady from Sissinghurst in Kent who was quite keen on nature but had a hankering for some reason to go and join Arthur C. Clarke in Sri Lanka. At the time I was a member of the Kent Trust for Nature Conservation Council and she seemed set on disposing of most of her possessions and her rather wonderful house. In the end with some help from Hector Wilks (chairman) she gave us her stamp collection which we sold for many hundreds of thousands of pounds, the contents of her house that we sold for even more and then the house itself for the benefit of the Kent Wildlife Trust. Being involved in Continuing Education Kent County Council put me on their Training Advisory Committee.

From 1985–1993 I joined the Council and other Committees of the Fauna Preservation Society and again from 2005–2008 when it had become Fauna & Flora International (FFI). In the first eight years John Burton, who went on to found the World Land Trust, was the director and we worked closely together. A remarkable man who had to weather a new chairman who tried to move it to Brighton from London causing temporary mayhem! The director in my second time on the Council was Mark Rose who joined me, Julian Fitter and Richard Keynes, great-grandson of Charles Darwin, in setting up a charity to help the Galápagos which didn't go far. A conflict seemed to arise when FFI became involved in using carbon as a conservation tool and my co-founding of a company in 1999 called Sustainable Forestry Management (SFM) which successfully used carbon in the same way but instead of public donations and membership income we used private sector investment. So I resigned which was a great pity as it's a good organisation.

The World Land Trust uses private funds to purchase large tracts of land by local NGOs for the purposes of protecting it whereas SFM raised funds as an investment. The Trust raised its capital by using the age old charitable technique called begging which I have done a lot of to create DICE as have so many of my friends, whether for a charity or creating a new initiative in academia. I used to joke that my knees had become flattened with prostrating myself in pursuit of support but the reality was that the large sums I eventually raised were done firstly in a gentle conversation and paperwork followed afterwards to satisfy the donor's lawyers or whatever. There was often an inverse relationship between the amount of work to raise money and the amount captured; a five-minute conversation often raised £1 million.

While dreaming of the future, I was still running field courses as far away as Zambia and had many close shaves with adoring middle-aged fans and other events. Articles in newspapers about my exploits had been appearing for some time even before I left Oxford and as usual they were exaggerated sometimes to the point of fiction.

"The School of Continuing Education at Kent has curious ideas on how people might wish to continue their education. Its Christmas treat is a day school lined up to consider 'The Behaviour and Conservation of Tortoises'", from a local Kent rag who further beat the tired old drum with, "It's nice to know there are those doing their bit to make life a little more bearable for the unemployed. And here's news of another concession, a chance to attend a day school at Canterbury University. Admission is free if you're out of work. Unfortunately you may not be into much of a hurry to book your place – the subject of the seven hour seminar is 'the behaviour and conservation of tortoise'". This course was repeated again in the Department of Extra-Mural Studies at Bristol University and there was no comment from their local newspaper.

So it was quite nice to have someone like Peter Brown of the English Department at the University publish a book called *Tortoises* containing D.H. Lawrence's poems with my encouragement which had some veracity. He was someone whose sage advice I relied on when forming my Institute and needed to deal with the jealousy and enviousness of some of my academic colleagues at Kent when he recommended I talk to Sandy Alexander, local solicitor and University Treasurer, who ran Vienna as an officer in the Buffs for a few months after the War.

I was still putting on courses such as a Saturday school with the RSPCA 1985 where I was chair of their Wild Animals Advisory Committee and then a Council member dealing with how animals are treated and indeed the games animals play. My lifelong passion for animals is bedded in respect for them but does not prohibit human use. Two participants who became close friends were Sir Robert Worcester who now lives in a castle near Maidstone and founded MORI, a polling company, and became Chancellor of the University years later, and the late Rt Hon. Alan Clark who lived in another castle at Saltwood in Kent. I gave the main speech at the RSPCA's 150th anniversary at Christ Church College August 1990 on animal welfare and the environment.

University of Michigan, Ann Arbor

In 1986–87 I had a sabbatical in the United States and became a Professor of Biology & Senior Research Fellow, Department of Biology & Museum of Zoology, University of Michigan, Ann Arbor. These appointments came about by accident. Fiona had joined me three months after I left the UK because we had just moved from South Street to the village of Wingham and she was settling the new house and the tenants while we were away. What we didn't realise was that she was pregnant before I left and discovering this on her arrival I desperately needed some form of medical insurance to cover the pregnancy and birth.

In the States you'll die on the street if you don't have a cheque book in your pocket or substantial medical insurance; indeed in seeking a job in the United States people's first question is about the health insurance that comes with the job. By being appointed as a full Professor and Research Fellow of the University, all arranged by Bill Dawson (Museum Director and now Emeritus Prof.) and Ron Nussbaum (who succeeded him, now Emeritus Prof. who was my intellectual host during my sabbatical), without pay or any other benefits, I was immediately eligible to join the Blue Cross Blue Shield health-insurance program. This covered pregnancy and hospital bills for just $700 a month in contrast to the cost of having a baby without insurance which would have cost $47,000 (or $106,000 in today's money) in Ann Arbor.

When I left Kent to go to Ann Arbor I spent some time at a conference at Northwest Missouri University. I trundled all the way there with one of the original IBM personal computers which I intended to use in Michigan but did not know that I should have locked the hard disk before travelling! While there I met David Galbraith who would later become a research fellow at DICE. A very bright biologist who mentioned that someone called Alec Jeffries in England had just published a paper in *Nature* about microsatellites according to David. Whatever they were! In fact Sir Alec Jeffries had developed techniques for genetic fingerprinting and DNA profiling. While in Missouri I was told not to carry a bottle of spirits outside unless it was in a brown paper bag or I would get arrested. Nearby the conference was an extraordinarily large church which had a car park for many, many thousands of cars.

Fiona told me when she arrived in Ann Arbor three months later she had a drink with a friend in the village pub before she left.

The publican asked, "Have you just moved into the village?"

"Yes."

He then pointed up the road or down the road.

She confirmed, "up the road", at which point all the locals downed their beer mugs in synchrony with their mouths open.

I was always curious about a mezzanine bedroom in our new house which had mirrors on the ceiling and hooks. Apparently the previous owner was the Madame of East Kent and had another establishment where she had been arrested as her under-aged son lived there when she was working which is against the law. Although we had only moved in three months before, and were now off to the States for a year, Fi told me, once ensconced in Ann Arbor, that the new tenants of our house while we were away had showed some concern at men with long raincoats knocking on their door in late evening. The problem was that they were fundamental Christians so we immediately had locks put on the gate into the walled garden which gave access to the front door.

Mike Radock was Vice President for Development & University Relations at the University of Michigan before heading the Mott Foundation at Flint. He was the husband of Helen who was related to me as her adoptive stepmother was my grandmother's sister. Between them both they extended the very essence of American hospitality and support which one so easily forgets listening to the news about America these days. They arranged not only an apartment at Observatory Lodge for us close to the centre of the University, on the corner of Washington Heights and Observatory Street, opposite undergraduate residency halls (now called Hill Dining Center), but also wrangled an old white gas-guzzling sedan for us and helped us through all the 'foreign 'ways of American administration. On Labor Day, when most universities commence, parents would arrive with their child in overburdened cars and install them in the building opposite. The parents were utterly exhausted from the effort and financial dissipation.

New male undergraduates would even put their stereo speakers outside their windows and play very loud music no doubt to attract the new female talent. There are many examples in the animal world of males who can call the loudest attracting the most females[106]! An out-of-State undergraduate student at Michigan University would need $70,000 for fees, food, accommodation and living expenses. A Michigan resident would pay half that which is still 107% more expensive than the national average but then the University is one of the ten best in the States. The annual out-of-state charges are roughly equivalent to the total cost of an entire three-year undergraduate course in a British University.

Mike and Helen lived in a wooded estate just outside Ann Arbor. The houses are very large and spaced out and many were designed by Frank Lloyd Wright. The large trees were treated every year with a large hypodermic syringe attached to a truck that injected nutrients into their roots.

Mike knew everybody and was extremely kind and considerate. His network of contacts and friends was without parallel, as he was principally responsible for raising huge endowments to the University, and he had that driven energy of many Americans. He introduced me to Tom Monaghan who had constructed the headquarters of his business from plans drawn up by Frank Lloyd Wright but never built. He had founded Domino Pizza Company and had an amazing collection of vintage cars which he showed me. Another character I met in the company of a lot of businessman, in one of the private houses nearby, where I was constantly served with overlarge glasses of Scotch and trying to keep sober and engage in coherent intelligent conversation which is quite difficult in the face of American largesse, was Bob McNamara. Like most of the others he had been a

---

106   Charlton, B.D., Ellis, W.A.H., Brumm, J. Nilsson, K. & Fitch, W.T. (2012) Female koalas prefer bellows in which lower formants indicate larger males. *Animal Behaviour* **84**: 1565–1571. doi:10.1016/j.anbehav.2012.09.034.

senior executive in Motown, otherwise known as Detroit being the centre of the motor industry, and who had been President of Ford, Secretary of Defense and President of the World Bank. A quiet man, who did not talk very much, sat watching everybody else and occasionally engaged in conversation. He was very calm and clearly popular as it turned out he had been a prominent footballer when an undergraduate at the University. It was Gerald Ford, former President of the United States, who I had dubbed 'the Band Aid President' as he followed the trauma of Nixon's presidency.

Ibnu Sutowo told me he had run Indonesia between Sukarno and Suharto, the first and second Presidents, and had become the wealthiest living Indonesian. He had set about nationalising the oil industry and was producing fertiliser at a dollar a tonne while a World Bank loan from the US was pricing fertiliser at $40. McNamara told Suharto, when he took power, to fire Sutowo otherwise he would cancel all World Bank loans to the country. Suharto said "No", thereby triggering McNamara's threat and precipitated the largest peacetime debt of any country.

One Christmas Ibnu stayed in Jakarta and he entertained me to Christmas lunch at one of his huge hotels in the city. He and I walked through the vast corridors to the best restaurant with staff bowing and some falling to their knees as we progressed. I don't think he was often seen in public and was usually conveyed in a bullet and bomb proof Mercedes Benz with thick darkened glass. I think many of the hotel staff assumed he was dead and were astonished at this very famous man suddenly reappearing. We sat down and as courtesy to me we had traditional English dishes and the best claret you can imagine. He was a man of immense intellect and generosity with great vision, and I held him in very high regard not for his wealth but for what he's been able to achieve. At one point he admitted that although well into his 70s this was the first glass of wine he had drunk in his life. He explained to me how in Indonesia they viewed corruption since he had often been accused of nefarious practices by his competitors and others:

Ibnu: *Suppose a friend does you a favour, do you feel a need to return this generosity at some point?*

Me: *Yes, of course!*

Ibnu: *So this is what the West calls corruption, isn't it?*

Me: *Yes it is but it's a question of whether someone is unfairly advantaged by not playing to the rules. Avoiding tax, insider trading, the rich using their wealth to intimidate others to do what they want and so on.*

Ibnu: *Who makes the rules – politicians in a democracy? Are politicians corrupt, does the democratic process ensure that the rules are fair and equitable? I don't think so. Favouritism exists in all societies and all societies have corruption in their midst as do their governments.*

Me: *So, is this why Indonesia has the governmental process of Dwifungsi ('dual function') whereby the Army would neither try to take power nor remain inactive but become enmeshed into all levels of Indonesian society, safeguarding the nation after Sukarno and the communists?*

Ibnu: *Yes. Many nations and idealists have tried to take us over. For example the Dutch tried to re-invade after World War II with the help of the British to reinstitute their colonial powers which had existed for hundreds of years. After fighting the Japanese my wife and I had to fight this incursion and then the communists attempt to dominate Sukarno which we had to stop. My attitude to corruption is whatever works is okay but if any part of our nation suffers as a result I will stop it.*

Between the Radocks and Ron Nussbaum our stay in Ann Arbor, and its demanding University, was made easy and most enjoyable. The University has a specialised department which takes research project outlines and rewrites them in multiple different ways for differing funding targets and for this service include a huge overhead. Of course their success rate was enormous but the University was driven by money and even an internal telephone call had to be paid for from a research grant you had even if you were a member of staff, visiting or otherwise.

Opposite the Museum of Zoology was an older building, the chemistry building. I was told it was staffed by a lot of old redneck professors who dumped all the teaching on the new young bright sparks that were hired at considerable cost by the University so that they couldn't shine through their research, for which they had little time or energy, with the burdensome teaching schedule. Meanwhile the old professors whiled away the time doing mediocre work. The Regents of the University lost patience and dug a very big hole right next to the Chemistry Department. The old chemistry professors were effectively told to 'shape up or ship out' while a brand-new state-of-the-art Chemistry Department was built in the hole. They were given time to improve their performance; until the new building was fully commissioned and staffed by the new appointments. By the time the new Chemistry Department was finished nothing had changed in the old Chemistry Department and it was soon razed to the ground.

I worked on research concerning the evolution of egg size, sex determination and stability and imbalanced sex ratios. The smell of hash wafted up from the basement research areas of the Museum of Zoology where I was told Robert Trivers and Richard Alexander were working on the naked mole rat colonies which although a mammal behaved as a superorganism. Someone let it be known that I was working on sex determination and it was misconstrued by those that heard. In consequence I faced a barrage of enquiries about how humans could have a son or a daughter by design. I realised that vaginal pH and frequency could tip the balance of the sex produced but was warned by the University of Michigan lawyers to say absolutely nothing.

During my sabbatical those involved in the First World Congress of Herpetology met at the University of Michigan as I was its Director and was hosting it at the University of Kent two years later during a very busy summer when I founded my Institute, a conservation NGO for reptiles and amphibians, and an international peer-reviewed journal in biodiversity conservation. They included the late Carl Gans, an eminent herpetologist at Michigan, who, when our baby son was overdue, suggested the cure was a large Chinese meal. Nine hours later my son Kieran Swingland was born!

While there, as a member of Faculty, I was asked my opinion as to the appointment of a Regent to the University (eight people who govern the University). Such an appointee must be eligible for a full professorship on relinquishing the post. The candidate in question was female, black, handicapped with a Hispanic surname; she ticked all the boxes in terms of positive discrimination. She was a zoologist but not one of any particular distinction or recognisable accomplishment and like many of us I didn't feel that she could occupy a full chair properly.

Back in England Richard and Daisy Fitter had been running the Fauna Preservation Society for many years and invited me to join the Council and the various committees. This was the first of two periods when I sat on the Council (1985–93, 2005–08) the latter being more recently in what is now called Fauna & Flora International.

Practical nature conservation, practical computing and a field course on the ecology and wildlife of Swaziland for 2 weeks quickly followed. I was not solely concerned with my own discipline as the natural scientist in the School and even arranged a part-time MSc/Diploma in Physics or Physics with Education, MSc/Diploma in Chemistry or Chemistry with Education, MSc/Diploma in Statistics, together with the relevant departments.

However the recidivist in me did find animal and evolutionary ecology more of a safe harbour and so took a large number of people on a study tour of the Galápagos Islands in 1988 organised with John Durant of the Oxford External Studies Department with Julian Fitter organising the on-ground arrangements; a marvellous trip which I repeated again taking members of the British Chelonia Group of which I was President at the time.

CHAPTER 11

DICE 1989–1999

Giving birth

After 10 years, while still working in continuing education, the Vice Chancellor Dr David Ingram, one of the most effective Kent VCs with excellent academic qualifications, having experienced all the VCs since Templeton (the founding VC), suggested an Institute was formed around me. He was very encouraging and supportive although it involved giving up my tenure and job in continuing education and taking the risk of raising all the funds for my salary, staff salaries and recurrent costs – everything.

As I've said before risk is inherent in any initiative which is why so many people don't achieve anything. They are not prepared to take the risk or perhaps they can't, knowing they have neither the skill set nor the bravery required. Leading from the front is a lonely business. It also requires a level of benign dictatorship since it was my vision and sense of what the world needed, and my skills at communicating and raising funds, that would make a success of the whole initiative.

While those that joined me could affect my thinking through their experience and ideas, I had to do what Edmund Burke suggested in the 18th century.; advocating steps toward legislative independence as he was sceptical of democracy at the cost of alienating his Bristol constituents. He defended the principles of representative government against the notion that elected officials should merely be delegates

This is not dissimilar to the situation where many members of Parliament were beavering away to keep the United Kingdom inside the EU (Remainers) even though their constituents voted in the 2016 National Referendum to leave (Leavers); only two of the Governing Party's MPs who still wanted to Remain had their constituencies aligned with them! MPs should only execute the majority feelings of those they represent and not pursue their own obsessions in contradiction.

However in being the unelected architect of DICE I had to side with Burke *pro tem*! To insure the future I only had to find the right people to join me and the money to keep everything growing. Only!

I was taking the biggest risk and it became clear that within the University, and amongst those joining DICE, there were those looking to their own personal advantage rather than the Institute's own development and progress particularly as its success and growth became more attractive. I was committed to the Institute's survival and growth, body and soul, and not to my own aggrandisement. Many of the novel ideas I instituted, which were successful, were copied by others in other universities to their own personal advantage; stolen ideas. Principal among them was the unique MSc in Conservation Biology which I drafted at the beginning and appeared, sometimes word for word, in other universities' programmes.

By this time (1989) Fiona and I had a 2½-year-old son and a six-month-old daughter. Fiona had temporarily retired from dentistry to take care of our offspring but at the same time we ran the First World Congress of Herpetology together, and I established an NGO to conserve amphibians and reptiles, the Herpetological Conservation Trust (HCT) with £1m gift, and an international Journal to address a multidisciplinary approach to biodiversity and conservation called *Biodiversity and Conservation* with Chapman & Hall now Springer; all at the same time.

The Congress was enormous with 1600 delegates from most countries in the world who consumed 6 1/2 tons of chickens, US delegates paid for those who arrived without any money mostly Russian and Eastern European, and we ran concurrent sessions with plenary lectures in the main theatre (Marlowe) in the city. The HCT (now renamed the Amphibian and Reptile Conservation Trust) became the leading NGO in Europe in reptile and amphibian conservation. I raised a total endowment of £3.5m and it currently owns and manages large reserves throughout the UK and elsewhere.

The summer of 1989 was the summer of insanity; no sane person would

First World Congress of Herpetology 1989

have taken on establishing and running so many major enterprises all at the same time when I didn't even have a permanent job any more.

I called my Institute the Durrell Institute of Conservation and Ecology (DICE) named after my very close friend Gerald Durrell who was so surprised by my invitation that he called his brother Lawrence Durrell in the south of France, made famous in Gerry's book *My Family and Other Animals* who had become a famous novelist especially for *The Alexandria Quartet*, and told him that the Institute was being named after him. The foghorn like voice on the telephone said, "A mental institute I presume!"

There was another reason I wanted it to be called DICE, apart from its catchy simplicity, and that was the risk I was taking with my young family in giving up the security of a tenured position and starting something where I'd have to raise all the money including my own salary and attract the best in the world to join me; a dicey situation. A University administrator called Ian Stone was very helpful before he retired and went off to the Isle of Man and the Arctic.

I named the institute DICE not just because of these risks but because I had known Gerry very well for 9 years and considered him one of the giants of conservation, along with Peter Scott and David Attenborough, and he was of my own temperament and experience in life as were the others. Loners like me, self-sufficient but sensitive to others, with considerable imagination and the determination to make the world a better place especially for animals, our best friends. In my innocence neither Gerry nor I had realised the portent of naming it after him as he accepted the invitation as just a gesture between friends which it was.

On 24 November 1989 Gerald and Lee Durrell, Dr David Ingram (Kent Vice Chancellor October 1980–August 1994), the Chancellor Lord Jo Grimond, and myself went through an informal ceremony in the Senate inaugurating this new Institute.

Gerry then gave an evening lecture at the University to which thousands came, most being accommodated in other auditoria with CCTV feed, and entranced everybody with his charm, erudition, observation and just being himself.

He said, "At long last this Institute represents a marriage between ecology and conservation: the science that tells you how the world works and the science of how to keep it working".

The following morning the University of Kent at its Congregation in Canterbury Cathedral honoured him with a DSc *in honoris causa*, clearing the other honorary graduands from the programme.

That afternoon back in the embryonic Institute, housed in Rutherford College's Masters Bungalow, Simon Hicks, the Jersey Trust secretary, came to offer a gift to my utter amazement. Unfortunately the University wanted to take a sizeable overhead, even though it was an endowment, so I couldn't accept the gift and sent it back with thanks.

Finding the right new blood, who were exceptional in their abilities and would fit in smoothly with everybody else, was extremely difficult but luckily once we started they found us. In constructing DICE I was aware that permanent and pensionable staff get old and many become deadwood. While we could not survive without such a core of world-class staff selected very carefully, we also needed an outer core of the best in the world to which we gave honorary titles according to their status and invited them to teach some of our modules while we accommodated them and look after them well. This meant the students were taught by the best in the world and there's nothing as powerful as advertising by word-of-mouth.

Creating DICE not only involved the raising of millions of pounds, but dealing with internal academic politics where being stabbed in the back is a daily occurrence, and it involved ensuring that I created programs to keep the recurrent costs paid and I had 'headroom' to raise the development costs. Academic politics are amongst the most vicious precisely because it is all to do with who is more significant or more important than another and not just money which is the simple axiom of the private sector. Many hilarious and dreadful things happened, including escaping through the window of my office when told that a particular very persistent and very boring person wanted to see me, but the look on students' faces when accepted into the Institute and the pleasure in being there and what they achieved afterwards was the lifeblood of my determination.

In the beginning the atmosphere and behaviour of some of my academic colleagues elsewhere on campus was similar to the behaviour of Michel Barnier negotiating the withdrawal of the UK from the EU, Brexit. On top of the risks and difficulties of creating a whole organism multidisciplinary Institute from scratch within a University whose closest disciplinary connection was biochemistry and microbiology brought the jealous knives out to punish me for the temerity of creating a new academic institution which was growing at an enormous rate, garnering funds and support across the nation and overseas, fuelled by my wide network of friends and like-minded people. Even worse, some of these friends were famous and powerful and this brought yet further retribution.

Facts from Faeces

I visited the Ujong Kulon National Park in July 1990. It is the last preserve of the rare Javan rhino where population estimates were concocted by the park guards from footprints to try and identify the individual, its sex, its age, and location; an entirely inaccurate means of surveying the small and endangered population where individuals were hardly ever seen. While the microbiologists rushed around collecting earth samples to take home I was left pretty much to my own devices and while staring at a pile of rhino faeces I wondered whether it could provide a more accurate answer. When mammals defecate the epithelial cells lining the gut are to be found on the surface of the faeces and it struck me that if we could collect the DNA my skills using population analysis might elucidate detailed information about the population structure and composition vital to conservation efforts.

The biggest problem would be obtaining samples of epithelial cells uncontaminated by the DNA of other organisms such as fungi, algae and other wildlife. I mentioned this to one or two members of the group of biologists that were with me and they thought it might be possible to get pure rhino DNA samples. But other than that all the rest of the procedures were foreign territory to them not being wildlife ecologists or knowing anything about the Javan rhino. I was told by Mike Walkey (Executive Director DICE) on my return to the UK that a colleague of his in the UK Patent Office had alerted him to a pending application that had been submitted, before we even landed, called 'Facts from Faeces' and the short brief description indicated it was probably my idea.

All of the procedures – collecting the cells, purifying the DNA, amplifying it through a process called polymerase chain reaction, and using the results with standard population mathematics and statistics – were in the public domain. It was putting the entire process together that was the only novel idea of mine. To secure a patent application, the details have to be improved within a specified length of time and so the applicants came to me and asked me to explain all the details, thinking I knew nothing about their patent application.

Not having any pecuniary interest in the outcome unlike them I put the whole process in the public domain in six speeches in 1991 – the RSPCA keynote speech at its 150th anniversary, Christchurch, Oxford; the American Museum of Natural History tropical rainforest symposium in New York which was videoed, the Savannah River Plutonium Plant and University of Georgia Ecology Laboratory 'Powder Mill' conference; IUCN Species Survival Commission meeting at London zoo; Wye College conference and a *New Scientist* interview; and lastly a Linnean Society talk 'Research and Training for Biodiversity'. I sent off the New York video in UK format to each of those trying to capitalise on my idea!

Near infanticide

Since I was determined that the solutions to the Earth's problems could only be tackled using a multidisciplinary approach involving far more than just zoologists, botanists and ecologists, I found existing departments took umbrage when I hired someone in their discipline such as a chair in biodiversity law or natural resource economics. What was worse was my reputation, integrity and track record internationally was the core basis of the fundraising needed and mustn't be threatened or damaged by the University's behaviour over the funds I brought in, much to the annoyance of myself and the donor. I also had to create a portfolio of training programs that would cover the recurrent costs such as the Conservation Biology MSc.

I made the rules and not the University (such as allowing staff to keep the whole of any consultancy fee providing they paid the full costs of any first-class replacement to cover their teaching or other duties) since the University had me creating this Institute without spending a penny so it was entirely self-sufficient. This further aggravated the powers in the centre especially when we contemplated leaving and certainly not paying for the services provided by the Registry as they were too expensive and kept trying to call the shots when I was trying to

University of Georgia Savannah River Ecology Laboratory 'Powder Mill' conference hosted by Whit Gibbons 1991. A very difficult site to visit being a foreigner, with a large number of nuclear reactors, with an angry alligator snapper turtle that wished I hadn't

create something exciting, different, effective, successful and solvent unlike so many other departments.

For a long time a small number of the University managers were prejudiced against the Institute although delighted by its increasing prominence and reputation in the world, delighted to bathe in the limelight having had nothing to do with its success. Rather the reverse. They were jaundiced that they could not control it and were also envious. I was determined that the funds I raised ended up in DICE. University administrators like to control everything especially the funds but insure all the responsibility rests with academics.

The Durrell Trust for Conservation Biology, DICE's Trust, originated when an endowment that I had raised was being sliced by the University for overheads and not wholly contributing to DICE, and of course potentially damaging my reputation with donors. With the help of my uncle Owen Swingland QC, a Chancery silk, and Sandy Alexander, the University treasurer and solicitor, a Trust was founded subsequent to Vice Chancellor David and Geraldine Ingram's visit to Jersey Zoo where Gerry was able to show him round his pride and joy in a golf cart, give him a very good lunch, and caused David to mutter that a Trust would be a good idea. This took place in March 1990.

I asked Owen to draft the Trust deed to insure my reputation was protected although not a Trustee which provided for my ultimate control in the Trust decisions by having a Founder's Committee inside the Trust with two Trustees; we each had a vote and I had a further vote as chair. So I could block decisions of the Trust if they misguided the money I raised, by giving it to Battersea Dogs Home, for example, but I could not make them spend the money the way I or a donor wanted.

If I had both powers I would *de facto* in law be a Trustee since I had a pecuniary interest by being a member of staff of DICE. This was put to the Charity Commissioners by Canterbury solicitors Furley Page whose senior partner was Sandy Alexander, the University Treasurer, using Owen's handwritten draft and was challenged by them referring it to their Commissioner who practised in this area. Needless to say that Commissioner was my uncle Owen who confirmed its legal probity and the Commissioners agreed the Trust with Furley Page who then charged me £726 presumably for the typing!

This protected my reputation and fundraising ability. In those days UK universities were novices about fundraising, unlike USA institutions, and stupidly valued a pound from a Research Council more than a pound from a donor because they were stuck on the financial imperative of research performance (RAE) for a large part of their government income, demonstrating my qualms about the downside of the RAE scheme I expressed to Dick Southwood

Universities were somewhat financially reliant on the RAE, a research assessment exercise (now Research Excellence Framework, REF) carried out by the government every four years, which was devised in part by Prof. Dick Southwood, Linacre Professor of Zoology, Oxford. He invited me to walk round the garden of Merton College after a lunch to discuss the mechanism of how research should be assessed, how it should be measured, which in his view involved a matrix of some description with which I was familiar. I said at the time this government-driven exercise would dampen innovation, initiative and experimental research and research papers, and future research would be constrained to short sharp sure-fire pieces of research that would be published in Nature that would carry the most Brownie points. Dick was the quintessential academic politician so I was certain that committees would be dominated by Oxbridge and Imperial College, Dick's background, creating a bias favouring the leading institutions and not the young yet vigorous entries into the higher education field such as the plate-glass universities of the 1960s, Kent being one.

A battle with bureaucracy, parish-pump politics and competing interests

The Institute had started in August 1989 with me, a secretary, a handful of research students and a loose gecko running round Rutherford College Master's Bungalow. By January 1991, within 18 months of establishment, it had a compliment of over 70 (a Founding Director, ten Visiting Research Fellows, six Senior Research Fellows, two Secretaries, 5 Research Assistants, and over 40 postgraduate and 25 diploma students). It had one of the largest portfolios of postgraduate conservation and ecology courses in Europe, and had a strong programme of professional short courses and conferences. It was developing research and development units in conservation genetics, wildlife management, wildlife health, mycorrhizal technology which could help destroyed forests recover faster, environmental management, and evolutionary ecology. The exponential rate of growth and the burden of the entire Institute fell solely on me.

On the 23rd July 1990 at a meeting of the then DICE Management Committee it was finally clear that the Institute could not continue to function at the University of Kent in the way that it had been established a year before having an unclear identity, a budgetary structure which was too complicated, being too entwined with the Biological Laboratory, and not being properly financially credited for its work. Moreover lawyers advising on the formation of the charitable trust were unanimous in criticising DICE's organisational establishment and lack of clear identity within the University if the Trust was to be formed. As a result Alexander and the Vice Chancellor discussed the matter and phoned me on the morning of 23 August 1990 offering to have DICE made either a Faculty, a department of the Science Faculty, or to remain in the Biological Laboratory in a `financial envelope'. I chose to become a department of the Science Faculty.

I invited the Jersey Wildlife Preservation Trust Scientific Advisory Committee to have its next meeting in Kent 13 September 1990. That evening members of JWPT staff, Committee members, the Vice Chancellor, Institute Fellows and Students, spouses and friends dined at my house. The following day 14 September 1990 a meeting was convened of the Trust to discuss the reorganisation of DICE and the draft Deed. This meeting established a Board of Management, chaired by Sandy Alexander, University Treasurer, to which DICE was responsible, and The Durrell Trust for Conservation Biology (DTCB), chaired by Lee Durrell. The first meeting of the Board took place 13 November 1990 when among other arrangements it was agreed that a general manager was needed to deal with the administration and finances. A general internal strategy document was also agreed.

In February 1991 I became concerned about the management of the Institute as the pressure on me, both developing and managing DICE, was becoming too much. I mooted the appointment of an Executive Director and a decision in principle was taken with the help of Keith Lampard (then Assistant Registrar and Secretary to the Faculty of Natural Sciences) at 7.10pm Friday 8 March that I would seek the means to support this appointment. Although Lee Durrell was enthusiastic about this and put up a small sum of money, Gerry asked me privately, when were together at Marwell Zoo alone with John Knowles, the founder, to relieve Lee of this over-commitment and I rang John Fairbairn. He provided the seed money for the post which was £100,000 pounds from a telephone call before the Esmée Fairbairn Foundation, which he created, became the elaborate institution it is today.

As a result, during the second Board of Management meeting at the University 11/12 March 1991 after discussion with staff, Fellows and Trustees, it was decided to ask Dr Mike Walkey, a zoologist and an old friend of mine from Queen Mary College, University of London, to accept the post of Executive Director taking over the administration, finances and general management and I became Founding Director overseeing the academic and institutional development. This was supported over lunch with Gerald Durrell at the Basil Street Hotel 15 March 1991 and the letter of appointment from the Vice Chancellor was issued starting the post 4 April 1991 part-time and from 1 October 1991 full-time.

It was clear that I could not create an Institute, mold its structure for what the world needed and be active in the outside world, and at the same time be at the back of the 'shop' running what I created and dealing with University politics. Mike Walkey who had originally interviewed me to get into London University in 1966 joined me as Executive Director 25 years later to run the show having demonstrated his remarkable abilities by running the School of Biological Sciences at QMC, London University under Prof. Alan Bevan who taught me genetics as an undergraduate.

From that time on, with the close relationship with Mike Walkey, I was not alone and together with the loyal friendships of the permanent members of DICE, we were far better placed to deal with the internal politics and fend off boarders.

The Durrell Trust for Conservation Biology was at last agreed by the Charity Commissioners late 1991. The Institute's first brochure was produced in June 1991 with the support of Denise Everitt (University Finance Director) who became a fan of DICE. The first issue of the international journal of *Biodiversity and Conservation* which I created was published in December 1991.

The Universities Funding Council Research Assessment Exercise 1992 ranked The Durrell Institute 9th out of 34 similar departments in British Universities alongside Cambridge University, King's College London and Bristol University putting it in the top third of environmental institutions in the UK We were only three years old, had only one UFC-funded staff member and had only four academic staff in comparison to an average of 22 in better ranked departments elsewhere. By 2001 we were ranked 5, amongst the top UK institutions in multidisciplinary biodiversity research in the natural and social sciences.

There is an essential flaw in academic's contracts since they are hired to teach but promoted on research which is an inherent conflict; the more teaching an academic does the less research they achieve.

DICE Prospectus 1994

Indeed one of the first comments made to me by Dr John Phillipson on my first day in Oxford was that he didn't teach because it meant many students would not have the benefit and in any case like most Oxford academics his contract of employment did not require him to do any teaching at all, revealing how Oxbridge maintained its ascendancy in research performance.

Being a brilliant research zoologist and stimulating teacher is not as you might think a passport to promotion. Academics are hired to teach but promotion is based on publication record in most universities and this is quite clearly a source of enormous tension. You can't pump out high quality papers if you're always teaching. Papers in Nature score very highly and if that is all an academic did they would get a chair (professorship) quite soon but such a promotion has its political side. Does your face fit? Do you make the University look good on the outside world? Do you pull in large sums of money for research or other programs? If you are constantly lecturing undergraduates it's unlikely to happen.

At Kent University during my 20 year stint there I helped move the promotional standards away from just research towards one's which embraced teaching success (measured by the number of successful graduates who got jobs), substantial research programmes (measured by money and quality), contribution to promoting the University and finally contribution to the wider society. Of course, this recidivistically slid back especially under VC Robin Sibson, who revered research excellence above all else, to just research which so favoured the elite institutions (not Kent) with light teaching burdens promoted by the RAE or REF.

Some private life

My family and I had moved in 1986 from my tiny 17th-century house in South Street near Selling to a larger Victorian house, Clement Cottage, ensconced in a walled garden down its own small road in the centre of the village of Wingham, a Domesday village. Six years later we moved up the hill about a mile or so to Herons Hall built in 1883 which sat in 2 acres with a single tarmac road.

The day after we moved in February 1992 I lit the only source of heat, a wood-burning stove, which set fire to the house as the previous owner had used apple logs which left tar residues on the chimney which caught light. The fire engine from Wingham could not reach us as our nearest neighbour refused to move her car parked in the road and it had to be redirected down the other end to get to us. Putting the fire out and getting access with their hoses to inside the chimney stack was very difficult and required tip-toeing between my son and daughter both under five and asleep on the floor of the upstairs room. One fireman put his foot through the floor which we later discovered was a hidden cellar.

We immediately set about improving the house scraping the condensed tar of two people's heavy smoking habit from the windows. The previous owner's husband had had a sudden heart attack going down the end of the field to feed the geese. The secondary glazing had a humid greenhouse effect on the sash windows which were rotting. The cellar had to be dug out of 40 tons of chalk through a half-buried window we discovered under the kitchen window which being hygroscopic had rotted the beams under the kitchen floor. We then added a fourth bedroom and a large living room allowing me to hide away in the original small living room now a study, and we added a huge conservatory for semi tropical trees, lime and orange trees and many other plants reminding me of the places in the world I had worked. I turned the enormous garden into a wildlife forest with thousands of trees we planted as whips and in their first summer in 1992 we had to rush around with watering cans and hoses making sure they took.

Then a large pond was dug with a JCB and lined with bentonite, waterproofing clay, which didn't work so we lined it in butyl. It immediately attracted all the wildlife imaginable including water scorpions, frogs, great

The transformation of Herons Hall 1973, 2008, 2010 and temperate conservatory 2009

crested newts, water voles (which eat through the lining, one hole above water and the other below for emergencies so as the water went down to the bottom hole!) and ducks. We then built an octagonal summerhouse with large leaded windows overlooking the pond from which we could read or write, or do emails while drinking wine at peace with this wonderful quiet forest and stunning pond shut away from the troublesome and noisy world. Herons Hall had an enormous old barn called the Black Barn of Ash which was on the site hundreds of years before the house and used as a store for incendiary bombs during World War II as RAF Manston was close by. The floor was made of handmade bricks and was last rebuilt after a fire in the very early 1900s. The final touch was a very large conservatory built by Hartley Botanics, planted with all those palms, olives and other species reminding me of the countries I've worked in as well as three life-size bronzes of a giant tortoise, seawater crocodile and a baby African elephant.

Settling the governance

New Financial arrangements for The Durrell Institute of Conservation and Ecology were put into effect from 1 August 1993. For internal purposes DICE was treated in the same way as the Laboratories in the Science Faculty. Its budget was determined in accordance with the special DICE Resource

Allocation Model (RAM) which followed the general principles of the University RAM and takes account of a) the much higher fees charged for DICE students, and b) donations towards the salary of the Executive Director and other externally funded staff. For 1993/94 and 1994/95, the budget would be adjusted in the light of the actual students recruited. (This was different from the rest of the University where budget centres receive/lose smaller additional cash amounts if their FTE student load exceeds/falls short of the target.) DICE had its own financial academic reserve. But I discovered the bizarre truth that if I fell short of any financial prediction I made for any particular year this deficit was carried forward into the next year even if all our costs had been covered!

The University's usual arrangements for the acceptance of research grants, contracts, and consultancies, would apply to the activities of DICE. DICE would contribute 15% of its income arising from research contracts, consultancies, short courses, (excluding any residential or catering charges) to the University as a contribution towards its central costs. The Executive Director was the Budgetary Controller for DICE and regular financial reports on DICE's income and expenditure was prepared by the Finance Division. General oversight of DICE's finances and expenditure was exercised by the DICE Management Board. This Board reports to Senate. Consonant with DICE's Laboratory status and practices elsewhere in this University concerning Boards of Management, the Chair and Deputy Chair will be held by non-salaried members of the University. The Board comprised Chair Sandy Alexander, DICE Founder, DICE Executive Director, Chair DTCB, University Finance Director, JWPT Council member, Dean Natural Sciences and Director Biological Laboratory. The Board of Studies comprised myself as Chair and all the staff and honorary staff.

Developing the programme

A new degree in LLM/MSc in Environmental Law and Conservation was proposed between the Law Board and The Kent Law School and The Durrell Institute of Conservation and Ecology in October 1993. This added to the portfolio of a taught MSc in Conservation Biology (1991) and the MBA (Environment) started in 1992 with The Canterbury Business School, as well as the Diplomas in Ecology (started in 1982), Raptor Biology (started in 1987), and Endangered Species Management (with JWPT started in 1985).

The MSc in Conservation Biology 1991 was the first Masters which helped launch the Institute's core programme and "applications from all over the world flooded into the University of Kent for the UK's first postgraduate courses in conservation biology with students from 17 different countries including executives from the United Nations and the World

Health Organisation – testimony to the heightened interest in the relatively new science of conservation. With a corresponding rise in demand for DICE's existing qualification courses in Ecology, Raptor Biology and Endangered Species Management will supply the need for comprehensively trained conservationists, something our beleaguered world has never needed more." So spouted the PR machine of the University. Thus began a whole suite of programs that provided a substantial recurrent income. Needless to say it was copied by Oxford, Cambridge and Imperial College.

Working with the Business School we developed an MBA in Environmental Management led by Walter Wehrmeyer (Research Fellow, DICE and now Reader at the Centre for Environment and Sustainability at the University of Surrey) funded by the Esmée Fairbairn Foundation. As often happens with ambitious academics the director of the Business School decided to take over this initiative entirely, which had great potential, cutting DICE out. The flaw in this kind of intellectual theft is that the thief is invariably unable to make a success of something that is not theirs! The MBA flopped. The LLM/MSc in Environmental Law and Conservation did not proceed as the appointee charged with driving this through failed to apply himself.

In November 1993 I visited the Université du Littoral in France to establish the Project Transmanche (an EU funded program of research cooperation concerning the Channel environment) and it was proposed by the then Deputy Vice Chancellor John Craven and the Pro-vice Chancellors, on the cross-Channel ferry, that a DICE undergraduate degree should be created as a means of providing resources to hire junior staff. This was precipitated by the DVC being unwilling to re-invest in our staff capacity, other than rely on my ability to attract significant funding for Chairs and research, ignoring the significant income from the Masters courses (I set the MSc fee very high, the same for UK and overseas students), unless we had an undergraduate income.

This broke my strategic programme for our development which was predicated on 6 months teaching and 6 months research allowing time for both taught students to complete their MSc theses and for staff to do their own research. By taking on a first degree teaching programme it would stretch out all year hampering this model and I was concerned that first degree graduates would further hamper our objective of full employment for our alumni (a postgraduate qualification being *de rigeur* in this complex area of conservation) which seemed to me in these early days the only statistic that universities should concentrate on.

I also obtained a substantial grant from ODA (DfID) of £150,000 in 1993 to establish work in tourism, conservation and sustainable development which has culminated in an MSc in Tourism and Conservation at Bridge

Warden College in association with DICE led by Harold Goodwin (Emeritus Professor of Responsible Tourism at Manchester Metropolitan University). I remember most clearly that after I had taken him to have a talk with the Permanent Secretary of ODA who I knew, and committed £150,000, Harold was incapable of coherency as we walked back down to Victoria Station.

In 1994 DICE was assessed by Higher Education Funding Council for England (HEFCE) for Teaching Quality Assessment and pronounced satisfactory.

I was awarded a Personal Chair in Conservation Biology in early 1994 although Vice Chancellor Sibson offered me a lower salary than the chairs I created by endowment.

I obtained an endowment of £800,000 for another Chair in DICE later in the year, the Ibnu Sutowo Chair of Biodiversity Management. The funds were ring fenced in an account called the Sutowo Indonesia Biodiversity Management Fund (SIBMF) until dispersed in 2004 at the request of Denise Everitt (Finance), Alister Dunning (University Treasurer) and Neil Oliver (Accounts) during a meeting with me and Prof. Nigel Leader-Williams (the Chair's incumbent). I agreed providing the Chair and an Institute Secretary were made permanent and funded by the University. Extraordinarily the University had taken a barrrister's opinion on this action by them prior to this move emerging!

As a pre-eminent Indonesian the University awarded Ibnu Sutowo an honorary doctorate in 1994 after one, ultimately senior, member of the Uni-

Professor Ibnu Sutowo, Doctor of Science, November 1994 Canterbury Cathedral.
Visiting Alfred Russel Wallace's tomb

versity, recently retired, tried to block it after he approached the Foreign & Commonwealth Office suggesting Sutowo was corrupt. The FCO rejected these niggles and the University rejected his claims about honorary degrees being exchanged for endowments. At the ceremony in Canterbury Cathedral half the Indonesian Cabinet attended which caused the first traffic jam of Gulfstream aircraft at nearby Manston Airport and was the only time such a huge gathering of Muslims could be seen at the seat of the Church of England. The party afterwards at Eastwell Manor was amazing.

In early 1995 Gerry Durrell and my father died.

In November 1995 a new Professor of Biodiversity Management was appointed, Prof. Nigel Leader-Williams who took up the role of Research Director and eventually Director. Georgina Mace (Zoological Society of London) and Nigel had originally applied for the position as a joint Chair but Georgina dropped out for family reasons. Georgina did come down for lunch in August with her husband and three children, one of whom needed special schooling but all schools were on their summer holidays and she was rather put off. Vice Chancellor Robin Sibson (1994–2001) made a ridiculous fuss about giving the entire chair to Nigel, as it was a joint appointment, but I was able to make him submit as the £0.8m was coming from Ibnu Sutowo via the Durrell Trust for Conservation Biology! Nigel went back to Cambridge in 2009 where he led a conservation programme and Georgina, who I have known a long time since my days in Oxford, is now Dame Georgina Mace FRS (University College London) for her outstanding work on measuring the trends and consequences of biodiversity loss and ecosystem change.

DICE Review after 5 years

Another battle with domineering bureaucracy

Robin Sibson wanted as few as possible departments and institutes, reorganising the University twice, forcing my independent Institute within the Faculty of Science into a shotgun wedding with the Biological Laboratory who were all microbiologists and biochemists. The Laboratory's founding Professor Ken Stacey was a real gent who came from the MRC Microbial Genetics Unit in Hammersmith, and then at another of the 1960s universities, the University of Sussex, and had a laid-back outlook on life; smoked full strength unfiltered Navy Cut Capstan cigarettes, the same tobacco as my father smoked just after the Navy. He was very supportive of me and what I was creating unlike his successors who wanted DICE under their thumb. Ken wanted me to focus my research on a specific area like environmental sex determination but I deliberately spread myself much wider in my interests and in my involvement with charities and other organisations. This was pivotal to the establishment of DICE.

The period from April 1995 until the University was reorganised again in March 1997, when we agreed that Anthropology and DICE should merge, was one of the most difficult and unproductive periods of DICE's history as the remarriage with Biosciences (renamed from the Biological Laboratory) was again forced by Vice Chancellor Sibson's second reorganisation. The RAE ratings announced by HEFCE reflected DICE's appalling treatment in the Biosciences Department culminating in an attempt late 1996 to asset strip the Institute and remove its identity by fully absorbing it into biochemistry and microbiology. I have a secret memo dated 21 February 1997 drawn to my attention from the then Biosciences Director which recommended the dissolution of DICE on fully combining with them involving the disbursement of those staff that Biosciences did not want, in other words the destruction of DICE.

Since my time in Oxford I have seen this competitive and destructive behaviour by academics in nearly every country. It is driven by jealousy and enviousness making it very difficult to start something new and substantial without a strong and achievable future relevant to global needs, powerful allies, very competent and loyal staff, and luck.

As DICE embraces both the social and natural sciences the appropriate department to marry was anthropology and I forced this marriage on Sibson who had no facility for imaginative entrepreneurship or modern innovation, any more than his absence of social ability. This was most clearly demonstrated when I urged him to talk to his dinner companion in 1996 who had just given me £0.5 million (Alan Heber-Percy) as a gift for helping to form the Countryside Alliance and supporting Robin Hanbury-Tenison *pro bono*. The VC would not embrace Alan in conversation. I intended to establish a Chair in Biodiversity Law, a vital part of biodiversity conservation, and a concomitant MSc in Ethnobotany with Kew to provide the income necessary to maintain an Ethnobotany Chair. Later that year DICE joined with the Anthropology Department.

In 1998 a new MSc degree in Ethnobotany, which started in 1994 after a dialogue between myself and Prof. Sir Ghillean Prance (Director, Kew) with a view to establishing an endowed Chair named after the then Queen Elisabeth the Queen Mother, was started. The Chair was to manage, and be financially supported by the MSc income and be jointly held between Kew and DICE. This initiative was overtaken by the coming together of DICE and Anthropology, Ghillean's and my retirement, and subsequently has become embedded in the current School of Anthropology and Conservation.

Anthropology used us for the first few years as a milch cow as DICE made money and they didn't. This was vehemently denied by the University administrators. A practice called virement, or using success to subsidise failure, instead of reinvesting in success.

A common prejudice in Universities as it's not possible to embrace all subjects (i.e. a UNI- versity) if they don't pay for themselves! DICE didn't having lectureships in such abstruse and useless areas as post-modernism of which there were two in anthropology, one of whom went off his head! Since then the School of Anthropology and Conservation has flourished with the influence of DICE and embracing the subject areas and imperatives of what the world needs.

Nevertheless, as I write, DICE is still subsidising the anthropologists!

Founding an Institute (DICE), an NGO (HCT), a journal (*Biodiversity and Conservation*) and putting on the First World Congress of Herpetology (FWCH), which had taken five years hard work, all at the same time (1989) needed superhuman energy and no need to sleep. I was completely insane but luck and fortune never arise conveniently. The international peer-

Mocha was our first Burmese and kept my shoulder warm as I worked all the time to create what I have and manage the outcome (2004)

reviewed journal *Biodiversity and Conservation* was my attempt to address the lack of a multidisciplinary peer-reviewed Journal in ecology and the conservation of biodiversity. It was started with Dr Bob Carling at Chapman & Hall and is now owned by Springer. Vol 1:1 appeared in March 1992.

Vincent Weir

Vincent Weir, another loner like me, and I quickly established an NGO conserving reptiles and amphibians the Herpetological Conservation Trust (HCT, now Amphibian and Reptile Conservation Trust or ARC) with Keith Corbett as the first officer and a committee of knowledgeable people. It was launched at the First World Congress of Herpetology 1989. I was a member of the British Herpetological Society Council from 1980 to 1983, a long established society, which was a respected academic organisation that was alarmed at this sudden explosion of activity but conservation was the main thrust of HCT not academic study.

The late Vincent Weir, who was my partner and funder, was a very retiring man who lived in Whitehall Place above the Farmers' Club, enjoyed the parades on Horseguards and never received any formal education coming from an august family. He could name every fact concerning the Household Divisions especially the Royal Artillery Mounted Band led by two musicians on large Shire horses used as drum horses. Since their hands are occupied with the drumsticks, they must work the horses' reins with their feet. My favourite was Pompey, the drum horse of the Royal Horse Guards (The Blues) 1938–1953 a handsome and very popular Drum Horse, and long after his death the Farrier Major of the time was known for selling 'Pompey' hooves to new recruits.

Vincent at 18 would race down to the West Country to observe otters in his Aston Martin and the one solid element as he grew up, lonely like me, were his love of animals. He gave me £1,000,000 to establish the NGO to conserve 'herps' and a further £2,500,000 which arrived by post without notice once we proved we were effective. He also asked me what other biodiversity needed help in the UK. And I said plants, butterflies and possibly mammals. 'Plantlife' was invented, and a charity helping butterflies was established. The British Mammal Society started arguing amongst themselves where the new mammal charity should be established, and who should head it, which made Vincent lose patience and gave his backing to bats.

From start to finish

DICE was first housed in the former Master's bungalow of Rutherford College, next to the Butler's bungalow, at the University of Kent. Such pretension! Tyler Court, a student hotel, was built over both bungalows. Those were the days of Kent's aspiration to be a fully collegiate University aping Oxbridge with a tutorial system and lectures. The DICE HQ worked well for the first year or so but we then moved to the research centre at the University and built an enormous prefabricated building out the back to house everybody. A very short time after we got all of us together in one place the Deputy Vice Chancellor took over our rooms and prefab and we became a diaspora again, spread across the University.

When asked by the original founding staff when we started what was the policy of the Institute the answer was simple. It was stimulated by an observation from Mike Walkey that I had a brain like the inside of a Byzantine cathedral and jetted across the world like Concorde!

I explained we worked by three tenets:

- Be the best otherwise you're fired,
- Work towards redundancy, teaching the world how to do what we can do and, once done, we will not be needed until others come knocking at our door to do the same for them,
- Finally JFDI.

This scared the pants of those new staff that had just joined having given up secure jobs elsewhere! Explanation was needed. I made the rules since the University had me creating this Institute without costing them anything, entirely financially self-sufficient.

An enormous number of events that were bizarre, devious, funny, satisfying, energising, learning and ultimately succeeding were just part of the daily mix. We inaugurated a DICE Annual lecture and invited the good and the great including Secretaries of State, geniuses, glitterati, and people who we respected. The first of which on 'Environmental Management and Sustainable Development' was delivered by The Right Honourable Michael Howard QC MP, Secretary of State for the Environment on 22nd January 1993. This was followed by such luminaries as Sir Crispin Tickell, Prof. Lord Bob May FRS, Dr Dick Laws FRS, and Prof. Sir Ghillean Prance FRS.

I even met Lord John Brabourne and his wife The Countess of Burma. I am a film buff and his film *'Sink the Bismarck!'* is a great film. We talked for 20 minutes but he needed to go. He was wounded when an IRA explosion killed his father-in-law and one of his twin sons.

I raised millions to fund posts, created Masters' programmes to provide income to cover recurrent costs, and we became established, if not comfortably, in the University. Over succeeding years DICE became more conventional as the University paid for more of the posts and today it is fully integrated and effectively dominates the School of Anthropology and Conservation.

In August 1999 I was suddenly forced to retire through ill health after ten years of creating four successful world class initiatives (FWCH, DICE, HCT and the journal) and was given 6 months to live if I carried on. "It will either be a heart attack or a stroke", said Dr Sheila Bliss, my GP. The cause was stress leading to ischaemic and congestive heart disease together with hypertension.

Those that caused it had neither the nous nor verve to create something this significant themselves in the first place but liked the idea, once the battles had been won and success was clear, of taking over. I was examined by a consultant psychiatrist, consultant physician, consultant cardiologist who all confirmed my very poor state of health and the reasons for it; I was retired very quickly with the enormous help and support of Wendy Conway (Personnel Director at the University). I got the impression the speed was driven by University nervousness at what I might do.

The adages of Winston Churchill that describes my mindset best are: "Success is the ability to go from one failure to another without loss of enthusiasm". It would have been impossible to create DICE at Oxford being so much more politically practised than Kent. Churchill was more succinct when he said: "Keep buggering on".

While Noel Coward, the 'Master', was of my own heart when he said: "Thousands of people have talent. I might as well congratulate you for having eyes in your head. The one and only thing that counts is: Do you have staying power?" And best of all, "Work is more fun than fun". He

DICE MSc 2018 Graduation

also said, "He must have been an incredibly good shot" (when told a very stupid acquaintance had blown his brains out). Which sums up what DICE faced in its formative years.

Today

Today DICE has over a thousand alumni in over 100 countries, addressing UN's Sustainable Development Goals and 15 Aichi targets of the Convention on Biological Diversity, and has spawned more than 20 winners of the most prestigious awards for conservation worldwide including 9 Whitley Awards (the Green Oscars), considered the Nobel Prize for biodiversity conservation. Since I had to retire Professors Nigel Leader-Williams, Richard Griffiths and Bob Smith have been driving forces carrying on the work I started with great verve and imagination.

Thirty years after I created DICE we got the final accolade as DICE continues to expand, develop and change. DICE was awarded a prestigious honour, the Queen's Anniversary Prize, in 2019 in recognition of our excellence, innovation and benefits to the wider world through "pioneering education, capacity building and research in global nature conservation to protect species and ecosystems and benefit people". As Professor Bob Smith DICE Director wrote to me, "I hope you're feeling proud about the news and that your brilliant idea and hard work have been recognised in this way!"

It has become one of the oldest research and postgraduate training institutes in the world embracing the natural and social sciences focused on biodiversity and conservation. It was unique in its multidisciplinary approach and hiring people who had excelled in the field conserving wildlife and the environment but had the intellect to publish in *Nature* too. It is the largest UK higher education institute to undertake this work, offering interdisciplinary undergraduate and postgraduate courses in wildlife conservation. To date, over 1000 conservationists have trained with DICE. DICE leads projects in over 50 countries, including research on human wellbeing and nature, human-elephant conflict, oil palm deforestation, online illegal trade in protected species, national park planning and ecotourism projects, and the mapping of biodiversity through eDNA.

I supported numerous candidates to be awarded University of Kent honorary doctorates – John Maynard Smith (evolutionary ecologist), Gerald Durrell, Professor Ghillean Prance (Director, RBG Kew), Professor Ibnu Sutowo, Professor Sir John Cornforth (Shell Research, Sittingbourne), Sir John Swire (from Mulu onwards), Sir Crispin Tickell (Darwin Initiative, proposed him as Chancellor), Lord Robert May (Oxford), Nicholas Baring (Earthwatch, lost Barings Bank because of Leeson), Jeremy Mallinson (co-founded JWPT now Durrell organisation), Professor Sir John Krebs (Oxford), Michael Bukht (at Haberdashers' with me, aka Michael Barry chef/radio controller), Professor Norman Myers (friend), Professor Jacqueline McGlade (Darwin Initiative, polymath), Sir Robert Worcester (met through animal welfare conference 1985 arranged by me while in Continuing Education), Lord Sandy Bruce-Lockhart of the Weald (befriended since 1979, KCC Leader) and Amanda Cottrell (introduced by Bob Worcester) – because they were friends and acquaintances who had accomplished significant work and in some way or another had helped DICE. They were all awarded their honorary doctorates.

While the Aristotelian aims of higher education in the last century were admirable and suited the times, a modern university in this century has no option but to focus everything on what gets graduates permanent jobs in a profession they like and are qualified for.

When I started there were few jobs in biodiversity, the only options being academia, museums or veterinary, none of which attracted me in the slightest. But by 1989 when I founded DICE the opportunities in biodiversity were growing and I concentrated my intellectual abilities on ensuring that the Institute produced people who the world wanted.

Most universities including Kent were at least 20 years behind me following tired conventional pathways which today will eventually bankrupt them as young people would rather have a job at the end (or an apprenticeship, learning the job on the job and being paid) and not be £50,000 in debt with a bright new shiny useless degree without a job. It could be as high as £65,000 in debt for a four year degree including a foundation year enabling universities to accept students unconditionally who are not up to university standards. The other difficulty is that many university staff couldn't get a job in the outside world and in consequence it means the unemployable are teaching those desperate to be employed!

Kiwi fruit

John Craig (now Emeritus Professor of Environment Management) wandered into my office one day at DICE, a long thin character in well worn Levi's, and just said 'G'day'. Sibilla Girardet from New Zealand who did an MSc with DICE on Aldabra Atoll and then a PhD at Auckland told John to contact me as she thought we would enjoy each other's company! We had a very long conversation around our shared vision, very clear about the future of ecological and environmental research and training in higher education. He was curious about how I brought DICE about as he was founding the School of Environmental and Marine Sciences in Auckland University and was experiencing the same biopoliticians and nay-sayers.

In April and May 1997 I visited New Zealand flying by Garuda airlines via Amman, Batu Besar, Jakarta (where I tried to get hold of Sutowo), Bali and finally Auckland to be picked up by Mick Clout (Professor of Conservation Ecology)

Congregation. DSc in honoris causa. Lord Mayor, VC David Melville and Judge Nigel van der Bijl, Recorder of Canterbury. Summer 2005

Fiona at lunch party at Augustine's, Longport, Canterbury after Congregation Summer 2005

who together with his wife Joan put me up. Mick and Joan were students in the Department of Wildlife and Natural Resources at Edinburgh when I was Demonstrator and he had become a leading authority on invasive species.

After visiting Wenderholm Regional Park I went to the School of Environmental and Marine Sciences (SEMS) at Tāmaki Innovation Campus, founded by John Craig along the lines of DICE, where I gave a seminar on 'Making Money from Biodiversity' and developed a LINK cooperation programme between both institutions backed by the British Council involving Neil Mitchell and Malcolm Bowman.

Flying to New Zealand takes 24.5 hours in the air and you feel like a desiccated Egyptian mummy by the time you arrive and need at least three days to get your sleep pattern organised. I use melatonin, an old trick to reset the biological clock for seasoned world travellers like myself, but it only works occasionally. What's worse is one's gut dries out which makes progress awkward. I spent some nights staying at the University Whitaker Hall while I made various trips, visiting the harbour, Auckland Domain, Māori performances at the Museum, the stunning portraits of Māori, and celebrated by buying a small stuffed kiwi.

I flew on to Wellington, the capital, to talk to the British Council director Paul Smith together with Nicola Johnson and Michelle MacCormack, and met Don Newman at the Department of Conservation, a well-known conservationist, who scooped me up and took me to South Island and then by boat to Maud Island from Nelson where we had a full Māori greeting. Afterwards we started hunting for frogs. The Maud Island frog (*Leiopelma pakeka*) is a primitive frog native to New Zealand. We slept in the Māori wharenui, a communal house, next to their meeting ground or marae. Don and I competed for who could snore the loudest!

Then to Picton and at nearby Ship Cove, where Cook landed on his three New Zealand trips, we had a full Māori handover ceremony before releasing the three hundred frogs, translocating them 25 km to nearby Motuara Island in Queen Charlotte Sound, the first time New Zealand frogs to have been moved between islands[107]. It was covered in lush forest when Captain James Cook used it to claim British sovereignty over the South Island in 1770 on one of his three trips to New Zealand. We then drove to Nelson Airport and Mick Clout picked me up at Auckland to his home. This whole conservation exercise was sponsored by Allan Riley of Ace-Doors Ltd New Zealand, one of my first experiences of private sector supported conservation.

Don cooperated with Gerry Durrell and me when the Jersey Wildlife Preservation Trust was reintroducing all the native species of plants and animals on Round Island in the Indian Ocean after the devastation caused by introduced rabbits. Don was a world expert on mammalian pest control

---

107   'Frogs/pepeketua'. Department of Conservation Te Papa Atawhai. Retrieved 24 November 2016.

but there was a general election happening on Mauritius, which owned Round Island, and the Opposition party, in trying to gain power, tried to declare the Round Island rabbits a protected species to discredit the incumbent administration's intent on eradication, which we were able to disprove. The opposition lost the election and Round Island was cleared of rabbits enabling Jersey to put back all the plants and animals they had been looking after at the Zoo.

This interesting expedition, to spread isolated and endangered species to a number of different sites, 'not all of one's eggs in one basket', is a strategic plan used in New Zealand on many species especially kākāpo (nocturnal flightless lekking parrot) which Mick was in charge of. Introduced predators such as rodents, weasels, corvids, and the brushtail possum, which destroys the vegetation and is controlled by aerial dropping of 1080-laced bait[108], were major targets. The Māori greetings are impressive as they hold biodiversity, 'their treasured things', in enormous regard which is written into the Waitangi Treaty. It originally meant the wealth of fish and shellfish but this has extended to all biodiversity, land and marine territory.

The Treaty of Waitangi is an agreement made in May 1840 between representatives of the British Crown and more than 500 Māori chiefs. It resulted in the declaration of British sovereignty over New Zealand by Lieutenant Governor William Hobson. In effect, Britain profiting from skirmishes between Māori iwi or tribes, and the French parlaying New Zealand away to Queen Victoria; at the time the Māori thought they were merely agreeing to the British keeping order not becoming a colony and losing ownership of their country. The English text and the Māori text differ in meaning significantly, particularly in relation to the meaning of having and ceding sovereignty. The current Waitangi Tribunal makes recommendations on claims brought by Māori relating to actions or omissions of the Crown, in the period largely since 1840, that breach the promises made in the Treaty of Waitangi.

I met Bob Mahuta who was the first Māori leader to negotiate a satisfactory compensation settlement with the New Zealand government for tribal land confiscated under European settlement in the fledgling colony. In a deal completed in late 1994, he won a package worth NZ$170m for his Tainui tribe for the seizure of 485,000 hectares of land in the North Island's Waikato Region 131 years earlier. Significantly for all Māori, the settlement included the first formal apology given by the Crown to the indigenous people for historical wrongs during colonisation. This iwi invested their payout in scholarships for their young men and women to be trained to the highest level as professionals – doctors, dentists, lawyers, surveyors

---

108   Green, W. (2012) 'The use of 1080 for pest control'. The use of 1080 for pest control. Animal Health Board and Department of Conservation.

and all the other professions that would help their tribe or iwi progress without reliance on the pākehā, settlers of European descent. I also visited Umupuia pa, a nearby Māori defensive settlement and marae, first settled by pākehā in 1866 in Ngai Tai iwi land.

On May 10, 1997 while in New Zealand I heard that DICE was free of the Biosciences Department and we had combined with the Anthropology Department at Kent University. Since I had created DICE to be a marriage between the natural sciences and quantitative social sciences it was a natural union but with one flaw we discovered later, namely our success would mean underwriting Anthropology's financial failure for quite some years.

To celebrate I drafted a LINK programme between SEMS and DICE which funded mutual cooperation and visits for some years until the British Council started to concentrate more on the arts rather than the sciences. John had had immense experience of working in fairly remote parts of New Zealand. On a regular basis we would teach in each other's establishments and it was great fun as I could enjoy a completely different perspective from the other side of the world about conservation and communities especially with the influence of the Māori people.

After a SEMS staff meeting it was clear that there were academics elsewhere in the University of Auckland who were not keen on this up-start School; a species of academic crocodile and biopolitician, which had blighted me in the formative years of DICE, the only 'species' on earth I would like to exterminate. Never concerned with enlightened initiatives and advancing academic development, these creatures are only obsessed with power, control and designing processes to support their own prejudices. This was all déjà vu to me since DICE went through the same ravaging for the first few years of its existence.

Malcolm Bowman, head of SEMS, took me to the Leigh Marine Laboratory for a planning retreat after which I invited Mick and Joan Clout to the General Store at Whitford to dinner to thank them for their hospitality and celebrate Fiona's birthday. I gave them a carved fishbowl from the Trobriand Islands. The next day I visited Tiritiri Matangi with John Craig, SEMS founder, who also led the project to turn this island from a sheep farm destroyed of native wildlife into a world-famous conservation area with all the wildlife put back. On my return I met Sibilla Girardet, a New Zealander who had studied with John for her PhD but had completed her MSc at DICE under me and spent some of that time working on Aldabra working on the genetics of the giant tortoises in April 1992. She did her PhD on the translocation of little spotted kiwi (*Apteryx owenii*), from Kapiti Island to Tiritiri Matangi Island, providing an opportunity to assess kiwi behaviour in an artificially restored habitat.

Before I flew home on the worst airline in the world, Malaysian Airways, I took John Craig and Anne Stewart to dinner at Vinnies, Geoff Scott's eponymous restaurant, in Herne Bay and had one of the best meals and wines in my life – Hunter's Gewürztraminer. Vinnies closed in 2016. This concluded one of the best trips I have ever made and I left in awe of New Zealander's conservation efforts and intelligence and with their country. I also continue to drink Hunter's Gewürztraminer to this day and remember my friends and memories in New Zealand.

I made many trips to New Zealand and spent a lot of time with John Craig and his wife Anne Stewart, who showed me New Zealand and opened many doors, and made many other friends including Mick and Joan Clout, Neil Mitchell, and Sibilla Girardet and especially Lindsay Saunders who I worked with a lot on ADB projects in Sri Lanka and China. I eventually bought a large apartment in Short Street in the centre of

British High Commissioner Martin Williams, Helen Clark PM and myself after a lecture I gave entitled 'Tigers, Timber and Trouble: wealth creation and careers in biodiversity' in Auckland Town Hall June 2001 supported by the British Council LINK Fellowship. Martin Williams was a First Secretary at the British Embassy in Iran when militants invaded the US Embassy in November 1979, taking 52 hostages. Contrary to the storyline of the American Oscar-winning film Argo, which tells how six American diplomats in hiding were rescued by the CIA, the British helped but were portrayed as being callously indifferent when in fact Martin risked his life. Another film U571 rewrote the Second World War so that American servicemen captured an Enigma code machine rather than British sailors. Hollywood seems to have a passion for rewriting historical facts

Auckland overlooking the bay.

John took me to his family bach, a modest beach home, at Waihi Beach in the Bay of Plenty on the east coast of North Island. On one occasion around Christmas my family joined me with John and Anne. At some point while everyone was having a fun time I took a walk by myself along the beach and got into conversation with an older man who was also having a breath of fresh air. It soon occurred to me that I was talking to Sir Edmund Hillary who climbed Everest with Sherpa Tenzing in 1953 and while neither of us mentioned this or our identities he struck me as a very pleasant but very self-contained kiwi.

Alliances – Countryside, Welfare, Food Co-ops and Cumbria

When Robin Hanbury-Tenison was still at the British Field Sports Society, his first proper job, the Countryside Alliance was being formed from three organisations: the British Field Sports Society (BFSS), the Countryside Business Group and the Countryside Movement.

In December 1996 I wrote a letter with Richard Meade and Deborah, Duchess of Devonshire to all the BFSS members urging them to join the RSPCA especially after I had successfully got both organisations to co-operate over The Wild Mammals (Protection) Bill and it seemed to us that this was an excellent opportunity to co-operate further. I was in a good position to try and help foster this partnership since I had been Chairman, RSPCA Wild Animals Advisory Committee and was until 1995 Vice Chairman, RSPCA Scientific, Technical and Academic Committee and Council Member.

The RSPCA was alarmed at the prospect of the very large membership of the Alliance swamping their much smaller membership and immediately the Council passed a motion insisting that all new members of the Society must sign an undertaking that they did not support hunting. Richard was Britain's most successful male equestrian Olympian, and Deborah Devonshire was an English aristocrat, writer, memoirist and socialite. She was the youngest and last surviving of the six Mitford sisters, who were prominent members of English society. She revolutionised the activities of Chatsworth in particular the development of commercial activities such as Chatsworth Farm Shop. She was also very keen on chickens as was I with my ayam cemani and wrote to me often.

Gerry Durrell and Maurice Swingland, my dad, died within three months of each other in 1995. Gerry had been in hospital for some time in London and at least went home to die. But my dad kept being cheerful with his GP instead of confessing to transient ischaemic attacks or TIAs which had been building up and culminated in a massive stroke which eventually killed him nine months later. I went to see him in a very good

THE COUNTRY SPORTS ANIMAL WELFARE GROUP
59 KENNINGTON ROAD
LONDON
SE1 7PZ

Dear BFSS Member,   29 February 1996

Following the enactment of the Wild Mammals (Protection) Bill (the Meale Bill) today, in which the BFSS and the RSPCA co-operated closely to produce an historic piece of animal welfare legislation, ending years of antagonism, there now exists an opportunity for us to continue to work together. For too long members of the BFSS have felt alienated from the RSPCA's animal welfare work because of the comments made by a few animal rights extremists within the RSPCA. We believe that the time has come when country people, and country sportsmen and women, should step forward and, once again, take their places in the ranks of the world's leading animal welfare organisation, remembering the role played by country sportsmen in helping to found the RSPCA.

The purpose of this initiative, which is undertaken by the signatories of this letter in their private capacities and not as officers of any organisation, is to encourage individuals to rejoin the RSPCA, and start to play a part in steering the RSPCA more towards its traditional role of caring for animals and away from animal rights. It may well be alleged that the BFSS is seeking to "infiltrate" or take over the RSPCA. This could not be further from the truth. The BFSS and other country sports organisations have no interest whatsoever in seeking to control any other organisation or charity. We hope that this letter will be viewed in the spirit of co-operation and respect for all animals, which we all share.

If you support the animal welfare work of the RSPCA, please ring 01403 264181 and ask for a membership form. If you do this right away it will enable you to send in your subscription before the end of March. You will then be entitled to vote for the election of Council Members at the AGM in June. £20 Joint Membership gives you two votes!

Yours sincerely

LORD MANCROFT
DEPUTY CHAIRMAN BFSS

THE DUCHESS OF DEVONSHIRE

BILL ANDREWES
DEPUTY CHAIRMAN BFSS

RICHARD MEADE OBE
FORMER COUNCIL MEMBER RSPCA
CHAIRMAN BRITISH HORSE
FOUNDATION

PROFESSOR IAN SWINGLAND
FORMER CHAIRMAN RSPCA WILDLIFE ADVISORY COMMITTEE
PROFESSOR OF CONSERVATION BIOLOGY, THE DURRELL INSTITUTE

nursing home that Jill North, his companion for so many years, had managed to get him into, rescuing him from hospital where he had been left with nothing to drink for an entire day. As I left him for the last time to fly to Jakarta, after spending a long time alone with him as he couldn't speak or retain any coherency in his actions, I glanced through the bay window at him, he had that expression I knew so well, "Isn't life a bugger!" I never saw him again.

Douglas Botting wrote Gerry's biography[109] (800+ pages) after Gerry asked me who should do it. He wanted Botting anyway. I only knew two things about Botting – he was an expeditioner like us both and he wrote a good biog about Gavin Maxwell who I never met but got caught up in his life especially with an otter (*Ring of Bright Water*). Maxwell was another expeditionary and explored with Wilfred Thesiger the Tigris Basin, home to the Marsh Arabs, where he was given an otter cub, Mijbil. The Marsh Arabs like many remote peoples do not denigrate homosexuality. It's just sex with a male or female, so what! Mijbil was said to be a new species *Lutrogale perspicillata maxwelli* (or, colloquially, 'Maxwell's otter'). The smooth otter is found in India down to Sumatra but in Iraq it's dubbed this subspecies.

Biodiversity and their habitats are used as political weapons by many politicians; for example, fed by the Tigris and Euphrates rivers, the marshlands of Mesopotamia are spawning grounds for Gulf fisheries and home to bird species such as the sacred ibis. They also provide a resting spot for thousands of wildfowl migrating between Siberia and Africa. Saddam Hussein, who accused the region's Marsh Arab inhabitants of treachery during the 1980–1988 war with Iran, dammed and drained the marshes in the 1990s to flush out rebels living in the reeds. After his overthrow by the US-led invasion in 2003, locals wrecked many of the dams to let water rush back in, and foreign environmental agencies helped breathe life back into the marshes.

The Countryside Alliance launched on 10 July 1997 and was formed to help promote and defend the British countryside and rural life[110], both in the media and in Parliament. I helped Robin Hanbury-Tenison *pro bono* by leading a small group of conservation scientists concentrating on examining research on hunting on the basis that whatever the outcome of our deliberations, for or against the Alliance's viewpoint, it would be published. This grew out of the BFSS Conservation Committee chaired by the Duke of Northumberland but eventually it led the policy-making of the Alliance.

I appeared on a live television debate chaired by Kirsty Young, former presenter of the BBC long-standing programme Desert Island Discs, a very astute individual who could handle the fact that half the audience were

109   https://www.telegraph.co.uk/obituaries/2018/02/09/douglas-botting-explorer-biographer-obituary/

110   http://www.bbc.co.uk/news/in-pictures-43113400

violently against hunting and the other half took a more informed view. The question of foxhunting was presented by some as a gratuitously cruel and to no purpose. It was simply a vicarious pleasure to satisfy a few in their bloodlust. They wouldn't accept that foxes were predators and do enormous damage to chickens, sheep, turkeys, and various other kinds of farm livestock. They favoured every other form of control other than hunting such as live trapping, shooting and snares; when I pointed out that these three are crueller than hunting there was uproar. Live trapping meant the poor animal waited for hours before someone came and ended up by shooting them. Anyone that can shoot a running live fox dead is a superb shot and most ended up wounded and dying slowly. Snares were the worst of all merely throttling the poor animal to death over many hours.

Patrick Bateson, the Cambridge zoologist, was funded by the National Trust to do some work on deer hunting[111] in the south-west of the country. The Trust banned deer hunting following his report, which said that hunting with hounds caused deer to suffer

When the Trust banned hunting with hounds from its land in 1997 it switched to culling deer with guns. But the Friends of the National Trust (Font) said this method of control is actually less humane and did not accept Bateson's conclusion. One argument was that a hunt only kills one individual animal – the hounds or 'tufters', used for isolating a deer at the start of the chase, are made to pick out an old one, perhaps, or one that should not breed; moreover shooting often left deer with injuries which subsequently killed them. Deer shot in the face, their lower jaws hanging off and full of maggots, starving to death. "Hunting either kills the animal humanely, or it gets away."

Professor Bateson said in his report that hunted deer sometimes survived the chase, only to die later. "More than once I've seen an animal that was hunted one day happily mating the following morning ... Since the ban, poachers moved in, killing deer at night with dogs."

Font and the Countryside Alliance paid for a study[112] by Roger Harris of the Royal Veterinary College in Hertfordshire and Douglas Wise of the University of Cambridge, which said that hunted deer do not suffer excessively. In the deer studied by Harris and Wise's team, only around 0.5 per cent of muscle fibres were damaged — less than the wear and tear suffered by some human athletes. "There was no evidence of extensive muscle damage," says Harris. Bateson accepts there is no clear evidence

111   Bateson, P. & Bradshaw, E.L. (1997) *Proc. R. Soc. Lond.* B **264**: 1–8.
112   Spedding, C. (2000) *Animal Welfare*. Earthscan; Harris, R.C., Helliwell, T.R. and others (1999) *Joint Universities study on deer hunting*. R&W Publications, Newmarket; Wise, D.R. (1999) *The Bateson report: Use or abuse of science?* Countryside Alliance, London; Wise, D.R. (2000) *Second stage submission to the Committee of Inquiry into hunting with dogs*. Home Office, London.

of the muscle damage he predicted. "I have to be more open-minded," he says. When research scientists delve into areas where humans and animals interact they must bear the consequences of their work, and a responsibility to insure no harm comes because of their work.

While the debate continues my view is that animals need to be respected and treated humanely however humans eventually use them; tying live chickens by the neck to a shopping bag to keep them fresh in hot countries,

The Rt. Hon. Tony Blair MP.
10 Downing Street,
LONDON.

11th February 1998

Dear Prime Minister,

We, the undersigned, write to you with reference to the Wild mammals (Hunting with Dogs) Bill.

The debate between those who are concerned about the welfare of wild animals and those who wish to protect hunting with hounds and other country sports has been intense. We believe that it is possible to find a solution to this problem.

Even though the arguments have become polarised, we believe that the majority of people are concerned with both the character of the British countryside and its biodiversity, as well as the humane treatment of animals.

We ask that, before any further action is taken, we could meet with a representative or representatives of Government to discuss ways in which it might proceed on this matter.

We have sent a copy of this and the enclosed letter to the Home Secretary and the Minister without Portfolio, though we have not sent it to any of the other Secretaries of State.

We should stress that none of the signatories rides with, nor is a member of, a hunt. Furthermore the views we express are personal, and do not necessarily reflect those of the organisations or bodies with which we are associated.

Yours faithfully,

Professor Patrick Bateson FRS
(Professor of Animal Behaviour University of Cambridge)

Professor David Bellamy
(Environmental Broadcaster)

Dr. Janet Kear OBE
(Conservationist)

Mark Miller Mundy
(Organiser of the Countryside Marches 1997)

Christopher Mead
(Author and Ornithologist)

Professor Christopher Perrins FRS
(Dir. Edward Grey Institute , University of Oxford)

Julian Pettifer
(Environmental Broadcaster)

Professor Ian Swingland
(Professor of Conservation Biology, The Durrell Institute, University of Kent)

John Wilson
(Angling journalist and TV Broadcaster)

or tying live crabs to a string on the end of a stick for kids to annoy their parents in Las Ramblas, Barcelona or the shooting of masses of tiny migrating birds in southern Iberia, has to stop.

A former respected director of DICE Professor Nigel Leader-Williams, who I wanted to join us when I came across him in the Luangwa Valley in Zambia working on rhino, published some work together with Professor Bob Smith, the current DICE Director, showing that land managed for hunting had greater biodiversity[113].

Robin Hanbury-Tenison wanted to retire from the Alliance and so we cast about for someone who could fill his shoes. At the time I was on the Council of the Zoological Society of London and Richard Burge was the Director General, a new post that hadn't quite embedded itself into the administrative culture of the Society. I believed that he could perhaps lead the Alliance and after introducing him to Robin suggested that John Jackson, the then chairman of the Alliance and the solicitors Mishcon de Reya, and Alliance president Baroness Ann Mallalieu QC should see him. They saw him at the House of Lords and after his appointment Richard asked me to be the Chief Policy Advisor, Countryside Alliance, 1999–2002 advising on all aspects of the countryside especially research for publications in peer-reviewed journals.

We started a Rural Regeneration Unit to capitalise on new ideas from our R&D enabling the RRU to support the economy, society and culture; endeavour to source and facilitate external funds; provide insights into future strategies; advise on technical capacity, and especially support the Food Co-operative programme developed by the RRU. This was originally somewhat separate from the Alliance and headquartered in converted stables in Staffordshire.

It was subsequently completely separated from the Alliance and run by a close friend Danny Dempsey from Cumbria who used to work for the Alliance. The RRU became established in Wales as the Welsh Food Co-operative and over the years it won:

- World Health Organisation Counteracting Obesity Award Winner
- Carnegie 'Rural Sparks' Award for Wales
- Public Health Wales Good Practice Award 2012
- Horticulture Wales Environmental Excellence Award 2013

and the statistics are:

---

113 Leader-Williams, N. (2009) Conservation and hunting: friends or foes? In *Recreational Hunting, Conservation and Rural Livelihoods: science and practice.* Dickson, B., Hutton, J.M. & Adams, W.M. (eds) pp. 9–24. Oxford: Blackwells.

No. of co-ops now promoting and marketing their own co-op	98 (90% of the 108 engaged)
No. of co-ops now offering Additional Welsh Produce	85 (79% of the 108 engaged)
No. of co-ops now offering different bag types and sizes	97 (89% of the 108 engaged)
No. of co-ops now communicating directly with their supplier	108 (100% of 108 co-ops engaged)
Total no. of customers	36,434
Total spend on fruit & veg	£147,562.05
Total spend on Additional Welsh Produce, e.g. eggs, milk, yoghurts, meat, honey, preserves, bakery items, etc.	£19,987.95
Total no. of bags	46,728
No. of co-ops achieved Sustainability	81 (75% of the 108 co-ops engaged)

The Welsh Assembly insisted on wholly subsidising the Co-operative which I was not happy with as it made us vulnerable to the budgetary fortunes of the Assembly whereas if we had charged a minuscule sum per bag we could have kept going and been self sustaining. As I feared, in 2016 the Assembly couldn't afford us anymore.

All of this came out of us observing large ladies with many children in the forbidding council estates found in the Cumbrian countryside; tough and resilient women who were used to taking matters in hand and dealing with whatever was needed. If asked how they cooked potatoes the response was, "Oh, I send the boy down the chippy". Looking at the countryside where many fields that had not been cropped of the carrots, brassicas, potatoes, and other useful food items I asked a farmer what his reaction would be if we had people to pick the vegetables and he would receive a small sum in return. For him, devoid of such a workforce and having received his subsidy from the EU Common Agricultural Policy (CAP), it was a further windfall. When we asked women whether they would be prepared to pick crops if we showed them how to cook it, help them lose weight, and share in the work of bagging a mixture of vegetables to hand out to the local community for free the answer was a resounding 'yes!'. They were keen on the idea, happy to be weighed and delighted for a few hours labour each week to get a free bag of vegetables.

I took a sample bag of vegetables, which always contained more than what was grown just locally, to the manager of my local Sainsbury who said he would charge me £35 for it. It all worked very well. I was at Clarence

House when HRH the Prince of Wales received a gold medal from the RSPB. As he passed by knowing me full well he asked how things were going and I mentioned that in his own principality, Wales, there was this successful food co-operative. Amazed at such news, since he had no idea, he immediately turned to his Deputy Private Secretary so that he could offer some support towards its future.

While still working with the Countryside Alliance a march was organised in central London called 'Liberty and Livelihoods' in September 2002, which attracted 400,000 people that descended in chartered trains and buses. I can only recollect that on one side of me was Vinnie Jones and on the other Edward Fox, and the police lining Whitehall shoulder to shoulder in front of all the buildings gave us a standing ovation. The Labour government at the time was not only deaf but couldn't count and disputed the number of people that attended the March but we had digital counters mounted in the access points to Parliament Square where we gathered. The shout went up: "Listen to us." And of course they didn't. The Hunting Act still received Royal assent in 2004.

I also tried to help The Santay Project in Guayaquil, Ecuador 2000–2002. Fundación Malecon was essentially an urban regeneration project and I was trying to oversee all the biological, ecological and environmental aspects of the Santay Project which involved turning the island in the middle of the Guayas River into a wildlife park of indigenous species so the urban population could experience what lived in their country especially Galápagos. The objectives were: (i) biodiversity conservation and improved forest management; (ii) improved institutional capacity to manage Santay Island itself; (iii) reduced the poverty level of the 2–3 million people living in the impact zone bordering the Island through expanding economic opportunities, improved social infrastructure, improved organisation for resource-users, and facilitating stakeholder participation in resource management; and (iv) adopted a supportive set of policies, especially regarding charging economic prices for access to Santay Island resources. Today Fundación Malecon has achieved the regeneration along the banks of the River but Santay Island remains untouched.

When I was 11 years old my father had taken me on occasion on some of his trips on behalf of the Ministry of Defence – HMS Ark Royal in Malta, Benbecula in North Uist to look at some radar mast, and the Royal Aircraft Establishment at the annual Farnborough International Airshow. On one occasion he took me to a very large 'field 'in Cumbria, Broughton Moor, where there were lots of little buildings nestled in a mosaic of substantial earth bunds surrounding each one. He explained to me that this was in case of an explosion. There was also a tiny railway and many other buildings in this extraordinary sight which I couldn't really at that age guess what it was for.

In 2004 Allerdale Council planned to buy the 1,050 acre former military depot known as 'the Dump'- the largest brown field site in the Europe – from the Ministry of Defence. It had to secure around £26 million from the North West Development Agency to fund the massive clean-up programme. West Lakes Renaissance (WLR), a consultancy company, would then oversee the development of the site on behalf of Allerdale. Renamed 'Derwent Forest', the site was to be turned into a massive forest park with 30 kilometres of paths and cycle ways, a visitor centre and a wind farm. Further exciting developments encompassing Olympic training, life style facilities, food co-operatives, local well-sourced produce for sale, specialised hotels/study accommodation, spas, restaurants, biodiversity conservation, sports and exercise facilities, alternative technologies and medicine, healthy living and eating, exercise methods which fit in with the individuals, better agriculture, cleaner food, better products, more inexpensive way of constructing buildings for business and living, which need less energy and use local materials, were all being consider for the future. By 2008 the North West Development Agency had not supported the objective, Allerdale did not have the funds by itself, and a few hardy individuals like me and Mark Fryer, who was at the time the leader of the Council, continued to support the project. Work to regenerate the former Royal Naval Armaments Depot site at Broughton Moor was announced in 2020.

CHAPTER 12

Business, politics and money 1999–2009

Sustainable Forestry Management Ltd

On Robin's and my return to London in 1999 after making a film for Channel 4 Productions about Mulu, 20 years after the RGS expedition, we became involved in establishing Sustainable Forestry Management Ltd (SFM) which operated as an ethical investor in sub-tropical and tropical forests. He was involved as an expert on local communities, tribes and ethnic groups, and me as an authority on biodiversity, conservation and international projects. Both of us had become convinced that a private sector approach to the conservation of forests and support of local communities dependent on those forests is a useful additional approach.

This opportunity arose out of the market for carbon dioxide and other greenhouse gases which had emerged since the Rio Earth Summit in 1992 where I helped draft the Convention on Biological Diversity (CBD), known informally as the Biodiversity Convention, a multilateral treaty, especially the paragraphs concerned with sharing of benefits with local communities of any commercially successful outcomes derived from their area and knowledge. SFM's business was to address these issues on an integrated, sustainable and ethical basis using the ability of trees to sequester (consume) carbon dioxide from the atmosphere efficiently. SFM built a global portfolio of forest-based enterprises with the help of commercial, financial, 'not-for-profit' and multilateral partners including leading participants in forestry. SFM's principal revenues were to be derived from supplying and trading carbon dioxide emission credits and offsets in the carbon market and from the harvest of environmentally certified timber.

Early in our ten-year life Henry Paulson of Goldman Sachs showed an interest in acquiring us and we was very excited about the prospect but it all came to nothing.

I advised on matters concerning the international scientific debate about forest and biodiversity conservation, carbon and climate change, science policy, standards, draft agreements and discussions in UN Framework Convention on Climate Change (UNFCCC), and elsewhere. I resigned from the SFM Board in late 2006 and acted as the Chief Scientific officer until the critical UNFCCC COP13 meeting 2007 in Bali.

My concern at SFM's inception was that forests were capable of earning their own living multiple ways if we adopted a more holistic approach instead of focusing exclusively on carbon. We could improved the standard of living of local people and conserve their forests using, amongst other approaches, ecosystem services (benefits provided by ecosystems that contribute to making human life both possible and worth living which can be monetised for the benefit of habitat conservation and local communities standard of living) and ecotourism. The narrow base of just carbon seemed to me to limit the strings in our bow and make us vulnerable.

I saw that as a result of The Marrakesh Accords in 2001, which created the rules for the Kyoto Protocol, forestry was largely excluded from the conventional carbon trading platforms (Kyoto and the EU Emissions Trading Scheme) and so only voluntary carbon credits were possible which are of far less worth than certified and compliant carbon credits accredited to Kyoto.

What was needed was to get avoided deforestation accepted in the conventional carbon trading platforms such that the carbon credits were certified and compliant with Kyoto. I was solely preoccupied with science policy and persuading countries to allow avoided deforestation's inclusion in the carbon trading platforms of Kyoto and ETS (EU Emissions Trading System). Avoided deforestation is the process of maintaining an existing primary forest untouched, in other words to conserve it. Avoided deforestation is part of what is now termed Reduced Emissions from Deforestation and Degradation (REDD+) since 2008 and adopted by COP21 Paris December 2015.

Since I believe that economic sustainability is the precursor to environmental sustainability, and in establishing DICE it had to earn his own living first and foremost and not be subsidised, we wanted to ensure that SFM would demonstrate that modest returns can be generated by investment in conserving the world's tropical and subtropical forests. It is now widely accepted that emissions of carbon dioxide resulting from human activity are a major cause of global warming. It is also accepted that given population growth and demand for energy the world will continue to rely on fossil fuels, a principal source of greenhouse gases alongside forest fires and vehicle exhausts, for the foreseeable future as they are cheap and available. Forests absorb ('sequester') and store carbon dioxide efficiently and provide the low-cost opportunity for carbon dioxide offsets for industrial enterprises, even a climax (mature) forest still absorbs carbon. Renewable energy sources are much preferred environmentally but will never create enough energy to meet demand without nuclear power.

This now provides the opportunity to restore some of the damage which widespread deforestation has caused over many decades as well as helping to mitigate global warming. Industrial exploitation of tropical and subtropical rural areas has often increased poverty in the developing world with about 1.6 billion people – more than 25% of the world's population – relying on forest resources for their livelihoods and global forest resources continuing to diminish at an alarming rate.

The destruction of old growth forests, watershed loss and desertification have damaged or destroyed the habitat of many of the world's most endangered species and vulnerable people. SFM's business was to address these issues on an integrated, sustainable and ethical basis. SFM was building a global portfolio of forest-based enterprises with the help of commercial, financial, not-for-profit and multilateral partners.

It worked very well and attracted serious investment and global advisers since in our view the best way to address the destruction of forests particularly old-growth forests was to supplant the income from timber that the logging companies wanted with an annual income from keeping the trees upright. As HRH the Prince of Wales said in 2007[114]: "Credits are available for afforestation and reforestation projects, but not for maintaining an old growth forest. And the European Trading Scheme excludes carbon credits for forestry in developing nations altogether… surely we have to accept that the pressing urgency of climate change requires a response that embraces rather than excludes primary tropical forests?"

The pivotal flaw in the company's policy was the exclusion of forestry by international regulation through the UNFCCC caused by NGOs, particularly three so-called conservation charities based in the UK. We therefore set about redressing this stupidity in every way possible by briefing our investors, attending all the international conferences and Conference of Parties (COP) to argue the rational and logical case for forestry being included, and hired significant voices such as Stu Eizenstat, a lawyer of ambassadorial rank, who was the principal negotiator for United States that created Kyoto.

We gathered together world leaders in business, financial markets, conservation, emerging market investment, science and human rights. Its officers and directors had over 200 years of relevant business experience and global networks of relationships. Its advisors were at the top of their professions.

I produced three books on the question of carbon, biodiversity, communities and income subsequently turned into a book for Earthscan. This was suggested by Lord May of Oxford, former UK Chief Scientist and President of the Royal Society:

1. Swingland, I.R. et al. (2002) *Carbon, Biodiversity, Conservation and Income: An analysis of a free market approach to land-use change and forestry in developing and developed countries.* London: Philosophical Transactions Royal Society London A: Mathematical, Physical & Engineering Sciences.

---

114   https://www.bbc.co.uk/news/uk-41901175

2. Swingland, I.R. (2003) *Capturing Carbon and Conserving Biodiversity: the market approach.* London: Earthscan.

3. Swingland, I.R. (2004) CO_2 *e biodiversita'. Un approccio integrato a favore del clima e del patrimonio naturale.* Edizioni Ambiente, Milano, Italy pp. 296.

International efforts

I and others worked to make significant changes in attitudes and understanding of the use of carbon in conserving old forests. With my New Zealand connections I helped induce a change in the law with the help of the Māori so that whoever owned the trees owned the carbon, and not just the Government, thus incentivising forest conservation – the Permanent Forest Sink Initiative (PFSI) is one of the government's sustainable forestry programmes established in 2006. It enables landowners to receive carbon units through the creation of permanent forests.

In October and November 2007 I was invited to Uganda where MPs were recalled early by the President to hear my presentation about forest conservation. Two old forests that President Yoweri Kaguta Museveni intended to convert into sugar plantations to repay a major election supporter I could demonstrate were worth more per annum in carbon payments. The newspapers next day said the President had reversed his decision.

> Dear Prof. Swingland,
>
> It was very enriching and motivating to have had a chance to meet you and listen to your presentations on both occasions when you visited Uganda to talk to the MPs. You made a huge impression on the MPs and the Water Ministers in Jinja. Your approach on the Science behind climate change and the threat that climate change presents was as if you are the AL GORE. The way you gave the current scientific information and correlated it to the chopping of trees was well received by all of us. Prof., I would like to keep contact with you to help our committee and my country on the way forward on afforestation, carbon trade and sustainable energy mechanisms.
>
> I am sure you attended the Bali UN conference [viz. COP13] on climate change. I was supposed to be on the Ugandan delegation but information on my accreditation came to me very late and parliament could not make arrangements in the one day that we were given. Was Bali a success? What did you achieve? I do wish you a happy and fruitful year 2007.
>
> Best regards,
>
> Kigyagi Arimpa John (MP)
>
> Deputy Chairperson, Natural Resources Committee, Parliament of Uganda

In Indonesia I organised a DICE Workshop with the British Government and British Council on 'Sustainable management and conservation' in Dumoga Bone, Sulawesi in April 1994. Most of the Cabinet and the Chief

Nobel Peace Prize to be announced today

OSLO

Former US vice president Al Gore and Canadian Inuit Sheila Watt-Cloutier, both champions of the fight against climate change, are tipped as favourites for the Nobel Peace Prize to be announced today.

A total of 181 individuals or organisations are known to have been nominated, and the Nobel committee may choose to put this year's spotlight on global warming, seen as a major threat to all of humanity.

This year's Nobel science prizes for medicine, physics and chemistry all went to discoveries that have practical applications in our everyday lives, and while each prize is selected by an independent award committee the trend could be repeated with a peace prize to those trying to save the planet.

But the five-member Norwegian Nobel Committee was tight-lipped.

"We've made our decision and it will be announced on Friday," the secretary of the committee, told AFP, refusing to say more.

Observers have thus resorted to the guessing game.

The head of the International Peace Research Institute of Oslo, Stein Toennesson, said he thought Gore and Watt-Cloutier had a good chance of taking the honours.

"This year when the cli-mate issue is at the centre of attention, the Nobel committee could choose to add its part to the awareness campaign by giving the prize to Al Gore and Sheila Watt-Cloutier," he told AFP.

Gore, now 59 and who served as Bill Clinton's vice president, has brought global warming to the top of the international agenda with his 2006 film "An Inconvenient Truth," which received an Oscar for best documentary.

Less known to the public is Watt-Cloutier, 53, also a die-hard defender of the planet.

The former head of the Inuit Circumpolar Conference, she has championed the rights of the Arctic peoples, whose way of life is dependent on the ice and cold and which is now threatened by temperatures that are rising faster than anywhere else on Earth.

A peace prize for the duo would come just weeks before the December 3-14 UN conference in Bali, aimed at finding a roadmap for the next set of emissions reductions under the Kyoto Protocol, Toennesson pointed out.

However, predictions on possible winners are pure speculation: the Nobel committee keeps the nominees' identities secret for 50 years, though those entitled to nominate candidates are allowed to reveal their choice.

AFP

THE REPUBLIC OF UGANDA

PARLIAMENT OF UGANDA

TO: ALL MEMBERS OF PARLIAMENT

INVITATION TO THE SCREENING OF AL GORE'S DOCUMENTARY - THE INCONVENIENT TRUTH

In light of the current climatic changes in Uganda, the British High Commission in conjunction with the Parliament's National Resources Committee invites all Members of Parliament for the Oscar Award winning Environmental Documentary dubbed **"The Inconvenient Truth"** to be presented by Professor Ian Swingland, an eminent authority on climate change and sustainable development from the United Kingdom.

The film will be screened at **Theatre La Bonita** (next to Emirates Offices, opposite Christ the King) on **Tuesday 16th October, 2007 at 10:00 a.m.**

Entrance is Free

Ruth Ekirapa Byoona
For: Clerk to Parliament

British Council Director, British Ambassador Roger Carrick, myself, interpreter and President Suharto in the Istana Negara Palace in Jakarta 1994 launching the DICE workshop

Scientist attended along with 100s of others. It was opened by President Suharto in the Istana Negara Palace in Jakarta.

It changed Indonesia's perception and inculcated them with a desire to make forests pay without chopping them down. This early event gave me an entrée with Indonesia that proved invaluable over ten years later. The UNFCCC Conference of Parties (COP) 13 in 2007 was to be held in Malaysia but at the last moment found itself unable to act as hosts and Indonesian stepped into the role. The Government of Indonesia was intensively engaged with me as they had taken over hosting COP13 at such short notice and wanted a significant 'win' which would put them in a good light in regard of forest conservation having had rather poor publicity in the past. This led to my intensive work during 2006–2007 leading up to the conference in Bali (December 2007) where I briefed Indonesian Ministers, the Cabinet, civil servants, institutions and NGOs (and many international individuals and bodies) culminating in the acceptance of avoided deforestation into the carbon trading systems and now adopted at COP21 Paris which has reinforced this as one significant solution

Many Governments, especially those of developing countries, are against the private sector directly investing in forest conservation using carbon as the tradable asset rather than the funds going through them. Rather similar to the three UK conservation charities which influenced the outcome of the Marrakesh Accords (the Kyoto rules) excluding forests from the carbon trading platforms for a range of dreamt-up technical difficulties and indeed the reaction of Government ministers over Iwokrama fulfilling its mission to be self-proficient (business to business) without aid!

In a UN decision-making meeting only government representatives and those not-for-profit organisations are permitted, the private sector being banned. The Kyoto protocol is a business instrument and without the private sector being involved it inevitably led to a flawed and perverse agreement in the Marrakech Accords (the Kyoto rules).

When challenged the conservation charities responsible for excluding forestry simply claimed that their objection to forests being included was that they wanted the private sector investment to come through them and not directly to forest conservation. Public sector investment in forest conservation, which in reality in tropical countries is mainly via international aid, was unlikely as rich countries which provide nearly all the aid were at their limit of about $150bn pa. Tropical Governments expect foreign aid to do most of the work[115] and that leaves only the private sector for the huge sums needed for forests. Of course politicians especially in the European Union want to plan and decide and control what the price of carbon

---

115 http://www.oecd.org/newsroom/development-aid-stable-in-2017-with-more-sent-to-poorest-countries.htm

should be instead of allowing the free market to set the price, a further flaw in a workable and effective system, which led to the price being far too low and not giving enough financial pain to polluters to change their ways.

Today

Now let's see what has actually happened since that breakthrough at the end of 2007, eight years later in 2015[116]. Article 6 of the Paris Agreement creates a new carbon trading mechanism. It manages to do so without mentioning the words 'carbon' or 'trading' or 'markets'. Instead these words are replaced by the term 'voluntary cooperation'. Carbon offsets are "internationally transferred mitigation outcomes". And the new carbon trading mechanism is a "mechanism to contribute to the mitigation of greenhouse gas emissions and support sustainable development" (with the catchy abbreviation MCMGGESSD).

Shortly before COP21 started Brazil issued Decree 8576/2015, establishing a REDD+ National Commission. The Decree confirmed Brazil's position that Brazil will not sell its REDD+ credits internationally. But this isn't because Brazil is opposed to carbon trading. Brazil wants to keep its REDD+ credits to offset its own emissions from its expanding oil industry[117]. On 8 December 2015, Brazil and the EU put forward a proposal on carbon markets. In a press release, the EU announced that: *the EU and Brazil have agreed and submitted a ground breaking proposal on rules to govern use of the international carbon market at the UN climate talks in Paris. The joint proposal demonstrates a willingness to engage in common and robust rules on accounting for all parties.*

The final rules of the new carbon trading mechanism have not yet been agreed. It will only start in 2020 at the earliest. That means years of negotiating a new carbon market mechanism to conserve forests under UNFCCC management are still a mess. If the carbon trading mechanism kicks off, countries generating REDD+ credits will have two options:

1. Keep the REDD+ credits to offset their own emissions from fossil fuels.
2. Sell the REDD+ credits to countries that will use them to offset their emissions from fossil fuels.

In the absence of the cap-and-trade system invented by Richard Sandor[118], and not allowing markets to set the price of carbon instead of Governments, neither of these options will reduce global greenhouse gas emissions. In both cases the reduction in emissions from forests would be offset against continued emissions from fossil fuels whereas we wanted the cost

---

116 https://redd-monitor.org/2015/12/15/cop21-paris-redd-and-carbon-markets/
117 https://redd-monitor.org/2015/12/15/cop21-paris-redd-and-carbon-markets/
118 https://en.wikipedia.org/wiki/Emissions_trading#European_Union

of pollution to increase through time. Rich countries could finance REDD+ if it creates a loophole allowing them to continue burning fossil fuels. But it is difficult to see why they would want to finance REDD+ if they want to clean up the atmosphere as it creates a loophole allowing forested countries to continue using fossil fuels. At the start of COP21, Norway's Prime Minister, Erna Solberg, announced that Norway wants to include REDD+ in carbon markets, so that in future Norway can claim to be 'carbon neutral'.

I helped to write a submission to the House of Commons UK Parliament –DEFRA Climate Change post-2012 [Environment, Food and Rural Affairs Committee] EAFRC Parliament 8 January 2007 and attending the Environmental Audit Select Committee on Voluntary Carbon Market, Committee Room 6, House of Commons 6 March 2007 during the Voluntary Carbon Offset Market Inquiry made a difference[119]. I gave oral evidence to this committee (Hansard 6th March 2007[120]).

On 16th February 2009 I was called when I was staying with Nigel and Shane Winser in Oxford. I was told that apparently the corporate investors in SFM had become concerned at the way things were managed. By the middle of 2009 SFM was in liquidation but at least we had shown the world what was possible since we had projects across the world which were working.

For me and Robin Hanbury-Tenison it was an exciting and sometimes satisfying decade but neither of us gained a penny from our significant investment. It was very hard work for me using rational and scientific argument against the vested interests of individuals, NGOs, ignoramuses, Governments and corruption across the globe to try and have a system that benefits everybody especially the conservation of the environment. Over the 10 years I learnt a lot about business with some of the top businessmen in the world and the luxurious manner in which meetings were conducted in some of the most remarkable venues such as the Savoy hotel, a château, a South African wildlife reserve, Jersey, and taking an enormous team to the all-important COP13 all-expenses-paid.

Earthwatch

Nigel Winser, you will recollect, effectively ran the Mulu expedition 30 years before and was now the director of Earthwatch Europe in Oxford. I was on the board of Earthwatch for 10 years until 2009 but I was able to help my old friend and extremely competent manager and networker

---

119 https://publications.parliament.uk/pa/cm200607/cmselect/cmenvaud/331/7030602.htm

120 https://publications.parliament.uk/pa/cm200607/cmselect/cmenvaud/331/7030603.htm

with a very positive disposition and outlook on the world. Born in Kenya he had enormous experience having been deputy director of the Royal Geographical Society (RGS) in Kensington masterminding expeditions in Kenya and Oman. Shane, Nigel's wife, Mulu expeditioner and RGS head of expeditions and fieldwork, was also working in the RGS underpinning the whole ethos of expeditions and exploration.

When Robert Barrington retired from the directorship of Earthwatch Europe to take up a similar position in Transparency International we had to find a new director. Nigel was well positioned, and I was confident he would be appointed, but things went wrong when I missed the key Board meeting because I was attending another Board meeting in Tenerife of the Loro Parque Foundation, a charity that conserves parrots. I even called the Earthwatch Europe chair from the Canaries and he assured me that Nigel would be appointed.

An interregnum director was appointed instead which the Board then decided to let go a year or so later but did not have the experience to do it. As a favour to Herschel Post, the chair, even though I was not involved in the appointment, I asked Gilbert Holbourn of Saffery Champness to help

Earthwatch Boston Birthday 2005. Back row: Gareth Price (Finance Director), Nigel Winser, Rick Bodmer (DICE Peru). Front row: Merril Magowan (US trustee), me, Clare Marl (Head Press & PR), Herschel Post

and they offered their head of HR *pro bono*, who held the Board's hand in managing the incumbent's departure, as I had helped to pass a lot of other business to Saffery Champness in the past.

On the second attempt, with some arm-twisting from me, Nigel was appointed and had an extremely successful time running this wonderful organisation. Earthwatch Europe had intelligence, initiative and ideas which grated in Boston USA, the headquarters of the organisation, that preferred to stick to the original model of just retail seats on three-week trips to assist scientific investigators.

In the end we brought peace across the pond with a number of fatalities but at least the survivors were happy. Whit Johnson even explained to a joint meeting of both Boards in Boston: "I wish we had an Ian Swingland here in the States." Flattery is flummery but I am sure well meant. Brian Rosborough who founded Earthwatch, had met with me, Nigel and many others at the RGS many years before, echoed this sentiment while I reminded him that we did try and establish Earthwatch in England but the charitable rules were difficult although sufficient to establish Earthwatch UK as a charitable extension of Earthwatch US. In the UK, volunteers had to covenant to support UK projects for four years, and then petition to get the tax on their contributions back! This is not necessary today.

In September 2008 I bid during a fund-raising auction in support of Earthwatch having agreed with Nigel Winser, Earthwatch Director in Oxford, to do it through a surrogate individual since I was a long way away on my mobile as usual. I won the item which was a trip for Fiona and me to join Nigel and Shane and visit the Earthwatch Samburu Station at Wamba in Kenya run by Dr Nick Oguge and the Il Ngwesi Eco-Lodge close to the Lewa Wildlife Conservancy 3–10 March 2009. We had the time of our lives in great company enjoying the hospitality of the Il Ngwesi and travelled north to the Samburu where Nigel and I were made Elders after I had opened an earth dam that would supply them with year-round clean water. The filtration system made from naturally occurring sands and gravel was designed by Earthwatch to prevent perpetual diarrhoea as most other short- lived sources of water were polluted by wildlife and livestock faeces.

Ochen Mayiani had something wrong with his eye so I sent detailed pictures back to Julian D. Stevens, Consultant Ophthalmic Surgeon at Moorfields Eye Hospital in the hope that either he or Bill Aylward (Director) could help as between them they had saved my eyesight when I went blind four times from 2008 – 2010. Unfortunately they came to the conclusion that the eye was too damaged to save. James Kinyaga, an Il Ngwesi Elder, was a supreme host and gave me, on all his people's behalf, a Maasai spear designed to kill black-maned lions using one's bare hands. Clearly it would be useful in Kent given the article that was published some years later (below)!

One morning Nigel took me for breakfast with Ian Craig, the driving force behind Lewa Wildlife Conservancy. Over the scrambled eggs Nigel let slip that I was the Founder of DICE at which point Ian fell to his knees and kissed my hand, and the scrambled eggs went flying. Somewhat surprised at this response from such an icon of African conservation, he admitted that any graduate from DICE he would hire immediately especially if they were Kenyan and likely to stay.

Iwokrama

The Iwokrama International Centre for Rain Forest Conservation and Development, Guyana was set up to promote the conservation and the sustainable and equitable use of tropical rain forests in a manner that will lead to lasting ecological, economic and social benefits to the people of Guyana and to the world in general, by undertaking research, training, and the development and dissemination of technologies. It was under the patronage of HRH the Prince of Wales, and I was appointed by the Secretary General of the Commonwealth and the President of Guyana to be Chairman of the International Board, the largest biodiversity project belonging to the Commonwealth.

Even though for thousands of years the Rupununi, who lived around the forest, had used it sustainably so that it was still fully intact, the purpose of President Hoyt giving it to the Commonwealth in 1989 was that it should prove a forest could earn its own living but over the years the organisation had merely survived on international aid. I immediately instituted a review of what actions were being taken to achieve its founding objective. The International Board instituted a plan to move it towards self-sufficiency but this faced a number of obstacles not least all governments in developing countries welcome international aid into their Finance Department or Treasury but are less happy with business to business arrangements, which bypasses their hands.

The Guyanese Ministers were uncomfortable with all this but were quickly assuaged when international donor agencies saw our determination to become self-sufficient, fulfilling our original promise; the donors overcame their financial exhaustion and started rekindling their interest in aid funding. Nine months after appointment I had turned it from certain bankruptcy to an increasing prospect of self-sufficiency, and had appointed able people who understood the nature of business with the help of Chris Mathias, a friend. What was more important, for some reason no Rupununi were on the Board so I got one appointed (Sydney Allicock) and I lined up a Guyanese to eventually become the Chief Executive Officer

DICE leads Professor Ian Swingland's mission to save planet

Kent Online. Wednesday, April 18 2012

To many people, dice are numbered cubes in games of chance.

To leaders in the critical business of conservation around the world, the Durrell Institute of Conservation and Ecology (DICE) is one of the University of Kent's greatest achievements. Yet it is barely known in the county of its birth.

Charismatic Professor Ian Swingland, whose list of credits in Who's Who and on his CV almost dwarfs War and Peace, founded it in 1989.

But the plain-speaking professor – whose outspoken views have sometimes brought him into conflict with administrators, but admiration from Prince Charles and the rest of the world – insists: "It's the best thing we've got but they don't blow their trumpet about it.

"DICE is something the university could do more about and capitalise on.

"Biodiversity is the biggest business in the world and DICE could be promoted more widely."

When creating DICE, he invited Gerald Durrell – author, naturalist and founder of Jersey Zoological Park – to give it his name and a generous donation.

He founded it for postgraduates. "I chose people from across the world that were doing the job, and staff with extensive field experience to train young people to run the world taught by those that had."

There are 36 applicants for each DICE place. It has 20 staff and 70 students. Swingland also set up the world's first "Green" MBA at Kent Business School.

From Swingland's Kent home near Wingham, full of treasured mementoes from his travels, he has journeyed to far-flung places with the aim of saving as much of the planet as he can.

A passion for Africa since living in Kafue National Park, Zambia, led to his support for tribes in Northern Kenya.

He is worried, but not depressed, by the loss of rain forests threatening habitats, the harassment of native tribes pushed into ever smaller areas, "a form of passive genocide", human poverty and repression.

"I don't get depressed about the future of the world, I'm an unassailable optimist," he says. "Everywhere we are losing species, even here in Kent. Eventually, we'll destroy everything or stop trading in something because frankly we cannot find it any more."

He is committed to rural regeneration, food co-ops and local sourcing and is working on all three across Kent in co-operation with Kent University and Hadlow College.

Prince Charles has commended him for his excellent work including Operation Wallacea, the largest expeditionary organisation for young people; the Rural Regeneration Unit, a successful food co-op, The Durrell Trust for Conservation Biology, DICE, the Amphibian and Reptile Conservation Trust and an international journal *Biodiversity and Conservation*.

As for climate change, it has "always happened." But it means that Kent could soon be growing oranges, peaches and apricots. "The biggest single factor in global warming is burning down forests," he says.

Supporting James Kinyaga and Ochen Mayiani of the Il Ngwesi Maasai people and Nasham Nkainito dam opening to supply year-round clean water for the Samburu. March 2009

(Dane Gobin). Although I paid one visit to Iwokrama my recollections of my involvement were pleasant interactions with the people of the country but also a considerable organisational mess on my arrival which needed to be sorted out.

HRH the Prince of Wales wrote to me a very kind letter from Birkhall 22nd January 2004 expressing his enormous gratitude for bringing my characteristic dynamism and imagination to a very worthwhile project. He expressed his great pleasure for the way in which I tackled the situation with determination at a time when he knew I had some agonisingly difficult family challenges to face.

In helping to draft parts of the Convention on Biological Diversity in 1990 where local communities would share the benefits of any natural resources, and their knowledge of their uses, should these assets become profitable, I was foreseeing the tale of Conrad Gorinsky of Guyanese origin who patented the key chemical[121] extracted from the seeds of the greenheart tree that are used as a reliable contraceptive by Amerindian communities. In 1968 he travelled on a BBC-funded expedition in the Amazon with Robin Hanbury-Tenison[122]. In 1999, during an international seminar on rights over biodiversity, Wapichana leader Clovis Ambrosio expressed his irritation at the news that US patents for plants grown in Wapichana lands straddling the Brazil–Guyana border had been registered in the name of Gorinsky:

> My people, the Wapichana, live in the Brazilian grasslands and in Guyana. With our common knowledge of the vegetation…. we use a plant named cunani for fishing. We also produce medicines extracted from a tree known as tibiru, or greenheart…. Many of our kinsmen don't even imagine what our knowledge can

121   Posey, D.A. & Balick, M.J. (2006) *Human Impacts on Amazonia: The Role of Traditional Ecological Knowledge in Conservation and Development*. Columbia University Press, 366pp.

122   Hanbury-Tenison, R. (1991) *Worlds Apart: An Explorer's Life*. Arrow Books. p82.

represent to the [Western] industry. That is why chemist Conrad Gorinsk[y], the son of a Wapichana woman and a German man ... researched the cunani and the tibiru while promising to help our communities with medicines, He never did.... Mr Conrad Gorinsk[y] has patented the cunaniol and the rupununi in the United States, Europe, and Great Britain. He has contacted multinationals for the exploitation of his 'discoveries'. (Wapichana1999:42)[123]

123 Vidal, J. (Wednesday 15 November 2000) Patenting life, Biopirates who seek the great-

THE IWOKRAMA
RAIN FOREST

GUYANA, SOUTH AMERICA

Two indigenous substances were also patented in Europe: cunani (*Clybadium sylvestre*) was patented in 1998, a potent neurotoxin, used to disorient and catch fish which Gorinsky patented as cunaniol for the treatment of heart disease; tibiru (*Octotea rodiaei*), also called tipir or greenheart, was patented in 1994 used by the local people to stop bleeding, a contraceptive and as an abortifacient, and given the name Rupununine, after Rupununi, the Wapichana homeland in Guyana. The National Indian Agency (FUNAI) tried, apparently without success, to guarantee compensation for, or the cancellation of, a patent registered in Great Britain to the chemist Conrad Gorinsky for the substance extracted from the seeds of the tibiru tree. "Tough, isn't it?" he said. "I was not the only person looking at the greenheart. I just picked up a nut and said 'what can I do with this?' I have analysed the chemical structure but I have not patented the tree or a life process. How can I tell the Wapishana about the science? They just

est prizes. *The Guardian.*

inherited the greenheart. They don't own it. I have invested in this with my own money".

Conrad Gorinsky belongs to one of the powerful families that for more than a century have occupied indigenous lands, primarily for cattle ranching, on both sides of the international border. Although the son of a Wapichana woman, Gorinsky is not recognised either in Brazil or in Guyana as a member of the Wapichana group because ethnic recognition is based on social rather than on genetic criteria. The Wapichana are angered that his family holds large portions of land at their expense[124] let alone his hijacking their home-made remedies using plants.

There are many examples of country residents of European stock, whose families have been resident for many years, pinching the indigenous people's knowledge of the uses of flora and fauna especially for pharmaceutical purposes acquired over thousands of years. According to the book by Mbaria & Ogada 'The Big Conservation Lie', Jonathan Leakey was licensed by the Kenya Wildlife Service's Convention for International Trade in Endangered Species (CITES) office to export *Prunus* bark in the early 1990s when his brother, Richard, was the director[125]. *Prunus africana* is a slow-growing indigenous tree species whose healing properties are said to have been discovered in South Africa about 400 years ago. Scientific research has established that pygeum powder, which is extracted from the bark of the tree, provides relief from prostatic hyperplasia, swelling of the prostate gland, and prevents the development of prostate cancer[126]. The trade in *Prunus* bark rose from 200 tons in 1980 to about 3500 tonnes, the vast majority going to the German market where Leakey was the main supplier to the pharmaceutical company Bayer, and what is called the African Cherry is now on the verge of extinction.

Unfortunately challenging the status quo by demanding that local people's ancestral lands and knowledge of natural resources, and the resources themselves, be returned to them can have dire consequences for those who try[127]. It is not only private individuals and governments but NGOs that often conspire together to disenfranchise local communities from their land, their resources and their knowledge for their own gain.

---

124 Posey, D.A. & Balick, M.J. (2006) *Human Impacts on Amazonia: The Role of Traditional Ecological Knowledge in Conservation and Development*. Columbia University Press, 366pp.

125 Mbaria, J. & Ogada, M. (2017) *The Big Conservation Lie*. Lens & Pens, USA.

126 Stewart, K.M. (2003) *Economic Botany* 57(4): 559–569. New York Botanical Garden Press, Bronx, NY 10458-5126, USA.

127 https://www.ogiek.org/news-5/news-post-08-02-912.htm

CHAPTER 13

Research in Action 1989–2012

Citizen Science

It has always seemed to me that science has to be connected to people and their communities otherwise it's irrelevant, *'What for?'* or just simply an indulgence by scientists for their own sakes. Even 'blue sky' research without apparent application at the time can ultimately lead to it being used. 'Citizen Science' is a modern expression of this sentiment so I was quite happy to be the judge of the Pfizer Environmental Art Prize for Kent Schools and the Kent County Council, Industry in Kent Environment Award, help the Endangered Reptile Center, Canada and together with E.O. Wilson at Harvard be a Trustee of the Biodiversity Foundation for Africa in Zimbabwe[128]. I was also deeply involved in Earthwatch and helping establish Operation Wallacea and the Wallacea Trust for many years which have taken thousands of people to work on science projects worldwide.

I was more concerned with being involved in substantial projects that would leave a lasting legacy of better conservation of biodiversity and an improved standard of living for the communities in those areas. The Zimbabwe-based foundation had ongoing projects concerned with strengthening capacity and institutional ability to conserve biodiversity on the continent but as you can imagine it has faced significant difficulties.

In 2001 my son Kieran, having tried a number of state and private schools, went to Great Oaks Small School which had been started by friends whose son needed better schooling. It is a small independent (secondary) school that provides a unique education for students with a wide range of abilities. They provide a holistic education which ensures their students leave as well-rounded intellectual, moral, social, aesthetic and confident young people. They support students in gaining qualifications that are appropriate to their individual needs and aspirations. Kieran went on to various universities but ultimately to the Sir Edmund Hillary Outdoors Centre at Tongariro, New Zealand and then to a UK facility.

I have always believed that education at all levels is critical if the environment is to be saved. There is so much erroneous information and misconceptions which have arisen during my lifetime while passion and commitment for wild ideas, as well as those that are sane and informed, has increased. So I accepted an invitation from Mexico to help establish The International Institute for Environmental Management in Mexico City to train undergraduate students from the region in a four-year programme.

---

128   http://www.biodiversityfoundation.org/about.htm

Indonesia and Zambia

I don't think this Mexican initiative came to much in dire contrast to a DICE Workshop 1993 on 'Sustainable management and conservation' in Bogani Nani Wartabone National Park, Sulawesi, Indonesia which was hosted by the British Council, DICE, and the Wallacea Institute. It was organised by Richard Phillips of the British Council in 1993. While in Indonesia this time I assisted in the establishment of The Wallacea Development Institute (WDI), Jakarta set up by Ibnu Sutowo, an exceptional man of many talents, to marry biodiversity conservation with private sector support. The DICE Workshop was housed in the luxurious research station built many years before for the Linnean Society and their work and refurbished by Ibnu Sutowo.

Ibnu and I became great friends as he was a man who had been through many trials and tribulations, and we found common cause in the use of the private sector in biodiversity conservation to the point that he established the Wallacea Institute in Jakarta which led to the formation of Operation Wallacea and the Wallacea Trust in the UK today. The formal opening ceremony for the DICE Workshop was at the Jakarta Palace by the President of Indonesian Suharto attended by all the ambassadors, the Cabinet, and hundreds of other guests.

The American Ambassador approached me and challenged me: "How the hell did you manage to make this happen? Even we can't." The two-

President Suharto greets me at the formal Opening of the Workshop, Instana Negara, 1993

week workshop embraced professional biodiversity scientists, many Indonesian scientists and Ministers, students, NGOs, people from over 26 countries, even the Chief Scientist of the country flew to Sulawesi. The closing ceremony was attended by Sutowo, Emil Salim and many prominent people in politics and development.

The problems we highlighted involved effective conservation worldwide and who should do it: Governments, universities or NGOs? The question of biodiversity conservation paying for itself, rather than being subsidised by the State or a charity, was thought to be to be of most interest providing continuity as grants or donations or subsidies could always be stopped. The establishment of WDI by Ibnu would execute this approach.

I also drafted a bid for British Council to the Asian Development Bank for a technical assistance Project (TA 1782-INO). I was the biodiversity consultant on this project which was concerned with the 'Biodiversity Conservation and Commercialisation of Protected Areas in Indonesia'. It was on this project that I met Tahir Qadri an exceptional staff officer in ADB with an incisive intellect and great character who was respected everywhere. He became a friend and we worked together on projects in Bangladesh and his son Khurram trained at DICE.

The core of this large technical assistance (TA) was the commercialisation of biodiversity assets. The project concentrated on the institutional, policy, management, organisational, legal, socio-economic, manpower, training, and GIS/IT techniques of using the biodiversity in protected areas for sustainable local development. We recommended commercialisation options for minor extractive products, research and information generating activities, and ecotourism. There needed to be performance indicators and case studies of amongst others, biochemical prospecting in the region, community biodiversity projects, and GATT 94, which aimed to promote international trade by reducing or eliminating trade barriers such as tariffs or quotas and ultimately led to the establishment of the World Trade Organization (WTO), and its impact on Indonesian biodiversity. We also outlined management systems and other developments.

I had asked Dr David Waugh to accompany me on this DICE Workshop as he had established the International Training Centre at Jersey Zoo and had become a lifelong friend after the numerous Summer Schools there and creating a joint Diploma in Endangered Species Management between DICE and the Jersey Wildlife Preservation Trust (JWPT). Gerry Durrell called it the 'desman', a diving insectivore mammal that he fell in love while on his expedition to Russia.

I was invited to advise on the management of the Kasanka National Park, Zambia just prior to becoming one of the first privatised Parks in Africa in 1994 but within the national Park estate of the Republic. David

Lloyd who owned the land on which Peter Moss had created the Cardigan Wildlife Park with my help had retired to Kasanka. I suggested we train local people and provided training at DICE for the Paramount Chief of the area.

Chief Chitambo IV (Freddie) came to DICE for several months and was a tremendous source of information as to how he governed his people and how they shared the benefits of what their region could provide. He was the great great grandson of the chieftain who had looked after the explorer David Livingstone in the final months of his life. Freddie used to do the rounds of his 30,000 strong rural communities in Kafinda, Zambia on a push bike. In particular, he was interested in the benefits from this privatised Park as everything flowed through him to his people. I can remember clearly he was obsessed by getting a maize grinder so he could produce mealie meal or nshima the basic carbohydrate in the Zambian diet (resembling mashed potatoes when cooked) and the logistical difficulties of how to get him to the airport when his suitcases had multiplied from one to 11!

Murder

One day in summer 1996 I was encouraging Shaun Russell to finish his PhD at Rhodes University so we could cement his future in DICE and that evening I was phoned by Shaun asking if I had heard from his wife Lin.

"No, I haven't Shaun, what's the matter?"

"I just got home from shopping and she's not here with the kids. They should all be home easily by now as Lin collects them from the local primary school nearby."

"Is anything I can do to help? Perhaps they've gone to an after-school event or something."

"No I'll look around and talk to neighbours to see if they know anything."

Later that night Kent police came to my house and not a week went passed for the next two years without them coming round or communicating to advance their investigation. Shaun Russell's wife Lin, their youngest daughter Megan, their dog Lucy and Josie her eldest daughter had all been savagely attacked that night, tied up and beaten to death, except Josie who just survived and together with her dad Sean was spirited away to King's College Hospital, London which had medical expertise to deal with her horrific injuries and to ensure that both she and Sean were safe.

It was one of the most traumatic things that I have ever experienced because Sean and his family were building a life and career in Kent with my Institute, and were one of the most joyful and lovely families I've known. This multiple murder became famous since no motive could be discerned that would have driven anybody in their right mind to have done such a thing.

Sean appeared on television to make a plea to the general public for anything that might help the police in their enquiries. He was so calm and clear, unlike the usual sobbing ranting of the bereaved in such circumstances, it was heroic. But there was clear evidence that at the time it occurred Sean was shopping for food and other supplies in Canterbury shops clearly recorded by CCTV. The police became suspicious of a number of people in DICE or wanted corroboration about this or that from me.

But the problem that I was left with by the police was their suspicion that somebody in DICE might be the culprit. Just by chance I was at a dinner and found myself sitting next to the Chief Constable of Kent and the conversation was inevitably about this tragedy. He mentioned that there was some drug addict who might have done it but the police had no direct evidence of him being at the scene. Nevertheless he was found guilty but won two Appeals against his conviction which reconfirmed his guilt. More recently another inmate has challenged the first inmate's evidence casting doubt on Michael Stone's imprisonment again[129].

Lin had not written a will and was unmarried to Shaun, putting all their savings in Lin's name, to save money when they came back to the UK. By dying intestate it meant that all their money would be inherited by her surviving issue, Josie. It also meant that Shaun was nearly bankrupt. I was desperately trying to think what we could do to help Sean and Josie. It was clear he could not remain in Kent, which would forever be associated with trauma and death. We therefore offered him a year's salary *pro bono* and I suggested to him that he should return perhaps to North Wales where they may get some peace and quiet. He was already minded to do this once Josie was out of hospital. Although she would need further surgery to replace the dent in her head it seemed an excellent plan.

Conversations with Lynda Lee Potter of the *Daily Mail* kept the story alive for years afterwards, and some income flowing, and Sarah Harman, sister of Harriet Harman, the Labour leader, and a Canterbury solicitor, was enormous support acting for the Russell's *pro bono*. Today Josie[130] with the help of her dad has been able to buy the original family home[131] in North Wales with her father close-by having secured a permanent position with the University of Bangor then membership of the Government Darwin Initiative expert committee following me (the very programme that got Shaun into DICE in the first place when we won one of the first grants 1992) and now the director of the Treborth Botanic Garden.

---

129   https://en.wikipedia.org/wiki/Michael_Stone_(criminal)
130   Russell, S. (2000) *Josie's Journey*. BBC Books, 223pp.
131   https://www.mirror.co.uk/tv/tv-news/josie-russell-shares-engagement-happiness-13231350

International chairs – Florence, MMU, Michigan, Auckland

To keep my hand in higher education elsewhere I accepted a Visiting Professorship of Conservation at the Dipartimento di Biologia Animale e Genetica, Florence University. Here I lectured and developed a European MSc concept in Biodiversity Management by course units or credits which would bring the Italian Laurea structure more into synchrony with the European wide system of bachelors (new Laurea 180 ECTS credits), master (new Laurea Magistrale 120 ECTS credits) and doctorate degrees (Dottorato di ricerca). I worked closely with Francesco Dessi Fulgheri and his wife Laura Beani and attended the Florence Postgraduate School of Vertebrate Behavioural Ecology Pistoia May 1987 as well as Florence Evolution & Ecology of Social Behaviour Conference Florence 19–24 March 1988 which was attended by the luminaries of evolutionary ecology and changed perceptions surrounding the subject forever.

Working with them and their colleagues especially Alberto Simonetta, a cultured polymath who taught me a lot about Florence with whom I stayed on one trip, was a wonderful experience and showed me how Italians blend work and leisure with an elegance, and seamless transition which the British have yet to learn. Not unlike the Norwegians who achieve the same mix even though it's colder. Both Francesco and Laura join me on a trip I led to Galápagos with another Italian academic Massimo Pandolfi, Urbino University. An unforgettable experience and one that I have cherished ever since.

The Department in Florence was next door to the Pitti Palace, a Renaissance building which was the home of the Medici with the Boboli Gardens behind us. Lorenzo the Magnificent on 26 April 1478 was with his brother and co-ruler Giuliano in the Cathedral of Santa Maria del Fiore (a magnificent but ugly black and white marble edifice just a few yards from the Pitti) when they were attacked in an attempt to seize control of the Florentine government. Giuliano was killed, brutally stabbed to death, but Lorenzo escaped with only a wound to the shoulder. I was told that the plotters were hunted down over six months on the instruction of Lorenzo through his Secretary, related to my confidante Alberto Simonetta, and had all who were involved in the conspiracy lynched from the battlements of the Palazzo della Signoria. Leonardo da Vinci was patronised by Lorenzo and in 1479 drew one of the 80 conspirators, Bernardo Bandini dei Baroncelli, hanging from the Palace. There was an old drawing of four bodies hanging from battlements in mediaeval costume in my room and I always wondered if it was by Leonardo da Vinci since my room was very old, very remote and almost forgotten?

I also agreed to be a Visiting Professor and the External Examiner for the MSc in Conservation Biology, Manchester Metropolitan University,

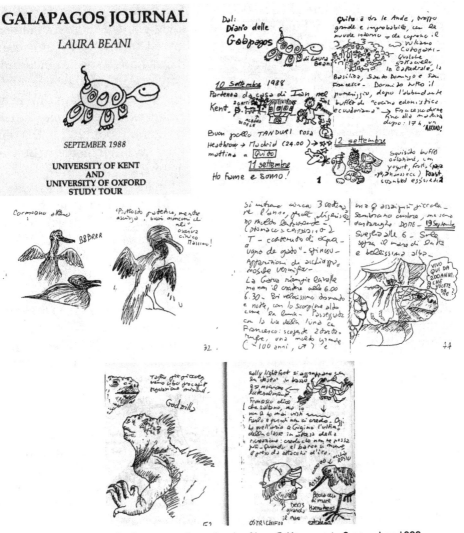

Laura Beani made this personal notebook of her *Galápagos* trip September 1988

and the External Examiner for the MSc in Biodiversity and Conservation, University of Leeds: alongside my pre-existing appointments at Michigan.

I worked with John Craig, Professor of Environmental Management, and founder of the School of Environmental and Marine Sciences (SEMS) for four years where I was Visiting Professor of Conservation Biology and Auckland Foundation Fellow. This was part of the established British Council LINK programme to develop new techniques to improve cost effectiveness and success in biodiversity conservation programmes worldwide, with especial relevance to Far East/Southeast Asia.

He retired from the School to live in Northland with his wife Anne

Stewart, where he established a 300 hectare family farm, with farm stay accommodation, a honey business and horses. He planted more indigenous tree species to supplement the old native forest on the farm and refurbished the wetlands. He has reintroduced many native species including kiwi. John had spent 36 years at The University of Auckland beginning in the Department of Zoology before moving to become the inaugural head of the School of Environmental and Marine Sciences (SEMS) at the Tāmaki campus and dealing with the same kind of university politics I had to endure. With the School's merger with geography and then geology he was appointed Professor of Environmental Management.

John is widely recognised and respected for his work in conservation and was instrumental in establishing Tiritiri Matangi Island in the Hauraki Gulf as an open conservation sanctuary. Originally this island was completely denuded vegetation and native wildlife as a sheep farm. Today it is alive with native species of plants and trees and wildlife and boarded walkways which attract thousands of people, all created by hundreds of local people and volunteers. The government Department of Conservation (DOC) claims the honours of making this happen but when asked for some takahē, like overgrown moorhens, they sent two males but were more cooperative over many other species including the tuatara, a species looking like a lizard, which the Māori consider to be a special treasure. John himself is respected by the Māori and is a master woodcarver.

He has received many international awards for his work in conservation including the New Zealand Order of Merit (ONZM) which Denis Saunders, former Assistant Chief of CSIRO's Division of Wildlife and Ecology, and I conspired to have him awarded. Denis himself has the Order of Australia (AM) and with his wife Vee set up the Sara Halvedene Foundation. He was president of WWF Australia. They had lunch with me May 13th 2013 at the Athenaeum to celebrate John's award 4 months later, never having met before.

John's research focus is in the area of sustainable management. He currently works as a consultant and stays an active researcher in the fields of conservation management, industry attitudes to sustainability, and urban ecosystem management although, like me, he started by working on the ecology of species. In his case this included: pukeko, takahē (*Porphyrio mantelli*), North Island saddleback (*Philesturnus carunculatus rufusater*), brushtail possums (*Trichosurus vulpecula*), kiwi (*Apteryx australis*), bell miners (*Manorina melanophrys*) and kākāpo (*Strigops habroptilus*).

Darwin Initiative

I joined the Darwin Expert Committee, a UK Government initiative announced at the Earth Summit in 1992 by Prime Minister John Major. He vowed to spend £100 million to conserve biodiversity much to the chagrin of attendees like President Bush Snr who disliked the Convention on Biological Diversity (CBD) agreed at the summit as he felt it would create unemployment in the United States. He spent five hours at the Congress. I contributed to John Major's speech and had suggested that perhaps his initiative could be called after an Englishman, the Darwin Initiative. Nothing was said over the extended timetable of this vast expenditure which alleviated civil servants concerned at the money being dispensed in one wallop! I was appointed by the Secretary of State for Environment, Food and Rural Affairs in 2000 and I am the longest serving member eventually retiring in 2009. The Darwin Initiative assists countries that are rich in biodiversity but poor in financial resources to meet their objectives under one or more of the three major biodiversity conventions: the Convention on Biological Diversity (CBD); the Convention on International Trade in Endangered Species of Wild Flora and Fauna (CITES); and the Convention on the Conservation of Migratory Species of Wild Animals (CMS), through the funding of collaborative projects which draw on UK biodiversity expertise.

It became clear that while DICE was graduating Masters alumni from many countries and were returning quite often to their wildlife conserva-

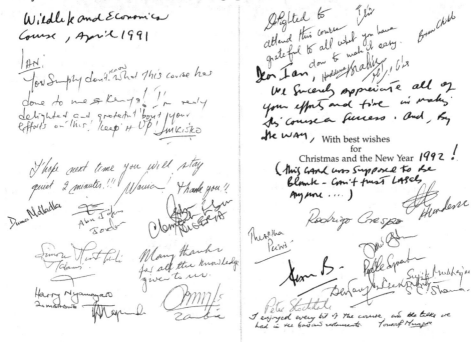

One of DICE's Summer Schools for senior staff in overseas wildlife departments from which many postgraduate students came on temporary leave for the DICE MSc spending their research time back home on a relevant area to their employer. Wildlife and Economics April 1991

DICE alumni at the Society for Conservation Biology international meeting 2002 at the University of Kent. The Society chose DICE for its first meeting outside the States and awarded David Attenborough a prize which I took to his house in London. Richard Griffiths is 2nd from left front row and I'm middle of the back row with Claudio Ciofi to my left. Claudio is an Associate Professor, Department of Biology, University of Florence

tion departments in their own country only to face prejudice from their own director who hadn't perhaps enjoyed the education that their returning staff member had been privileged to receive. So we introduced a two-week Summer School for directors and executives of such conservation departments and ministries. This was funded by British Council and other sources and it had a remarkable effect not only on our students experience post-graduation but on our recruitment to our Masters courses and indeed PhD programs. Of course I called on my huge network of contacts to come and talk to the participants as I did in the student courses and everyone seemed to get something out of it.

I instituted an annual three-week programme for all the senior people in conservation from the many countries from which we recruited students. It seemed to me obvious that we should make certain that our graduates on returning to their posts would be looked on favourably since their bosses had also had a taste of what we could do.

In July 2002 the Society of Conservation Biology held its 16th Annual Meeting in Canterbury the first ever meeting of SCB to be held in Europe. This internationally diverse meeting attracted 1050 delegates from 74 countries, around the meeting theme of 'People and Conservation'.

The End?

All this and the multiplicity of responsibilities, ideas, money, interpersonal friction and the exhilaration of creating something worthwhile like DICE that would help the world, and help young people's careers, began to take its toll and in the summer of 1999 I visited my GP who told me to my horror I was on three weeks' medical leave immediately and that I would never return to the University.

This consolidated two lifelong habits; that all my GPs are women and I have to take multiple pills every day to keep going. It also meant having to have periodic scans for the last 20 years when things seem to be going wrong.

The shock of being told that I could not carry on as a member of staff and baby-mind my Institute at the University of Kent was profound not because of my prophesised death, with which I had little concern, but being devoid of anything constructive to engage my energies and brain. I had to do something else to keep my mind usefully occupied.

I was devastated. My God the world went quiet and I was both distraught and devoid of purpose. I would go mad.

One of the routes forward was to offer environmental advice. I consulted the family solicitor Peter Gottschalk. His advice was that consultancy carries a liability and by offering my services through a limited company, I would be protected. I therefore chose the name Herons Hall Ltd and always operated using this company as a means of limiting my professional liability.

What saved me was serendipitous and my good friend Robin Hanbury-Tenison. We had been together in the Royal Geographical Society's expedition in Mulu Sarawak 1977 to 1978 when he was leading the expedition with another good friend Nigel Winser, and I helped him with the Countryside Alliance. Robin invited me to return in 1999, some 20 years later, to see the forest, the Penan people, and make a film for television, 'The Lost World of the Penan'. He would go in his guise as co-founder of *Survival International* concerned with tribes and their treatment, and as the expedition leader, and I would follow behind as one of the original scientists. We had quite a few expeditions in the weeks that we were there and the film was well received and I think won a prize. Since then we have both tried to help the Penan people who were treated somewhat prejudicially.

Saving forests and forest people using the destroyer's greed

During this documentary I urged Robin at the end of the film down the path of 'dancing with the devil', the environmental and community destroyers, and 'not carrying placards', railing against some perfidious outrage or appalling acts against tribal peoples; convincing those in charge by argument, and by using their avarice, to change their minds and not have a demonstration outside their offices. Rather like Ō goshi (hip throw) in judo, where one uses the energy of the opponent to defeat them, this approach took root when we returned to the UK soon afterwards in establishing Sustainable Forestry Management Ltd.

Even mature rainforest absorbs carbon dioxide and since it's one of the five gases that have increased in concentration over my lifetime (e.g. CO_2 has gone up nearly 23% – Global Mean CO_2 1946 310.3ppm, 2019 400.9ppm), it made sense to use the new trading activity of carbon as a conservation tool to supplant the annual income from timber with annual income from carbon; in other words commercialising biodiversity assets for their conservation and for improving the standard of living of those communities reliant on those assets. Carbon might even be the currency used in ecosystem trading.

The flaw was in the absence of land rights so prevalent in those tribes and communities that have occupied areas for thousands of years without bothering about legal ownership and which national politicians have benefitted from – and the shenanigans of the international community involved in establishing the rules of the Kyoto Protocol in the Marrakesh Accords.

The Kyoto Protocol is an international treaty which extends the 1992 United Nations Framework Convention on Climate Change (UNFCCC) that commits State Parties to reduce greenhouse gas emissions, based on the scientific consensus that (a) global warming is occurring and (b) it is extremely likely that human-made CO_2 is the principal culprit. The Marrakesh Accords is a set of agreements reached at the 7th Conference of the Parties (COP7) to the United Nations Framework Convention on Climate Change, held in 2001, on the rules of meeting the targets set out in the Kyoto Protocol.

For more than a quarter of a century, I have debated with a friend of considerable intellect the question of global warming, whether it's happening at all and the extent to which the scientific community have falsified the picture. He's a flat-earther but can mobilise quite powerful arguments.

While I remain ambivalent about much of the information, some of it fraudulent data from respected institutions, there is no doubt that there are perturbations in the climate which we have not experienced during our lifetimes or indeed for many hundreds of years before.

Over millions of years the earth warms up and cools down. We are currently going through a period of warming up. Because of global industrialisation we have spewed vast quantities of pollutants into the atmosphere and some have now formed a blanket around the world, a duvet, which is affecting our climate and magnifying the natural cycle. It is not only factories that have caused this but exhaust fumes from vehicles and also forest fires all of which make a significant contribution.

Approaching many capital cities that I have flown into, particularly in the tropical sub-continent and China, you can see a thick brown layer, thousands of feet thick, hovering over the entire area choking the people who cause it. Photochemical smog's effects cause damage to the respiratory system and environmental systems with the release of nitrogen oxide (NO), ozone and volatile organic compounds (VOCs). These effects are worse when the sun is highest because the pollutants react with it. According to a recent study in Nature, led by Johannes Lelieveld[132], director of the Max Planck Institute for chemistry in Germany, more people now die from air pollution than malaria and HIV combined. They include 1.4 million people a year in China and 650,000 in India. This compares with about 180,000 a year in Europe. Smog also occurs in cold weather and nearly killed me in London in 1952 with bronchopneumonia caused by coal burning, the main heating fuel.

---

132   Lelieveld, J., Evans, J.S., Fnais, M., Giannadaki, D. & Pozzer, A. (2015) The contribution of outdoor air pollution sources to premature mortality on a global scale. *Nature* **525:** 367–371.

CHAPTER 14
International Consultant

Australia

One of the first consultancy projects that I was involved in concerned kangaroos in Queensland 1989. I was appointed one of the International Scientific Authorities on the Queensland Kangaroo Management Programme supported by Greenpeace and the Commonwealth of Australia. The principal issue was grazing competition between various species of Kangaroo and livestock. The farmers wanted to maintain a massive cull so there they could have better beef production per square mile. As principal consultant on the Queensland Kangaroo Management Programme I was asked to provide a Proof of Evidence as to whether the proposed management plan for the State of Queensland, based on a mathematical model using sex ratios, culling returns, and population predictions as indicators would sustainably manage five species of kangaroos that were felt to be in competition with grazing domestic stock. There were numerous flaws in the proposed programme as it was largely based on shooters' returns and at a specific point a large-scale cull would be precipitated. A previous Premier Johannes Bjelke-Petersen was notorious for his disregard of the environment and for proposing oil drilling in the Great Barrier Reef and sand mining on Moreton Island, rather like President Trump. The latter to extract titanium for Dulux super white paint owned by ICI.

I worked with the late Graeme Caughley on this problem with which he was familiar; a much respected ecologist who was mathematically very astute. Graeme had worked in Zambia when I was there and was a New Zealand population ecologist, conservation biologist, and researcher. He combined empirical research with mathematical models, and spent most of his working life in Australia. It was a tragedy that he died at the age of 56 since in my view and others he was one of the best wildlife population ecologists.

However it was better that a foreigner acted as the scientific consultant not least because of the strength of feelings around the subject. As the Judicial Tribunal got closer and closer I learnt that the other consultant scientists or experts were becoming either unavailable or dead! I was briefed that I would need to go to Brisbane but various bodies were concerned for my safety and I would have to have bodyguards.

The day got closer and closer until we received a message from the then Premier of Queensland Mike Ahern: "Don't send Swingland." My Proof of Evidence precipitated a withdrawal of the proposed model before the Judicial Tribunal and a new management plan was instituted.

Southern African Wildlife College

John Hanks, with the support of WWF South Africa, and the main funding from The German Development Bank (KTW), asked me to be a curriculum adviser for his new Southern African Wildlife College in 1996 that he was building near the Kruger National Park's Orpen Gate in Limpopo Province. I flew to Phalaborwa airport with Christian Barnard sitting beside me. I noticed his very arthritic hands and had no idea who he was until I noticed the deference with which he was greeted when we landed. Then it dawned on me that he was the famous heart surgeon who had carried out the first whole heart transplant. When I arrived at the accommodation I found I was living in a tree house with Malcolm Coe, my friend from Oxford, but it was an interesting and stimulating time creating and devising a curriculum to train Protected Area Managers. Assessing the needs of the continent and the increasing value of its best renewable resource, wildlife, which needed conservation but was a challenge since daily we seemed to be losing the war if not every battle. The only other wildlife training colleges in Africa are the College of African Wildlife Management commonly known as Mweka College established in Tanzania in 1964, and the Garoua Wildlife College created in Cameroon in 1970 to provide in-service wildlife training for Francophone government agencies in sub-Saharan Africa. Since its inception, Garoua College has trained over 1,300 students from 24 different countries.

Peru

Soon afterwards I led a team from DICE in Peru in April 1996 on a two-week mission organised by the British Council with funding from the British Embassy to advise and implement a collaborative research, training and commercial programmes between DICE and the Peruvian Government, Agencies and Industry in business in the environment, sustainable tourism, biodiversity conservation, protected area management, and the establishment of an EcoFund for equity investment in companies with good environmental potential or performance. We planned workshops, development projects, postgraduate scholarships, professional in-service training facilities, and the EcoFund. This followed the visit to Peru in 1995 of the UK Secretary of State for the Environment, by the Rt Hon. John Gummer MP (now Lord Deben) which I accompanied.

Peru stunned me. A multicultural country with dry plains along the coast, the Andes down the centre and to the east beyond the Andes lies the Amazon basin. The sophisticated Inca culture, its organisation and architecture along with superb environmental engineering, subsequently dominated by the Spanish conquistadors, has delivered a rich tapestry of extraordinary accomplishment.

Like Zambia, whose main language is English with their numerous tribes and languages, Peruvian's principal tongue is Spanish with many indigenous languages such as Quechua which are all decreasing mainly because they are spoken not written languages. The indigenous or ethnic groups called Amerindians constitute around 26% of the total population. The Quechuas and the Aymaras form a large proportion of the indigenous population who live in the Andean highlands and still speak Quechua or Aymara, and have vibrant cultural traditions, some of which were part of the Inca Empire. Dozens of indigenous cultures are also dispersed throughout the country beyond the Andes Mountains in the Amazon basin. This region is rapidly becoming urbanised. Important urban centres include Iquitos, Nauta, Puerto Maldonado, Pucallpa and Yurimaguas. The mestizos comprise about 60% of the total population and are of Amerindian and European descent. European descendants constitute around 6% of the total population. They are descendants of the Spanish colonisers.

Many roadside snacks are available in Peru as in so many other tropical countries and one of the favourites are roasted guinea pigs on sticks like a lollipop or *cuy* (pron. 'kwee', onomatopoeic sound derived from the guinea pigs call when hungry); once I recovered from the teeth sticking out at one end, and the stick up the anus in the other, the taste was somewhere between turkey and pork. A painting of the Last Supper hanging in Cusco Cathedral which shows Jesus and his 12 disciples feasting on a Cuy! Some 65 million of these small animals are consumed each year in Peru.

Another roadside delight is chewing betel nut, a social activity, akin to having a cup of coffee, wrapped in coca leaves which alleviates altitude sickness. Alejandro Camino, the well-known anthropologist who joined us throughout our trip, gave me this to keep in my cheek or under my tongue to ward off acute mountain sickness which affects more than 50 percent of people who ascend higher than 8,000 feet (2,400 meters) in a relatively short time span. It's caused by the lower levels of oxygen in the air at high elevations; your lungs can't take in as much oxygen as they're used to and your heart and lungs have to work harder to keep your blood oxygenated.

As a bronchitic, until I was 16 years old, reared amidst the lethal London smog, this combination of a plant leaf and nut alleviated the effects of altitude which made me feel dizzy, tired with a mild headache and stopped me sleeping while the coca leaf alone can suppresses hunger, thirst, pain, and fatigue. It's a pity it's illegal in the UK. Sure, it stains your teeth, and when you spit it out on the footpath it leaves a big red mark, like a blood stain, but betel nut/coca leaf chewing is a popular pastime on the streets of

Peru. It is said to get rid of parasites. I first saw vicuna, the flighty member of the camel family, when high up in the Andes from some distance. In my woozy state I was not entirely certain but others were sure.

The Chasqui, Inca messengers who ran throughout the empire to deliver messages, chewed coca leaves for extra energy. Atahualpa[133], the last Inca emperor, established his capital at Cusco where he would send Inca runners for sea fish for breakfast and although many miles away a relay of Chasqui would deliver them to his table. They also carried secret messages lightly tattooed on their scalps. There is a strong suggestion that a counter-current heat exchanger[134] is evident in the descendants of the Chasqui. An arrangement of blood vessels, in which heat flows from warmer to cooler blood, usually reducing heat loss, enabling them to spend long periods in freezing conditions, standing on snow in bare feet, with more equanimity than us!

The Emperor was famously assassinated by the Spanish invaders who cared about nothing other than stealing all the gold they could find; indeed it is endlessly recounted that Atahualpa offered to fill an entire room of gold and silver once if they didn't kill him. They did. Soon afterwards Cusco Cathedral began construction in 1559 as a monument to the conquistadors' religion, Roman Catholicism, and is plastered in presumably Inca gold. Inca gold ornaments are the most exquisite I have ever seen and we were shown round a private bank, the Wiese Bank, by the owner which had a display of gold and precious stone jewellery as well as a gallery of pictures of all the presidents of Peru in order. There was one gap with no picture which would have been Allan Garcia 1985 – 1990 who destroyed the Peruvian economy and attempted to nationalise the banks!

The British Ambassador John Illman was our marvellous host who welcomed all of us with open arms although not his pet llama in the garden who spat, a way of expressing irritation or displeasure with other llamas. John, who was a very committed man and in love with Peru, introduced us to everyone significant in business and the environment, and showed us all around the country.

We visited many Inca sites and temples where their exquisite buildings made of very large stones fitted together with precision and ingenuity that couldn't be matched today. At one site I was shown the solution to a problem where a source of water was on one side of a hill and the Incas wanted it on the other. So they drilled a hole, with a circumference equivalent to a man's arm, from one side to the other with a slight inclination to ensure that it flowed without help! Today no-one had figured out how that was achieved. At another site I felt an enormous sense of energy and Shaun

133   Hemming, J. (1993) *The Conquest of the Incas*. London: Macmillan. ISBN 0333106830.
134   https://en.wikipedia.org/wiki/A._Roberto_Frisancho

Sacsayhuamán Cusco, Perú (courtesy *Diego Delso, delso.photo, License CC-BY-SA*)

confirmed that many lay lines met at the same spot.

The DICE Mission to Peru March/April 1996 included Shaun Russell, Stuart Harrop (who was about to leave the RSPCA and join DICE with a chair in Biodiverstity Law), Walter Wehrmeyer (research fellow in Business in the Environment), Harold Goodwin (ecotourism) and Ken King (a personal friend who was Managing Director and Chief Investment Officer of Rexiter, a State Street Global Alliance Company, based in London. He had worked for the Central Reserve Bank of Peru as an economic adviser (from 1967 to 1969). Chris Brown (British Council) was also tremendous in organising all the presentations and lectures we gave and I remember especially the one given by Ken King with an audience of financial experts and bankers who were blown away by Ken giving the whole thing in Spanish with a Peruvian accident!

We came to move forward with several areas of mutual interest to the country and to the Institute; business in the environment, cleaner technologies, tourism, conservation and sustainable development. We organised a subsequent 'Industry in the Environment' Workshop arranged by the British Council in Lima September 1996 involving Walter Wehrmeyer, one of the two major programmes being focused on tourism, conservation and sustainable development. The main programme was an aspect of the commercialisation of biodiversity assets, and a continuance of the ODA-funded project (1994–1997) at DICE under Harold Goodwin and me, extended to Peru. I got the funding for this DFID-funded project Tourism, Conservation and Sustainable Development Project led by Harold to examine tourism, environmental impact and sustainable management system in three sites with national collaborators in Indonesia, Zimbabwe, and India.

I was also able to be one of the first successful applicants for a Darwin Initiative funded project in DICE enabling us to review and established an IT database support for developing countries (Zimbabwe, Indonesia, Peru), established DICE training programmes and a Masters' course in Biodiversity Information, training postgraduates from the target countries, conducting training workshops *in situ* under Shaun Russell. (We could never find our hotel in Lima through the maze of unnamed streets, and taxi drivers were no more informed, so Shaun used to get us back with his GPS without which we would never find our beds!)

Cooperative agreements were reached between DICE and a large number of organisations and national institutions; SIL working on behalf of Peru's ethnic minority groups (Carlos Bolona), National Agrarian University La Molina –Centre for Conservation Data (Manuel Rios), CONAM National Council of the Environment (Paul Remy), PROFONANPE Peruvian Trust Fund for National Parks and Protected Areas (Alejandro Camino), MITINCI Minister of Foreign Trade and Tourism of Peru (Pablo Lopez de Romana) and British Council/British Embassy to organise and direct an Ecotourism Workshop mid-1997 involving a casebook-driven approach with developers/operators observing technical experts planning a sustainable tourism R&D programme on-site (i.e. where the Workshop takes place) which reinvests in conservation, assists local socio-economic investment, and national development.

Jorge Caillaux is a Peruvian lawyer, head of the Drokasa group of environmental lawyers, who work on biological diversity and access to genetic resources, trade and environment. Jorge in particular was perturbed at the theft of Peruvian biodiversity of commercial or medicinal value as I was when preparing the Biodiversity Convention for the 1992 Earth Summit. Our conversation concentrated on a vine called Cat's Claw commonly known as vilcacora derive from the Quechua for *Uncaria tomentosa*. Jorge was concerned that it was vulnerable to foreign exploitation for gain without benefits being shared either with the country, or with the Quechua people who, as is usual worldwide, knew something of its medicinal properties and gave the information away.

DICE identified the roles of some partners – DICE as the overall foreign partner, SIL as the business managers, CDC as the biodiversity managers, PROFONANPE as the suggested regional training centre funders, MITINCI as the Government participants, and lastly CONAM as the body to whom the policy output will be delivered but with opportunities for other partners to emerge. This grouping is called The Peru Ecotourism Forum. In preparation for this research and development programme, DICE also offered both SIL, CDC and CONAM, a Darwin Initiative MSc one-year scholarship in the business, biodiversity and policy aspects of ecotourism respectively; Jorge Chavez, Natalia Verand, Jose Salazar Barrantes and Alfredo Narvaez joined us.

Swaziland, and Apple and Pear Research Council

I helped develop the Swaziland National Biodiversity Strategy and Action Plan for UNDP and Swaziland Environment Agency (SEA) 1997–2001 and build on and reinforce existing national strategies and plans, such as the National Environment Plan, to allow the Kingdom to meet its obligations under the Convention on Biological Diversity (CBD) and the Conference of Parties (COP).

For the next three years I was the Advisor for the Swaziland Biodiversity Information Management System, a LINK programme funded by British Council. Swaziland has formally adhered to the Convention on Biological Diversity and other international protocols concerning biodiversity conservation and sustainable utilisation. Moreover DICE was already assisting the country in formulating the national plans and policy through a UNDP/Government of Swaziland (GOS) programme. This facility and link scheme was welcomed by the principals in Swaziland Environment Agency, Swaziland Biodiversity Strategic Action Plan (SBSAP), and the University of Swaziland (UNISWA) including the DFID Environment Advisor to GOS, and all relevant GOS Ministries and Departments as a step towards a powerful planning tool and human capacity building for national development which is totally compatible with the GOS standard for land use planning. UNISWA handled the data systems and SEA had the tool available for reference updated monthly by UNISWA-based National Biodiversity Data Unit that was created through this Scheme.

I returned for a further year to build on and reinforce existing national strategies and plans, such as the National Environment Plan, to allow the Kingdom to meet its obligations under the Convention on Biological Diversity (CBD) and the Conference of Parties (COP). Ara Monadjem of University of Swaziland became a particular pal and helped enormously with biodiversity information. Rod and Lungile de Vletter (World Bank) and his wife at Phophonyane Falls Lodge and Nature Reserve were also very friendly and supportive. Sinaye Mamba (museum), Ted and Liz Reilly (Big Game Parks) and Kim Roques (All Out Africa, social enterprise & eco-tourism) were helpful in trying to formulate the best approach. Ted, who owned Mkhaya Game Reserve which was established in 1979 to save the pure Nguni breed of cattle from extinction, had hyrax freely running through his house and was close to the King. There was a proposed Green

Chert mine[135] near Mgywayiza in the north of the Malalotja National Park which I visited on Sunday 14th September 1997 with Richard Boycott (Senior Warden, Malolotje Nature Reserve) and Robin Hoogwoert (Manager, Knight Piesold, Mbabane). The Taiwanese miners have still not proceeded.

It was fascinating to work in Swaziland not least because of the strenuous efforts made to conserve the flora and fauna by many people but also that it's one of the last remaining absolute monarchies. King Mswati III effectively rules every aspect of the country and his father Sobhuza II sat on the throne for 82 years and 254 days, the longest verifiable reign of any monarch in recorded history. The problem was the King would make a rule or law and behind-the-scenes his mother (the 'She Elephant' or Ndlovukati) would take issue with him and by the following day everything had changed.

King Mswati III. The annual Reed Dance 1997

I attended a reception for King Mswati who turned up late in traditional costume with his retinue of wives. I was briefed that he was the only son by Sobhuza who had no issue at the time of his father's death. There were three or five red feathers in the King's hair of the purple crested lourie which denoted his supremacy. The wives said very little and smiled. Some of them he chose had been taken by the King's men when he saw them at the annual reed dance or Umhlanga where unmarried and childless Swazi girls who are virgins parade themselves hoping to be chosen by the King.

I had to fly back from Swaziland to attend an interview at DEFRA to be Chairman of The Apple and Pear Research Council (APRC) 31 August 1997. I arrive at Heathrow not feeling particularly well and was taking penicillin prescribed in Swaziland. As I brush my teeth in a Heathrow hotel I noticed that I had spots all over my face undoubtedly from being overdosed with 600mg penicillin tabs in Swaziland where I was working developing the future biodiversity conservation plan with the government,

---

135 http://www.sntc.org.sz/discuss/eiacomments7.html

the University, and the private sector.

Anyway I jumped in a taxi and headed for the Department of Environment, Food and Rural Affairs but as I went past Kensington Palace there was a sea of flowers on the grass outside and the taxi driver explained that the Princess of Wales had been killed in Paris while I was flying. I was appointed part-time Chairman of the Apple and Pear Research Council (APRC) by the Department for Environment, Food and Rural Affairs (DEFRA) from 1997–2003 responsible for the management, development and direction of all near-market research concerning apple and pear growing and the industry. When I returned to the Swaziland I watched her funeral live on the colour television of my American friends Dale and Irma Allen in their garden studio where I was living.

APRC raised its funds by exercising a levy on the acreage of apples and pears grown by any farmer and invested it in near-market research to help the industry grow. I asked Robert Mitchell, a Kent top fruit farmer, to be vice-chairman and in the six years we did a lot of useful work including discovering a gene from an apple which could deal with dental caries, Dental Caries p1025 Project[136]. One species of bacteria called *Streptococcus mutans*, which is only found in humans, had been identified as the primary cause of dental caries. Dental caries remains a major public health problem, with the incidence as high as 45% in five year old children (1993 Children's Dental Health National Survey). In 1998, the cost of dental fillings alone to the NHS was approximately £210 million. *S. mutans* is not readily controlled through conventional oral hygiene techniques. Charles Kelly's group at Guy's Hospital had developed an approach to prevent infection by *S. mutans* involving an antimicrobial agent. In this approach, human trials with this peptide had shown that following a small dose, recolonisation by the bacteria is prevented for at least 3–4 months. Their aim was to genetically modify plants, specifically apples and strawberries, with a gene which codes for the production of this peptide. If successful, this would enable the delivery of the antimicrobial agent through consumption of the fresh fruit product or a derived product, such as a fruit juice or yoghurt.

I suggested to the head of a very large family-owned chain of supermarkets and Government minister that eating four apples with the gene a year would ward off caries or stop its progression which would help the many that couldn't afford a dentist. He had a fit, frightened that it would be seen at genetically modified (GM) and it would kill his huge business under the cynical anti-GM movement prevalent at the time. Before we could have the industry capitalise on this and other discoveries the independence of the

---

136   Delivery of antimicrobial agents in fruit to counter tooth decay. 1993. A research application to the APRC from Blakesley D., Massiah A. & James D.J. (Plant Breeding and Biotechnology, HRI-East Malling), Kelly C. Ma J. (Department of Immunology, United Medical and Dental Schools, Guy's Hospital, London).

APRC was challenged as the government wanted to cut costs and so we agreed to be absorbed into the Agriculture and Horticulture Development Board.

At that time there was a huge political pressure storm against genetically modified products. Headlines such as 'Frankenstein food' were all over the newspapers encouraged by the beneficiaries, organic organisations. Organic products became the new fashion pushed by the strap lines of being devoid of nasty chemicals and sprays. These products are more expensive but were even described as tasting better which is not true. The Soil Association started by Lady Eve Balfour was established to promote the maintenance of good practice in farming and not a chemical-soaked landscape with no biodiversity. So while I support the general objectives of minimising chemicals the organic movement still allows spraying with sodium, potassium and copper on top fruit and organic potatoes have a much higher bacterial count than those grown in the conventional fashion.

What we should be aiming for is CLEAN food however it is produced and genetic modification is just a modern technique of doing the same thing as we used to in crossbreeding and pollinating by hand. Of course, people get upset when they hear of luminescent jellyfish genes being put in something completely different but the benefits of genetic modification to feed the ever increasing world population on the same amount of land without destroying all remaining natural areas of biodiversity, and making sure the crops are resistant to pests and diseases eliminating the use of chemicals, is a no-brainer. I visited enormous greenhouses industrially creating new genetically modified crops in the Gobi desert as the Chinese are not reticent about trying new approaches to feed their enormous population unlike the British where the anti-GM nutters, pulling up experimental crops, have put British agriculture back 20 years and damaged our future. Of course companies like Monsanto have played cynical games with GM to maximise profits which have damaged developing country farmers and played into the hands of pressure groups. However Monsanto (now owned by Bayer) made a commitment in 1999 not to commercialise sterile seed technology in food crops in which seed produced by a crop will not grow.

Development Banks

Indonesia

When I was directing the 1993 DICE workshop in Sulawesi, the British Council, who were helping with arrangements, asked me whether I could draft a proposal to the Asian Development Bank for a project to do with biodiversity in Indonesia. This bid was successful and I acted as the Biodiversity Consultant, Biodiversity Conservation and Commercialisation of Protected Areas in Indonesia, Asian Development Bank (TA 1782-INO) 1993–1995.

The core of this large technical assistance was the commercialisation of biodiversity assets. Worldwide there are many products that can be extracted from the wild which can help local communities increase their standard of living. One example is the vegetable ivory or tagua nut which is the very hard white endosperm of the seeds of certain South American palm trees which can be carved into jewellery or other products mainly for the tourism industry. Other palm nuts are found in many parts of the world. The problem for the small rural communities living close to the raw product is getting it to the markets where they can get the best price. Those with transport whether boats or trucks or cars often demand excessive prices to get the finished products to market. If the community can work together the problem is often solved by acquiring their own means of accessing these more remunerative places. The project was established by me to help this process in Indonesia and we concentrated on the institutional, policy, management, organisational, legal, socio-economic, manpower, training, GIS/IT techniques of using the biodiversity in protected areas for sustainable local development. The recommendations generated included: commercialisation options for minor extractive products, research and information generating activities, and ecotourism. We also helped with management tools to gather performance indicators and case studies of, amongst others, drug prospecting in the region, community biodiversity projects, and GATT 94 (now the World Trade Organization) and its impact on Indonesian biodiversity.

Bangladesh – Sundarban and Gorai

After the biodiversity commercialisation project in Indonesia, which Tahir Qadri had overall responsibility for, he asked me to be a Staff Consultant on a project concerning Biodiversity Conservation in the Sundarban, Bangladesh in 1996 (Asian Development Bank (PPTA BANG/96-188). The Sundarban is the largest mangrove forest in the world in the coastal region of the Bay of Bengal and considered one of the natural wonders of the world. I formulated the paperwork and it was recognised in 1997 as a UNESCO World Heritage Site of Bangladesh although much controversy lay behind the application. The Bangladeshis thought that while there were some advantages to this recognition it would outlaw any use of natural resources within such sites, clearly underlining their existing activities which we could see from satellite images. However UNESCO World Heritage Site recognition will allow the use of natural resources providing a sustainable management plan is agreed with the participants, shareholders and the office responsible. It is the world's largest delta.

Our mission was to set the terms of reference for a feasibility project to manage the Sundarban Reserved Forest for the benefit of the local people, national development and to improve the integrity of the ecosystem. I returned the following year on a loan fact-finding mission (ADB/97-363 Loan Fact-finding Mission) to assist the mission in reviewing the Final Report of PPTA 2724-BAN by the consultants.

I reviewed the draft proposal sent by the Bank to the Global Environment Facility (GEF}, redrafted the proposal in a form suitable for GEF/World Bank, helped by Gonzalo Castro who flew over and, because of a national strike (hartal), we ended up into two Dhaka hotels a kilometre apart unable to see each other because it was too dangerous to go outside as the riots were armed and we would stand out and probably be killed. I was in the Sheraton hotel where ADB had offices in the same compound whereas Gonzalo was in the Sonarqaon. We did everything by email via Washington with a deadline of 48 hours. We subsequently won a US$12m grant for the project and I arranged for Gonzalo to visit the Sundarban in the Forestry Department's luxurious Edwardian launch with bedrooms used by Tahir and me earlier.

Women fishing fry (kapenta) using mosquito nets Kafue NP Zambia 1973

I visited many villages along the way and was perturbed by the large quantity of fry they were taking from the river which would affect their future fishing prospects just like the women in the Kafue River using their mosquito nets.

I sloshed through the thick mangrove mud to the very shores of the Bay of Bengal. There was a dead chital or spotted deer which on closer investigation was partially eaten by some cat of which there are four species in the Sundarban, three of which are quite small. As I wandered away to follow the rest of the party, who had all disappeared for some reason, I glanced back after a few yards at the kill to see a full-grown male Bengal Tiger standing over it glaring at me. The only thing to do was to freeze without looking directly at the animal and start believing in the existence of a God. After a bit, the tiger, presumably convinced there was more meat left on the deer than on me, picked it up, turned round and ambled away, dragging the deer carcass.

Once out of sight I started shouting for my assistants who started emerging from some distance away from behind trees and other vegetation bearing the excuses, "You were so close to the kill sir, there was no way that we could save you from the return of the tiger, which we knew would come back as the deer was hardly eaten, and probably get eaten ourselves". It was the word 'return' that got me riled. Why didn't they tell me? I fired them all on the basis of the usual ecological principle that the chances of being eaten in a crowd by a single predator are much less than standing alone.

The tigers regularly attack and kill humans who venture into the forest, human deaths ranging from 30–100 per year[137] from about 180 tigers left. The Sundarban tiger was in competition with the human population since neither species liked the wild boar for different reasons; the former because they could fiercely defend themselves and the latter on religious grounds. In consequence both species targeted the deer which although flighty once caught was no problem and deer populations were under pressure from two predators; far speedier than humans so tigers opted for the easy option, eat humans.

The Sundarban was beset by a range of significant problems. Human settlement was not allowed but tolerated under the management of freedom fighter Major Ziauddin Ahmed who spearheaded battles against the Pakistan occupation army in the Sundarban as commanding officer for the First East Bengal Regiment during the Liberation War of 1971 (recounted in his book 'Muktijuddhe Sundarban'). Major Ziauddin[138], also known as an 'emperor without a crown' was very influential in the Sundarban region and newspapers said he was injured in a gun battle with forest bandits in 2013. He had major interests in fisheries as chairman of Dubla Fisheries Group, was the municipality chairman in Pirojpur District within the Sundarban between 1989 and 1991 and it was reported he had later started a non-political organisation for the forest's protection. His dominating presence controlled everything that happened in the Sundarban and his methods were sometimes barbaric according to reports.

The Conservator of Forests in Bangladesh controlled the forests and the first time I met him he had mountains of paper on his desk, was eating digestive biscuits and sneezed causing everything to collapse. His authority

---

137 Goodrich, J., Lynam, A., Miquelle, D., Wibisono, H., Kawanishi, K., Pattanavibool, A., Htun, S., Tempa, T., Karki, J., Jhala, Y. & Karanth, U. (2015) *Panthera tigris*. The IUCN Red List of Threatened Species. IUCN.

138 https://www.thedailystar.net/country/bangladesh-bd-freedom-fighter-maorj-ziauddin-ahmed-major-zia-sundarbans-no-more-1440172

over the Sundarban was no doubt tempered by Major Ziauddin but it was said on good authority that to obtain the post of Conservator the incumbent had to pay and then recover his costs from the officers below him. This was little different from what I had seen in many other countries and the Asian Development Bank was well aware of the situation.

As a consequence, the Asian Development Bank (ADB) said in 2005 it had cancelled the biodiversity project with Bangladesh due to failure to meet conditions for the project loan. The bank had approved a 37-million-dollar loan for a conservation project in the Sundarban forest in 1998 but during implementation, the project, "encountered difficulties with design and financial management." With about three quarters of the loan period elapsed, only about one quarter of the project had been implemented as of end-December 2004 and "only one quarter of the funds had been disbursed," the ADB said in a statement from its headquarters in the Philippine capital. Following an ADB mission in October, the bank decided to cancel the balance of the loan, amounting to about 25 million dollars, and at the request of the government, reallocated it to an emergency flood damage rehabilitation project costing $180m. The original project was intended to develop a sustainable conservation system for the Sundarban, part of the world's largest remaining contiguous mangrove area, and reduce poverty of the 3.5 million people living around the forest

The last time I was in Bangladesh was 1999–2001 as a member of the Panel of Experts, World Bank. The Gorai River is a tributary of the Padma River (a distributary of the Ganges) starting near the Indian border in the north, near the Farakka Barrage which has dramatically changed the nature of the River, and running straight down Bangladesh parallel to the Padma. The Gorai is the main source of fresh water refreshing the predominantly saline waters of the Sundarban. We oversaw all the biological, ecological and environmental aspects of the Gorai River Restoration Project which aimed to redress the problems of decreasing flow caused by siltation at the offtake from the Padma and damage to the integrity of the Sundarban Reserve Forest as well as affecting all the communities downstream.

The Indian Barrage was designed so that the waters of the Ganges would flow down the Hooghly River to flush out the sediment deposition from Kolkata harbour without the need of regular mechanical dredging. It has created a disaster in both India and Bangladesh with millions of people having to move because of flooding on the Indian side and the opposite on the Bangladesh side where the Gorai is now dry most of the year. During the eighties and nineties the flow in the river gradually slowed down, especially during the dry season. The river discharge was decreasing and the annual sedimentation rate was significantly increasing.

The calamity arose from good intentions. In a typical year, over 70 per

Panel of Experts, World Bank

cent of the country is flooded during the monsoon season. But even though water in puddles and ponds is abundant, it's usually polluted and unsafe to drink. Efforts were then made to switch to groundwater that started half a century ago in response to epidemics of cholera, dysentery and a high infant mortality rate. Up to 10 million shallow tube wells were drilled in a bid to provide rural Bangladeshis with safe water. But many draw water from shallow, arsenic-rich sediments. The initiative worked but traded one health disaster for another. Current estimates are that one million wells are now polluted with arsenic, leading to what the World Health Organisation calls "the worst mass poisoning in history".

The best engineers in the world when managing water are the Dutch who were very involved in trying to solve the blockage at the start or offtake of the Gorai River. They experimented with underwater concrete structures that would cause vortexes to scour out the sediment accumulating at the offtake. Fortunato Carvajal Garcia was the head of the team from Royal HaskoningDHV in charge of the Gorai River Restoration Project and seemed to have endless energy and verve in a project that still continues using annual dredging allowing the river to flow once more! This has slowed environmental degradation in the Southwest region and in the Sundarban by ensuring fresh water flows in the wet season and augmenting these flows during the dry season.

Sri Lanka

A project concerning Protected Area Management and Wildlife Conservation of Sri Lanka 1999 that addressed the inadequate institutional framework, legislative framework, weak institutional capacity of the Wildlife Department, overexploitation of protected areas, and missed income opportunities and lack of benefit sharing. We successfully developed and refined an institutional reform agenda indicating the steps the Government needed to take prior to Loan approval and those that needed to be taken as part of the Project. By identifying gaps in the current project design we prepared terms of reference for the activities that still needed to be undertaken. Also prepared a GEF block B grant proposal and GEF concept paper, obtaining the Government's concurrence, including that of the Biodiversity Focal Point, on the actions proposed. All this was done with Lindsay Saunders, who is a close friend, and Jayantha Jayawardene, Rohan Pethiyagoda but especially Sumith Pilapitiya, an exceptional conservationist.

The conservation of natural resources is blighted by corruption in many countries in which I worked. Biodiversity is no exception and indeed it was clear yet again that prominent and powerful people were benefiting from exploiting the wild animals for their own gain especially elephants. Much of the time we were incarcerated in the Oberoi Hotel in Colombo and protected by armed guards and concrete barriers against the Liberation Tigers of Tamil Eelam (the LTTE, also known as the Tamil Tigers) which had been involved in the civil war for decades. Occasionally we could sneak out to the Galle Face Hotel which was not far away and could relax in old world surroundings removed from the glitz and marble of the modern air-conditioned Asian hotel. This hotel was started in 1864 by four British entrepreneurs and was elegant spacious hotel, lacking the false graciousness of the Oberoi (now Cinnamon Grand Colombo) and not protected by guards or barriers. It didn't have air-conditioning which is wonderful since the filters are hardly ever changed in these noisy machines and sometimes make me feel ill. One of the most pleasurable times was having large gins and tonics on the Galle Face Green while watching a total eclipse of the sun with Sumith 11 August 1999 while discussing elephant trafficking, corruption within wildlife departments, personalities, and the cure.

Working in different parts of the world was giving me enormous experience to draw on when teaching. If DICE was to fulfil its mission I, at least, should be fully immersed in what was going on worldwide. I encouraged the staff to take every opportunity to work around the world and I hoped that their accumulated expertise would attract similar opportunities whether it is consultancy or research projects. The University, of course, felt they could levy extraordinary overheads on any consultancy opportunity, which were quite ruinous, and since DICE had to earn its own living to survive I simply told my colleagues that they could keep all the fees from such a consultancy providing any duties they had were covered by the best in the world for which they would pay.

China – Xinjiang, Urumqi, Ningxia and Shaanxi

Since 1993 I had acted as an international staff consultant to a whole range of projects particularly with the Asian Development Bank as well as the World Bank and the Global Environment Facility (GEF). The GEF grant money is refreshed every four years starting at the Earth Summit 1992 in Rio whereby the rich countries fill the pot and poorer developing countries use it for economic externalities, those things they couldn't expect to pay for themselves. Most of the money is in the polar countries and most of the biodiversity is in the equatorial countries. The insights, corruption, hilarious ruses, and trying to grasp the true reality both in negotiation and on the ground certainly taxed all my abilities and intellect.

"Does anybody know where Swingland is and how I can get hold of him?" This message from Bruce Carrad (ADB) got through to me somehow or other to which I responded, "What's up?". "Where the fuck are you and are you free!" was the direct response from him. Australians and New Zealanders are often quite direct, a very refreshing change from the tangential way of speaking amongst the British who intimate their view without being pointed.

Over March and April 2002 I was appointed Biodiversity Specialist, PRC-GEF Country Planning Framework – Land Degradation in Dryland Ecosystems (TA3657-PRC), Asian Development Bank. In effect the whole of western China had turned to sand because of the Tragedy of the Commons and because winds blow from the west in China slowly turning a third of the country into a desert. The Chinese Government and the three largest aid agencies the World Bank, the Asian Development Bank and the GEF wanted solutions to the problem. I was flown directly to Beijing and then to Xinjiang where I had my first meal of a steaming mound of fatty mutton and very strong liquor. It was freezing cold outside but everyone was smiling and good humour in a multitude of languages I didn't understand.

My job was to review all the biodiversity information for the western third of the People's Republic of China (including the identification of sites characterised by species richness, habitat diversity, importance in maintaining vital ecological processes, the conservation status of the ecosystem, uniqueness of ecosystem); status of biodiversity and identified particular strengths and weaknesses of these arrangements; status and adequacy of the Biodiversity Conservation Action Plan (BCAP); policy and institutional issues associated with biodiversity conservation, and made recommendations for improvements; estimated the potential value of ecosystem services associated with current and proposed protected areas, and the potential value of tourism and other non-destructive uses of biodiversity in Western PRC. Proposed possible investments in biodiversity conservation that would generate significant economic returns from direct utilisation or

First time in China. Ürümqi, Xinjiang March 2002. Quick lunch with Uighurs, Xinjiang, 2002

Wind barriers in Gobi Desert Xinjiang 2002. Dancing with a Uighur girl. Xinjang 2002

The end of the Great Wall of China completed 220AD. Dunhuang, Gansu, China 2002

from the associated ecosystem services, as well as contributing to poverty alleviation.

There was a team of over 40 Chinese consultants and probably a dozen international consultants. We travelled by coach all over western China for weeks. Many of the people we met were Uighers who are Muslim especially around Ürümqi. Uighers are of Turkic ethnicity that live in East and Central Asia, primarily in the Xinjiang Uyghur Autonomous Region.

I experienced and saw some amazing sites; a railway inundated for 5 miles in one night by sand moving, a field where crude oil was oozing up around my feet, a 7 mile long canal now with buildings emulating Venice in the middle of the desert, a lake so reduced in its contents it was nothing but a lot of crystalline minerals, dancing with Uigher girls dressed up in traditional costumes, standing in a valley full of all the original *Prunus* spp., the original fruit trees, walking round a deserted casino on the border between China and Kazakhstan, and tackling the eccentricities of many Wild West hotels in the area which were incredibly basic, cold but always with smiling, charming people who tried their best.

On my second visit March and April 2005 Bruce, who had only just joined ADB when we met in Bangladesh with Tahir Qadri and myself, took me aside and expressed his exasperation with the products from my first visit not because of me but because of the material he got from everybody else.

On this occasion I was a Staff Consultant, PRC-GEF Country Planning

Niu Zhiming (ADB Beijing), me and Buce Carrad (ADB HQ). Ninxia desert at Mongolian border.
2005

Framework – Land Degradation in Dryland Ecosystems, and worked on sustainable biodiversity management (RSC No. C51110-PRC, Technical Assistance for Preparing Ningxia Integrated Ecosystem Management Project and Shaanxi Qinling Ecosystem Protection Project. Asian Development Bank). I worked very closely with Bruce and also Niu Zhiming, who worked for ADB-PRC in Beijing. Niu became very close, like a son, and indeed met my own son in Indonesia (see below).

Qinling Botanic Garden golden takin 2005. Terracotta horses and warrior. Tomb Qin Shi Huang, the first Emperor of China. 2005

Old Man. Gobi Desert, Xinjiang, China 2002. Kieran Swingland and Dr Niu Zhiming 13 December 2017

On my previous visit I headed into five provinces but focused on Ningxia and Shaanxi as the best two sites to prove the concept and manner in which this dryland degradation could be tackled using Integrated Ecosystem Management (IEM). I had to review all documentation and prepare issue papers covering biodiversity conservation and management, innovative approaches for the future and international best practices on sustainable biodiversity management. Specifically draft; the final PPTA paper covering the Ningxia Integrated Ecosystem Management Project and Shaanxi Qinling Ecosystem Protection Project and appendices; GEF

Yinchuan wetlands and Mingcui lake system. Ningxia Province March 2005.
L to R. A consultant, Li Hongsong, me and Madame Ma

PDF-B grant applications; draft final MOUs; project documentation suitable for supporting TA implementation; liaise with donors.

Another trip to China in 2006 was before I formally retired in 2009, I acted as the GEF Leader, ADB TA 4640-PRC Ningxia Yinchuan Integrated Ecosystem Management Project establishing the first example of ways in which the problems can be addressed and PRC objective of getting 25 million people a year out of rural subsistence could be met. I raised millions from GEF as a grant. I had to identify priority sites for project interventions

Helankou rock painting of a deer and a leopard

Mongols plundered the imperial tombs west of Yinchuan in 1227. The Western Xia dynasty 11–13th century made significant achievements in literature, art, music, and architecture. During the Mongol conquest of Western Xia, Genghis Khan died. Winemaking continues to boost the economy of what is still one of the country's poorest areas and very good it is too! Flocks of great bustard frequent the tombs

Warlord and National Revolutionary Army general Sun Dianying's ruined house in Yinchuan. He attempted to conquer Ningxia, but was defeated by an alliance led by the Ma clique in 1934

in accordance with the criteria agreed under the PRC/GEF Partnership; and identify suitable GEF investments. The Helan Mountains to on the western border of the province were full of biodiversity and had clearly been a refuge for early human settlement.

In November 2008 I gave a speech at the International Conference on IEM Approaches and Application conference in the vast Friendship Hotel, a labyrinthine monster that used to house the People's Army. I had invented the IEM approach in the development of all the Chinese projects. Afterwards I flew to Yinchuan where I met Li Hongsong and Shuli Cui who became close friends when I worked in the province and we had drinks and dinner at the Flying Tiger then at the Hui Moslem Museum hosted by Chang Limin, Li Yaping (orthopaedic surgeon who fix my back years before), and Cai Xiaogin (who ran the State Farm and on one occasion, playing a game with dice, I 'won' the Farm!). Chang Limin hadn't been able to talk to his daughter who was studying in Germany for some time so while at the table I called on my mobile and was able to get her on the telephone much to his emotional delight. He then rushed off and came back a few minutes later with some of the best red wine produced locally which is better than anything I've tasted in Europe.

The next day I flew on to Urumqi, Xinjiang and stayed at the Sailimu Hotel to see my dear friend Lindsay Saunders with whom I have worked all over Asia on development bank projects. To finish off what I thought was my last trip to China I flew to Beijing where I stayed at the Shangri-La and had the farewell dinner and drinks with Niu Zhiming and his entire family at the Dayali Restaurant.

But four years later I attended the Yinchuan International Workshop on Integrated Wetland Management conference at Sand Lake Resort in Ningxia supported by the Asian Development Bank. I was able to renew my friendship with Lei Guangchun of the Beijing Forestry University and many old friends while we made field trips to Shahu and Yuehai. Niu Zhiming then took me to Yinchuan where we stayed at the Kempinski and visited the south-east desert with his wife Celine and his son Eric. Li Hongsong and Shuli Cui then took me off to have a haircut which involves massaging the neck and head, the most relaxing massage you can imagine before dinner.

Bi-lingual symposium volume. (Cover Anna Swingland.)

My very last trip to China was in summer 2013 at the invitation of Lei Guangchun of the Beijing Forestry University. Lu Cai met me at the airport and after various receptions and welcomes John Grace (Edinburgh University), a very old friend, and I had a meeting with the University Vice President Youqing Luo, Department of International Cooperation. Afterwards we gave presentations about the School of GeoSciences, University of Edinburgh and the Edinburgh Centre for Integrated Forestry, and The Durrell Institute of Conservation and Ecology (DICE), School of Anthropology and Conservation, University of Kent, and then Beijing Forestry University faculty members and the students gave presentations on the topic of biodiversity conservation, ecology studies, wetlands carbon and hydrological studies. John and I then gave a range of lectures. We then visited the Miyun Reservoir studying site and overnighted in a family Inn (Cheng Tao Xiao Zhu Folk Inn) by the Great Wall.

I had a long conversation with Yang Dan, ADB Country Deputy Director and Hamid Sharif, ADB Country Director, about various possible projects in China which ADB should be supporting. After a short discussion with John Somers, First Secretary, Scottish Affairs, British Embassy I visited The Forbidden City and Mausoleum of Mao Tse-tung. A dinner with Niu Zhiming, Tim Coles (MD Operation Wallacea), John Grace, and Lei Guangchun developed the idea of a Qinghai Tibet Institute and Qinghai OpWall Research Stations.

The core of our visit was the development of a possible distance learning Masters degree in biodiversity and business. Edinburgh University would validate it, DICE would provide numerous units as part of the taught programme and Beijing Forestry University would cooperate in ensuring that it reached as many people worldwide as possible. It was going to consist of six months courses and six month's research but in a final meeting at DICE some months later, when I and Fiona was able to spend an hour or so with all the parties (Fiona had so much experience in running a very successful distance learning Masters degree in the environment at SOAS), the idea did not seem to develop.

Sweden

In 2010 I was made a member of the Swedish Research Council (Vetenskapsrådet) and the Swedish Research Council for Environment, Agricultural Sciences and Spatial Planning (Formas), Science Evaluation Board. The research councils appointed two committees to evaluate their investment in biodiversity research from the perspectives of the quality and strategic direction of the science (Science Committee) and the relevance of the research (Relevance Committee). The Science Committee consisted of 10 international experts representing a wide range of science relevant to biodiversity.

In 2012 I was invited again to be a member of the Swedish Research Council (Vetenskapsrådet), Linnaeus Midterm Evaluation which involved a number of prominent guests to examine the progress of the Linnaeus grants which are intended for research environments that have already achieved international excellence in their research fields, or environments that could attain a leading international position if provided with extra support. The most important criterion used in choosing the recipients of Linnaeus grants was the ability of the research environments to perform internationally competitive research. The Linnaeus grant is a complement to the basic resources of the universities and intended to influence the strategic prioritisations at the university.

My charitable involvements ranged from Earthwatch, the Wallacea Trust, the RSPCA, The Kent Trust, and the Darwin Initiative, started by the UK government at the 1992 Earth Summit, the DICE Trust, and many others also gave me an insight into NGOs, their effectiveness, and how their imperative to survive so often overwhelms their raison d'etre.

Wolong National Nature Reserve is located 130km (80 miles) from Chengdu, the capital of Sichuan Province. It is the core part of Sichuan Giant Panda Sanctuaries, one of the World Natural Heritage Sites in China. March 2005 before the Wenchuan Earthquake 2008 destroyed the Reserve

On January 1st 2007 Buckingham Palace announced that I had been made an Officer of the Order of the British Empire (OBE) in the New Year Honours List for 2007. The citation recognised my services to conservation.

In late 2009 Nigel Winser organised an incredible dinner at the Athenaeum, close to my birthday, to which most of my friends and colleagues in so many areas of my life gathered together to celebrate my retirement from nearly all my commitments but to celebrate all their achievements as well.

ADOPTION CERTIFICATE

Help the panda is to help ourselves.

The Giant Panda
"Ian" is adopted
By Ian Swingland

Wolong Panda Club
Jul. 2005

Hua Mei ('China USA') mother with 'Ian' first born of twins. I adopted Ian July 2005. I tried to call the baby Fiona when I was told it was a boy! Amazed a zoologist could get it wrong! You try sexing a giant panda?

Investiture 2007

Retirement, Guy Fawkes night. Athenaeum 2009

Me, Buster and my ayam cemani near the pond

'Tom', my ayam cemani cock. The breed I always wanted for 27 years since I saw this magnificent breed in the Jakarta bird market. It is black inside and out

CHAPTER 15

Pioneers pay a Price 2010–2017

The Good, the Bad and the Ugly

On 11 February 2010 I was suddenly awoken just after seven in the morning by a knock on the door. I saw three men and a woman dressed in black uniforms from Her Majesty's Revenue and Customs (HMRC), several unmarked vehicles – and two feet of snow. Far from fully awake, I was bewildered and confused. I was shown a search warrant that concerned one of the principal investors in Sustainable Forestry Management (SFM), a company called Green Planet. My only thought was that it had something to do with being contracted by SFM in November 2005 to provide this investor with scientific information about forestry and climate change.

What I was about to experience was how the powers-that-be can turn helping out a 'friend' who asked for some assistance into a cynical ploy to defraud.

Although I was never arrested and had not been in charge of running anything as a non-executive member of SFM (I had resigned in 2006) – I clearly needed some legal advice very quickly. I was recommended to use a firm of Canterbury solicitors who attended my interviews with HMRC and assured me that there was no substantial evidence against me. While we waited to see what would happen, my solicitor ceased trading, his firm was declared bankrupt and his junior – who handled my case – emigrated to Switzerland in the middle of my case! But he achieved one very good thing by introducing me to two excellent Counsel who both lived in Kent, the county that had been my home for 40 years and my family's for over 400 years, and they got me a top firm of instructing solicitors.

Three-and-a-half years' later I received a summons. There were five defendants facing seven counts most of which concerned their own personal tax affairs – except me. The trial was classified as a Very High Cost Case (VHCC) and in my opinion a waste of both public money and time. There were seven QCs (two for the prosecution alone), eight junior counsel, five instructing solicitors and an army of HMRC and Crown Prosecution Service (CPS) personnel – plus a vast amount of digital information, 99.9% of which was totally unrelated to me. It dragged on twice as long as the trial judge wanted – for six months in the end.

From the start it became quite clear that the Crown Prosecution Service was out for my scalp because I had more of a public profile, having received an OBE for services to Conservation, and would give the publicity concerned a huge lift for the benefit of HMRC and the CPS. My minuscule part caused HMRC no loss whatsoever but it cost me a fortune to defend myself by having to live in London during the week, additional legal costs before I was awarded legal aid, and forfeited a six-figure sum to a Proceeds of Crime action brought by the CPS after the trial even though the count for which I was found guilty (Count 3), is not an acquisitive offence!

I was charged on two of seven counts:

a) Count 1 – Cheating the Revenue in respect of Carbon Research & Development (aka Green Planet) and

b) Count 3 – Conspiracy to commit fraud by false representation, contrary to Section 1(1) of the Criminal Law Act 1977 in respect of limited liability partnerships by Biomap Services Ltd and Environmental Management (GB) Ltd.

For Count 3, I had heard of neither company and so, not surprisingly, there was no evidence that I had anything to do with them.

Six long, stressful and wearisome years after the trauma had begun the trial started on 13 September 2016 at Southwark Crown Court under His Honour Judge Jeffrey Pegden QC. My daughter was working as a book-binder in Ludgate Hill not far from the Court and she kept my spirits up every week when we had dinner together. At weekends, back at home in Kent, Fiona glued me together.

A week after the trial started, highly inaccurate articles about me appeared in every national and international newspaper worldwide[139]. I can't believe that, during the first week of the trial, members of the jury did not see the extensive headlines about me plastered over the London *Evening Standard* newsstands at London Bridge Station close by the Court, with every tabloid and broadsheet newspaper carrying extensive stories ('World Famous Conservationist accused of fraud', etc.). The reports were bound to have coloured their views even though the judge stressed that the jury should not be influenced by the news media – or look me up on the internet. As someone said, "The one newspaper article I saw used you as a kingpin and famous whereas the others were hardly mentioned. Being a tall poppy is not easy anywhere!" That says it all.

The judge imposed an Injunction (in place until early 2019) on any reporting or dissemination of information about the trial as, amongst other considerations, the press articles were prejudicial to me and untrue (e.g.

---

139   http://www.thetimes.co.uk/edition/news/scientist-accused-of-lending-name-to-60m-tax-fraud-j7zfcd9hb;   http://www.telegraph.co.uk/news/2016/09/20/re-nowned-conservationist-was-involved-in-60m-tax-dodging-scheme/; http://www.standard.co.uk/news/crime/worldfamous-conservationist-was-part-of-60m-ecopro-jects-tax-scam-a3349231.html

stating I was accused of something to do with HIV research!). As Mark Twain said, "If you don't read a newspaper you are uninformed. If you do read a newspaper you're misinformed."

The process of jury selection was interesting and quite different from that portrayed in American legal procedural dramas on television. Forty possible jurors were herded into court and one by one selected alphabetically. But after being told the trial might last for many, many months, half approached the judge for a confidential conversation. They were excused and by the end of the trial we only had a 10-person jury deciding the verdict which jeopardises the outcome.

The case droned on relentlessly for nearly six months until 3 March 2017. My legal team and I sat silently while the prosecution read out lengthy statements – in entirety – from thousands of documents. They produced one prosecution witness after another, most of who knew me well and, when asked about me, declared that I was honest, had integrity and could be trusted.

The first prosecution witness was asked by my QC whether I was honest at which point he broke down and proceedings were suspended so he could leave Court in order to recover. In his closing remarks my QC said, "I can't remember a prosecution witness becoming somewhat emotional when asked to consider the character of a defendant. Asked by me whether he thought Professor Swingland was an honest man."

When, having composed himself, he returned to court with his description of me he said:

> I've written some notes so I can be more composed. You ask me about Ian Swingland. I gave you an answer earlier about the 1970s and the biggest team of scientists and explorers from the Royal Geographical Society sent into the forest on Borneo. One of his projects was to look at the effects of deforestation, particularly on small animals. He's earned a worldwide recognition for his work for four or five decades and his work has encouraged generations of young scientists. In all my interactions with him he was never greedy for money for him, it was all about his work and I believe he would never involve himself in anything untoward. To answer your question: Is he an honest man? Yes.

One prosecution witness after another all echoed the same sentiments: a frontline soldier, a commander in Afghanistan; a retired director of Kew Gardens; head of SFM Australasia; a wealthy SFM investor; a well-known environmentalist and life scientist, who had known me for 39 years; my long-term family solicitor in Canterbury, who had known me for 40 years; and a lifelong friend and national benefactor, who rang me and came to Court; and a famous explorer said I was totally honest, adding he is not just an honourable man, but a passionate one.

Our perception of everything that we saw and heard was that I was clearly 'a decoration' for HMRC and the Crown Prosecution Service who were determined to get a conviction of a high-profile individual, a godsend to their PR and publicity machine, and so justify the multi-million pound case.

I had always trusted the legal system until then; sadly, I now recognise that the law and justice are two very different things. HMRC has virtually unlimited powers, far in excess of any other statutory authority including the police; powers that can result in the ruin of people's lives without cause. HMRC and the CPS are heavily entwined. Alison Saunders[140], the Director of CPS (or DPP) during my prosecution, was heavily criticised in reports[141].

My worst crime was being a bad judge of character; indeed, a shocking judge of character. Being by nature 'naïve' – according to all my friends and those lined up as prosecution witnesses – I trusted people. I believed them. I took their integrity for granted. I assumed them to be honourable. The HMRC and CPS gang were gleeful, self-satisfied; they sat in a huddle in court and served up everything they could find to the prosecution irrespective of it being factual or otherwise, palimpsest or maliciously interpreted.

Right at the end of this very long and arduous trial it came to my turn to take the witness box. The Judge warned the prosecution QC, whom he had already ticked off from time to time for stringing things out, that he would only give him two hours after lunch in which to cross-examine. I believe, after so many months, the Judge understood I was exhausted.

My junior barrister said:

> You didn't disappoint over the last few days in the witness box. The team is a superb one and we all work together very well – that doesn't always happen I can tell you. We are both lucky in that regard. I can confidently say, however, that all the professionals in Court 2 very much admire the man of conviction and achievement in our midst: I thought your intellect and integrity has been highlighted in the last few days.

On 3 March 2017 I was acquitted of the major Count 1, an acquisitive offence, but found guilty of Count 3 which is not an acquisitive offence – i.e. I garnered no pecuniary gain from it.

Count 3 was cleverly devised: the jury would be intent on finding the principal defendant guilty and, since you cannot have a conspiracy of one, they would have to find me or the other defendant charged on this Count

---

140   https://www.telegraph.co.uk/news/2018/12/29/alison-saunders-much-criticised-former-cps-chief-becomes-first/

141   https://www.telegraph.co.uk/politics/2019/03/10/alison-saunders-banned-professional-dealings-cps-watchdog-warned/

guilty too – even if we were both saints. I was the main target being of more worth to the Prosecution.

All this based on two letters drafted by the Green Planet investor to which I added some paragraphs concerning mycorrhiza and on UNFC-CC and forests. They were *non-sequiturs* irrelevant to the content of the author's letter. In good faith, I stupidly signed those letters. If only... if only... I had known then what I know today. I was given a suspended sentence and two years' later I lost my OBE when the injunction was lifted. Still – at least I had won one in the first place and my relationships still hold where it matters.

There is an old saying: 'as soon as a man gets rich he goes bad – and as soon as a woman goes bad, she becomes rich'; echoed by Bernard Mandeville's view: 'you can have riches and vice, poverty and virtue – but you can't have riches and virtue'. I gained no riches.

Two years later, in 2019, the trial judge sat three times again at hearings reducing the exorbitant bill I was sent towards my defence by the Legal Aid Agency (out of the blue and years' after the trial ended). The judge concluded that since

> the bulk of the case was not taken up by Professor Swingland's case at all ... he was in the witness box for three days, so a much, much shorter period of time was required to deal with his case which fell within far narrower parameters ... Moreover, of course, it is particularly noteworthy, as I have emphasised, that Professor Swingland was acquitted of Count 1, which was the guts of the case...[thus] he was acquitted of the main bulk of the case. Count 3 involved the signature upon just two documents approximately nine months apart and the effect of Professor Swingland's signature was, in essence, what might be described as gilding the lily.

He reduced the gargantuan bill to 15% of that demanded.

The Legal Aid Agency subsequently applied to the High Court for a Judicial Review in November 2019 – without a decision so far and this is still ongoing – a horrifying 10 whole years after it all began. It all centres on points of law with the LAA versus Southwark Crown Court not me. Even though I'm only an Interested Party, and any costs should really be borne by the government, with one government department against another, the Single Judge decided to have a rolled-up hearing sometime in the future[142], instead of rejecting this application which is legally out of time and flawed. This means I may have to pay my legal costs in defending the trial judge's decision and possibly theirs in attempting to reverse the decision if the High Court denies justice! During this time I have felt my life to be on hold, suspended and waiting for things to return to normal. This sorry

---

142   https://www.telegraph.co.uk/news/2020/08/03/free-independent-brexit-britain-could-do-without-rule-unelected/

story is forming the basis of an exciting murder thriller called 'Croaked' using my herpetological knowledge of poisons to eradicate those who put others in harm's way for their own benefit. 'Justice delayed is justice denied', or, as Kafka put it in *The Trial* (German: *Der Prozess* 1915), "What awaits us is error, not justice."

Aftermath

I had never been embroiled in any legal difficulties until this living hell was visited on me; ten very long tortured years. I stood accused as a common criminal and every aspect of my private and professional life was paraded, prodded and penetrated by an agency with more power than any other. Sleep deserted me and I was forced to spend my 70th birthday in the dock.

Sir Thomas More: [in his prison cell]

> *If we lived in a state where virtue was profitable, common sense would make us saintly. But since we see that abhorrence, anger, pride, and stupidity commonly profit far beyond charity, modesty, justice, and thought, perhaps we must stand fast a little – even at the risk of being heroes.*

Apart from all the support I received from the judge, the court functionaries and counsel, I was heartened by all the prosecution witnesses' opinions of me and their personal statements. I also appreciated the many hundreds of messages of support from across the world; indeed, even from people from whom I had not heard for many years.

Here is a small sample:

- I was sorry to read of your issues with the court case and how it was presented in the media. From knowing you, I was certain that your involvement in this case would have only have come from your passion to conserve the natural environment.
- All ok with you Prof.? I am being a boring judge. Just get well old friend.
- This is a shocking story IAN. Being an honourable man makes it relatively easy for unscrupulous people to con you. It is devastating. I think you are immensely brave holding up so well.
- I thought it would be totally crap and as usual innocent people end up being the fall guy.
- There appreciate things are not great. You know where I am. I can call and visit anytime. I also think you should come and attend some events. You are most welcome.
- Happy Birthday Ian, Really wish you were not going through

this current difficult time, I am sure all is going to finish well for you.

- I am so pleased to hear that this ordeal for you is over. It must have been horrible beyond words.
- Happy birthday my friend. Stay strong. I am thinking of you. Xx
- Can't imagine this is a good birthday but hope you can rise above the shit and celebrate another year. I will be thinking of you when I raise a glass later today. I bet when you were that blond sun-drenched naïve young man down in the Indian Ocean that you had no comprehension of turning 70!
- IAN YOU be careful and do not let yourself get caught up in the nonsense of others and keep breathing slowly. Lower the stress. Am sitting in a car from Hanoi to Langson province. The door in Auckland is always open to you.
- Ever since I saw the story in *The Times*, I have been thinking about you and the dreadful position you find yourself in. I can hardly begin to imagine what an awful impact the trial must be having on your life. I sincerely hope you will be able to ride the storm and that you will emerge exonerated. If by any chance there is anything constructive I can do for you, please do not hesitate to let me know.
- You have been in our thoughts and prayers Ian and I am so pleased that the truths are winning. Well done. Keep strong good friend.
- Thinking of you and hope you are OK. Give 'em hell!!
- Hang in there, stay strong and healthy.
- I was most sorry to read in the national press that you are involved in a Court case and, as I have told mutual friends and colleagues, I know that whatever the case may reveal, you personally would not have acted act in any way, for personal gain.
- I would like you to know that when you let me come on the Ecology Diploma with my dodgy academic record it made a huge beneficial difference to my life. Whatever the rights or wrongs of your present situation I wish you and your family well for the future.
- *Nil bastardum carborundum!*
- Stay strong. Those who know you, know what you are about, so good luck.

- I continue to stand by you and what you stand for.
- I imagine life is far from enjoyable at the moment. The one newspaper article I saw used you as a king pin and famous whereas the others were hardly mentioned. Being a tall poppy is not easy anywhere! Anyway just wanted to know I am thinking of you in difficult times and hope you get some of your own back.
- I went to London last night for a concert and picked up a copy of the *Evening Standard*. I was horrified to see your photograph and report of the trial. I do of course realise the trial must be reported but had quite forgotten about it after all this time. I really hope that it does not cause you too much concern and that you are vindicated by the eventual verdict. Please let me know if there is anything that I can do to help you in clearing your name.

I was not vindicated. "Let Right be done.[143]" It wasn't!

---

143   Sir Robert Morton QC in *The Winslow Boy* by Terence Rattigan. 1946. The year I was born.

CHAPTER 16

The End

"Begin at the beginning," the King said, very gravely, "and go on till you come to the end: then stop". Lewis Carroll, Alice in Wonderland Chapter XII, 1865

What have I learnt in 74 years?

From a shy and lonely kid I had to learn to be social, apparently gregarious and able to be articulate. I soon developed those skills in the Mile End Road as well as a sense of humour and found I was able to engage with anybody, whoever they were, and have them join me in my various expeditions in life as well as my creations. A good idea that benefits both the planet and the people is very difficult to make into a viable reality and successful from nothing. For some reason humans, especially academics generally will do everything they can to be obstructive, although in my experience while Americans are very competitive they applaud and support success in a way that the English do not.

Someone once said to me about DICE: "You should basically stuff the place full of talent and allow that talent to bloom. So you have to have something that makes the great people want to come and work for you. And it's never money. You can always earn more money at a bad University because they need you more." He was right. The best people function by passion not pay. That's exactly what I have done with everything I've been involved in.

It is strange that I have found myself more comfortable in other countries and with other nationalities than I do the English. For example, I felt at home in China, totally relaxed in the Seychelles, happy in Indonesia, at one with nature on Aldabra and in Borneo, and stimulated in New Zealand; mostly with indigenous people and in some of the wildest and most remote places on earth. The Scots and the Cumbrians are tribes apart where I've experienced great warmth and resolve quite distinct from those in the south, the English. It's the small-mindedness and middle class prejudice that gets my goat! In one word, stupidity. "It's discouraging to think how many people are shocked by honesty and how few by deceit", Noel Coward 'Blithe Spirit' 1941.

There is no doubt that I have kicked a lot of traces over and upset conventional mindsets but always with a constructive purpose that has proved effective.

I have felt distinctly uncomfortable on University Committees, on Company Boards, and official gatherings. While confident in front of very large audiences, when I've given major speeches either about my research work or charities or about the organisations I have created, there was a difference. The difference is that at official gatherings idiots who talk too much and say nothing, or politicians, or people with their own vested interests, pervert the conversation and the outcome. Whereas making a presentation or speech to an audience you're solely in charge of what was said and the answers to questions.

The last job I applied for was in 1979, over 40 years ago, and ever since then every appointment has either been offered or I have fashioned a role in something I've created. Working for others is often quite difficult as most managers are not up to the job, have their own prejudices and inadequacies, or simply want to dominate and use or abuse.

When I retired on Guy Fawkes night 2009 a huge number of people from all walks of life in conservation, entertainment, politics and business turned up at dinner in the Athenaeum and I was given some lovely and relevant presents; Jonathan Kingdon's African mammal drawings (the Wellcome edition), a map of Aldabra by J.C.F. Fryer 1910 and two photographic albums of Fiona and my trip to Kenya in March 2009 all organised by one of my close friends, Nigel Winser. Nigel, Robin Hanbury-Tenison and I then gave a demonstration of how adept we were with Penan blowpipes loaded with poisonous darts. They were spot on but I needed two shots to burst a balloon.

For me it was a very emotional evening and the heartfelt ambience of the occasion will remain with me and my family forever.

Guy Fawkes 2009

The standard film screened by the BBC every Christmas is *It's a Wonderful Life*.

The film illustrates some home truths or clichés:

a) Things of true worth are not measured by money (SFM was an ideal for me – forest conservation using a different approach, not charity or subsidy – but for others it was money. DICE was an obvious idea, a charitable donation to improve the world but to the University it was money),

b) Keeping up with the Joneses is for idiots (a competitive nature is damaging),

c) Your life has purpose (everyone – everyone – is worth something, a belief that drove me towards continuing education),

d) Appreciate how blessed you already are (take account regularly),

e) Don't hire someone just because they are kin (it always goes wrong),

f) Bad guys don't always get punished – or the penalty is insufficient (not only that, they seem to live longer whereas the good guys worry about truth and honesty which wears them out sooner), and finally,

g) Marry the right person (did that) and rear great children.

Mark Twain said it better: "No man is a failure who has friends." Those I have in spades!

It's strange; while I have disliked humans since I was a nipper, yet I've spent my life helping others even though I have sometimes been taken for a ride. It comes from my upbringing: having to strive for everything and watching others try and fail.

> Ah, but a man's reach should exceed his grasp,
> Or what's a heaven for?
> Robert Browning 1855

I discovered that helping others changes the world and, while I have flaws, I have managed to spend all my life doing what I love: working with animals and helping others who like animals by giving them a leg up. My enthusiasm and belief in the potential of people means I have sometimes been less wary – less sceptical – than was wise.

> He who learns must suffer, and, even in our sleep,
> pain that cannot forget falls drop by drop upon the heart,
> and in our own despair, against our will,
> comes wisdom to us by the awful grace of God
> Aeschylus 525-455 BC the father of tragedy

That said, I continue to prefer the company of animals to that of humans. Animals are far more reliable, far more honest. At the same time, I have always treated every human, whoever they are, equally and fairly.

So, unless I go insane – which I don't intend to do – the rest of my days should be comfortable with my family – Fiona, Kieran and Anna and her husband Steve – and my many true friends. I may survive the next decade as I am told I'll die when I am 86 by my actuarial friends. We'll see!

I'll continue to do just the same as always – namely, getting up in the early morning, brewing up a large mug of char, emailing or Skyping my friends (most of whom live far away), giving Buster, my beautiful gold cocker, a small part of my full English breakfast and a walk, then going down to the local pub for lunch with a friend or inveigle them to London. Miss out the evening meal and go into couch potato mode with a book or TV.

Buster, Herons Hall 2014

Perhaps draft an obituary or two, so that friends are remembered accurately, rather than attend funerals that are as bad as cocktail parties, many turning up just to be seen-so I generally don't. People's Memorials should be in the hearts and minds of those that knew them and not a ceremony or a Cenotaph.

Finale

Do I have a bucket list? I think I've done just about all of it; been attacked by sharks, shot at (and fired back), 'stabbed 'in the back and had cobra venom spat in my eyes (animals are at least honest about their actions). Been accused of things I never did. But charity is learning how to forgive others. Wisdom is knowing how to forgive yourself.

Bathed in the enormous pleasure of watching my creations go from one success to another, seeing one alumnus after another achieve recognition, and above all changing the world for the better. Relished extreme and beautiful isolation for years and come out better for it; lived in the remotest areas of the world from desert islands to central African woodlands, from rainforests to the Gobi.

> There is pleasure in the pathless woods,
> There is a rapture on the lonely shore,
> There is society, where none intrudes,
> By the deep sea, and music in its roar:
> I love not man the less, but Nature more,
>   LORD BYRON, Childe Harold 1812–1818

So I don't want to be big-headed about it, but I've been to all the places I want to go. I've done all the things I ever wanted to do. I've met all the people I really wanted to meet. I've seen whatever I wanted to see. Now the life of an old curmudgeon beckons but I'm not upset about that – not at all. "An Englishman will burn his beard to kill a flea."

It's a pretty calm life, a fairly peaceful life. I no longer have any mega projects and I have ceased to care what others think. A few false 'friends' have shown themselves up for what they are: loyalty is only really tested when it is needed. And, from time to time, find more remote places on earth where I can be at absolute peace and think with clarity, absorbing nature.

Away from people – whether they be good or bad or ugly.

> Do not stand at my grave and weep
> I am not there. I do not sleep.
> I am a thousand winds that blow.
> I am the diamond glints on snow.
> I am the sunlight on ripened grain.
> I am the gentle autumn rain.
> When you awaken in the morning's hush
> I am the swift uplifting rush
> Of quiet birds in circled flight.
> I am the soft stars that shine at night.
> Do not stand at my grave and cry;
> I am not there. I did not die.
> Mary Elizabeth Frye 1932

APPENDIX

Where did the Swinglands come from?

Where did the very unusual surname of Swingland come from[144]?

A swingeing wheel is a device never seen in England as water retting and heckling was more commonly used in Scotland and elsewhere to prepare flax for spinning. However swingeing was still in used in Belgium for the preparation of flax and was evident in country villages. It consists of a light wheel made of wood and the spokes are platters set at an angle. This wheel is fixed on a hub and rotates by the action of a treadle, at the end of a bench or table. The flax is taken in a bunch and brought against the platters so that as the wheel rotates the flax is scarified and made into a sort of 'kapok' from which yarn is produced. Flax was largely produced in Belgium and this proved to be a very significant piece of information.

If the name is Anglo-Saxon it must at some time have been known on the Continent. Flax is grown in the Low Countries and Swingland means the land where the swingeing wheel was used. The Netherlands then must be the original home of the Swinglands. It did not seem out of place to argue that if the patronymic was derived from the language of a people it was not unnatural to look for traces of the family's residence in the same country and amongst the same people.

Overslingeland 'overswingland' signpost southern Netherlands close to Flanders just north of Antwerp

---

144 Compiled from family papers covering ca. 400 years especially those of my paternal grandfather Charles Swingland 1883–1941.

The first appearance in London of the Swinglands, according to the first record, took place at about the end of the seventeenth or beginning of the eighteenth centuries, i.e. between 1689 and 1744 in the reigns either of William & Mary and George II of England.

The state of England at this period, and the reasons which may have induced a Swingland to have left his native shore to settle in this country, was the particular troubles and the bloodshed in The Low Countries with which Spain had deluged both Belgium and Holland for the sake of an impossible ideal urged on by the greediness of a Roman Catholic Church in the name of religion.

The backdrop to these events was the Edict of Nantes (French: Édit de Nantes), signed in April 1598 by King Henry IV of France, granting the Calvinist Protestants of France (also known as Huguenots) substantial rights in the nation, which was still considered essentially Catholic at the time. In the edict, Henry aimed primarily to promote civil unity. Nearly ninety years later, in October 1685, Louis XIV, the grandson of Henry IV, renounced the Edict and declared Protestantism illegal with the Edict of Fontainebleau leading to the intense persecution of Protestants.

Belgium at this period was united with Holland under the domination of Spain since the middle of the preceding century with a fierce and determined opposition against the Spanish power. The Inquisition which had set foot in the Iberian Peninsula was latterly applied to the Low Countries. It had fired the Netherlanders with hatred and inspired them to endure almost utter ruin rather than submit to the heartless and wholesale butchery. They had borne their bitter experience for many years previously and in spite of the divergence which at last divided Holland from Belgium they were united in their resistance of the Spanish oppression.

The United Province of Netherland (which was the term by which the Low Counties were then known) consisted of Holland and Belgium (Belgium did not secede from this connection until 1833) at last succeeded in establishing the Dutch Republic with the Princes of the House of Nassau as Stadtholder. The Spanish soldiery which had cowed the populace and exacted their subsistence for so many years, at last, withdrew and left the people impoverished but relieved.

It is hardly necessary in this story to recount all the horrible details which at last enabled a noble people to throw off the yoke of the Roman Catholic Church which it was the ambition of Spain to fasten upon them. They can be found fully recorded in Motely's *Rise of the Dutch Republic*[145]. Suffice it to say that the spirit of revolt in the name of Protestantism gave the house of Orange Nassau the throne of Holland. Before the country could however repair the damage of these terrible years further difficulty

---

145 Motley, J.L. (1857) *1555–84. The Rise of the Dutch Republic*. Harper, New York.

arose with England and the Thirty Year's War began (1618–1648). Whatever the condition of the people of the Netherland must have been at this time, and for the 100 years previous, the severe religious strife it aroused, was supposed to conclude these hostilities. If a Swingland lived in the Low Countries during any part of this time and had experienced the miseries which had reduced the population to beggary and starvation it requires very little imagination to understand what brought about this migration.

When a person is young and healthy and above all has a high spirit there is no explanation needed to account for a phenomenon which might in an older person be considered to be foolhardy. I think there is little doubt that Swingland must have determined he could not have less to endure if he tried his fortune in a new land. Indeed the nature of the Swinglands has always been rather determined and conservative especially in the attachment to old places and things. It would therefore be a hard wrench for him to make a change but when one's existence is threatened by the loss of a livelihood it forces the courage to break with those we love and try new fields and pastures.

When the Thirty Year's War was ended the capitals of Europe were well sounded as to the form of peace. The Peace of Westphalia was a series of peace treaties signed between May and October 1648 in the Westphalian cities of Osnabrück and Münster, largely ending the European wars of religion. The Treaty was well advanced in its outline, when two important supporters of the cause of the Low Counties died, namely Frederick Henry the Stadtholder and Cardinal Richelieu of France.

Negotiations were, therefore, lacking in important particulars for the support needed to assist the Netherlands and when in 1648 the Peace of Münster was eventually signed the people of Antwerp and the country of the Scheldt found themselves under a ban which destroyed their commerce for the next 150 years. After 80 years of constant hardship the people's most ardent desire was for Peace but when the Peace of Münster was proclaimed it was favoured by all States of the Netherlands except Zealand and Utrecht.

For two years the negotiations which had preceded the signing raised the hopes of all as the prospects came nearer to putting an end finally to the burning of towns and heretics, the battles of Civil Population against the fierce Spanish Soldiery and the unremitting effort of the nobility led by the Royal House of Spain to force the Roman Catholic doctrines upon them. These doctrines ill-fitted a people definitely veering away from the Latin influence as the doctrines of Luther and Calvin became more widely known. Yet the result of all these negotiations and the Congress held at Münster and Osnabrück by the Emperor with the principal German States, Spain, France and the Netherlands after the careful sounding of every capital in Europe fastened a yoke upon Antwerp which diplomatic action and busy intrigue could not have carried out with more consummate skill.

The principal city of the Scheldt River was henceforward doomed. The treaty was the greatest deathblow which could have been given to any thriving and enterprising people. One writer in a letter dated from Antwerp in 1616[146] shows the forlorn condition of Antwerp during the opening years of the seventeenth century.

> *Antwerp, I own, surpasses all the towns I have seen in the magnificence of its buildings, the breadth of its streets, the strength, and the beauty of its fortifications. We only spent a single night there, and gave a morning and afternoon to visiting the town in our friend's Carriages, so as not to tire our horses. We saw all. Two sentences would suffice to describe the state of the place and you must accept them as literally true. Magna civitas, magna solitude; for all the while I was there, I never could count in the whole length of any street, more than forty persons at once. I saw neither carriages no horsemen and though it was a weekday not one of us saw a pennyworth of goods bought or sold in the shops. Two porters and a ballad monger could have carried off between them all that were brought together in the Exchange, upstairs or down. The English factory was filled with scholars disciplined by the Jesuits; the House of Osterling (Hanseatic Merchants) stood empty. Grass grew in many of the streets. Such was the state of Antwerp in 1616 and it was worsened by the awful Peace.*

The citizens of Antwerp were for the next century and a half to struggle to free their port from the iniquitous closing of it by the Dutch. As the Scheldt, a little below Antwerp, runs through Dutch Territory the particular clause in the Peace Treaty was interpreted to mean that the waterway between Antwerp and the Sea might not be used by other than Dutch ships.

Unlike Bruges, it was not the silting up of the port which had stopped their trade but baneful politics and commercial jealousy. Efforts were made from time to time to overcome the difficulties and hindrances. An English company was formed called the Ostend Company but again politics ruined it. To secure support for his Pragmatic Sanction the Emperor, Charles VI, dissolved the company in 1731 after it had risen in prosperity and favour over nine years. Other attempts were made to force the passage but each occasion threatened to end disastrously as Dutch war ships fired on any but Dutch ships.

This ban was not lifted until 1792 when Dumouriez gained military victory at Jemappes. But if Antwerp was in despair in 1616 what must have been its condition in 1648 or even 1700 after Louis XIV unleashed terror against Protestants in France. This period covers the early life of Newbrough Swingland with Catherine and their nephew Newbrough. To any energetic dweller in Antwerp such an embargo on trade could offer no sol-

---

146   Anon. Transcribed by Charles Swingland, 1941.

ace to a yearning appetite and anyone determined to make a livelihood for himself had no choice but to escape from the manacles which thwarted his efforts; in other words to leave his home and look afield for new avenues of employment and trade.

This dramatic page of history seems to fit the story associated with the early life of the Swinglands. The trade which he followed in England at 10 Rood Lane, London was that of cork cutting and glue-making. These trades were known in Antwerp and the Netherlands. Even these days Flemish ponies and horses have a claim to fame. And when it is remembered that from Spain comes the cork for cutting and that Spain had had a long though wearisome connection with the Netherlands there appears to be some possible connection with the Netherlands and the Swinglands. These facts furnish strong possibilities that the establishment of a business in London by the Swinglands of cork cutting and glue-making furnished a powerful indication of the district from which Newbrough came and where he learned his trade.

Cork cutting was evidently a trade brought to the Netherlands through its connection with Spain, and glue-making can only be economically carried on where horses and cattle are reared, giving another direct clue to the origin of the Swinglands. Both these point to a connection with Flanders of which Antwerp is the principal port and to the shipping trade because both these articles are necessary to ships.

As Spaniards had for nearly two centuries dominated the life of the people it is more than probable that strains of the Spanish blood should be found amongst our family. It has often been remarked, even at this distance of time, amongst members of our families' complexions not dissimilar with the Flemish or the Spanish. My own great uncle Clifford established quite a good trade connections amongst South Americans for no other reason than that he was believed to be a Spaniard.

My great aunt Evelyn had often been asked whether she is Spanish owing to her having dark skin and black hair. Leslie Bodley, whose mother was Miss Emily Bodley, my great grandfather's youngest sister, is very dark complexioned and his own son is definitely of a dark swarthy complexion which may be deemed to show that some connection must have existed with a dark skinned race. Emily married Thomas Bodley who established business as a builder at 35 Fairfoot Road, Bow. At first he experienced difficult times but of late years accumulated a good amount of property. He was a churchwarden at St Leonards Bromley. My great uncle Thomas Bodley was of medium height and muscular. He was very hard working and persevering and had a typical Devonshire temper. He was descended from the Bodleys, iron masters of Exeter and in direct descent from Sir Thomas Bodley who founded the Bodleian Library in Oxford.

Another extraordinary feature of this phenomenon is that the sons show traces of a dark complexion when they are children of Swingland girls and the daughters when they are daughters of Swingland males. We may perhaps be able to find some traces in the build of the Swinglands. Usually the frame is broad and heavy thick set with powerful muscles and broad shoulders. The neck is usually short and strongly rooted whilst the head is of a Frisian or Anglo Frisian type with heavy eyebrows. These to my grandfather's mind indicated a Flemish origin. There are strong indications of the origin of the family in Flanders, heavy development mentally and physically they certainly may be classified with the Flemish type, and until other evidence can be discovered to controvert these ideas, the Swinglands must be considered as having a name which is Anglo-Saxon and Teutonic, a trait which emanated from the Flanders and a physique which can be traced to many similar products of the union of the Spanish and Flemish races.

Where did the first-comers, Newbrough Swingland and his wife, land? Where were the nephew's father and mother? Was his father killed in the army abroad? Was he involved in one of the several insurrections which occurred in this country in the Jacobite cause or was he one of the several garrisons abroad of the English army which followed in the wake of the restored Charles of England.

The elder Newbrough Swingland became Parish Clerk at St Margaret Pattens, Rood Lane, Eastcheap in the City of London in 1729. And from this indisputable fact it may be deduced that even in those days Parish Clerks were not appointed to those responsible positions unless they had arrived for some years at a substantial position in life. The office of Parish Clerk was more important then than it is nowadays because the positions had not been stripped of their communal and municipal importance. They were comparable to the later dignity of Town Clerk. One might therefore be assured that Newbrough Swingland arrived in England many years before he was appointed to this office. I suggest therefore that it must have been late in the 17th century. As however his death did not take place until 1761 he must have been very young probably not more than a boy when he came. It does not follow that his wife came with him and it is not known whether he formed one of a crowd of refugees which fled from the fearful persecution of the French Marshal Villars in the reign of Louis XIV.

The Duke of Marlborough about 1708 entered Antwerp (100kms south from Overslingeland) in the course of his attack on the French army, after winning the battle at Oudenarde 80kms south, and thousands of refugees came to England. They were in a pitiable condition and destitute. About 2000 of them came and were encamped behind St Mary Matfelon Church (Whitechapel Church). A public subscription was made and £22,000 was

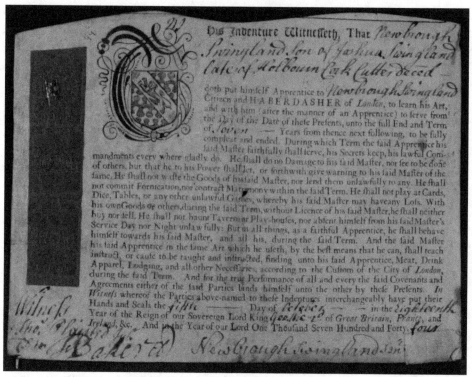

Apprentice Indenture for Newbrough Swingland, the son of Joshua Swingland (deceased), to work under Newbrough Swingland (his grandfather), citizen and Haberdasher of London, 18 October 1744 in the 18th year of the reign of George II

raised to enable many of the families to go to Ireland or America. The metropolitan Borough of Stepney has a picture of the encampment. Was a Swingland amongst these immigrants? Did Newbrough arrive here as a boy or as a young married man? A significant fact remains. No mention is found at St Margaret Pattens; neither of his marriage nor of the birth of the nephew. He may have come into the Parish as a married man and been later joined by his nephew but I know nowhere else to search. I conclude therefore that these Swinglands came to St Margaret Pattens Parish as new settlers.

One of the perplexing facts is how few people called Swingland exist today. We don't produce a disproportionate number of females nor do our males die precipitously. However we do move around a lot and can be found in places as far apart as New Zealand and the United States. The Swinglands originally came through Kent as refugees and dispersed not only to London but eventually to the South Island of New Zealand as well as the east coast of what is now the United States. They initially sought sanctuary in Canterbury where the west transept of the cathedral houses a Huguenot Chapel which still conducts services in French every Saturday. Newbrough senior established what became a substantial business centred on cork at 10 Rood Lane, London. This is now the site of what is nicknamed the 'Walkie-Talkie' building and was awarded the Carbuncle Cup for the worst new building in the UK in 2015.

A relative's obituary of yesteryear reads:

> Mr Philip Swingland, formerly Clerk in Charge of the Bond Stores at Greymouth, south island New Zealand was born in East London, England, in the year 1838. He emigrated in 1862, and settled in Canterbury; but was on the gold diggings in Otago, and worked at Mount Ida goldfield and other places. Mr Swingland removed to the West Coast in the year 1865, and joined the Customs Department in 1867. He takes a lively interest in charitable matters, and within the space of twelve years forwarded nearly £400 to Dr Barnado's Homes in London, all gathered by private canvass during his leisure hours. Mr Swingland is a devoted Oddfellow, and a Past Worthy Grand Master of the Order. He now (1906) lives in retirement at Wanganui.

He died three years later.

INDEX

Symbols

11+ 33

A

aardvark 93, 94
Abbott 132
abhorrence 304
Abu Dhabi 29
academic politician 177, 210
Access 38, 178
accused 138, 201, 234, 300, 301, 304, 310
AceDoors Ltd 228
acquisitive offence 300, 302
acquitted 302, 303
actuaries 11
adaptation 41, 49, 169, 189
adaptationist 167
Admiralty Underwater Weapons' Establishment 3
Aeschylus 309
afforestation 163, 164, 243, 244
Afghanistan 301
Afon Teifi Site of Special Scientific Interest and Special Area of Conservation 170
African Banks 190
aftermath 175
agent 11, 54, 64, 278
aggression 38, 40, 158
Agricultural Research Council, Unit of Statistics 58, 106, 107, 173
Agriculture and Horticulture Development Board 279
Ahern, Mike 270
Ahmed, Major Ziauddin 282, 283
air raid shelter 16
Alban, Steve 191
Aldabra 22, 33, 55, 98, 104, 105, 107, 108, 109, 110, 111, 114, 116, 119, 121, 124, 125, 126, 127, 128, 130, 131, 132, 133, 134, 135, 137, 138, 139, 140, 141, 144, 147, 149, 151, 152, 154, 158, 164, 170, 171, 172, 173, 175, 181, 185, 186, 187, 188, 189, 226, 230, 307, 308
Aldabra Atoll 22, 33, 55, 98, 104, 105, 108, 110, 111, 125,

135, 139, 140, 141, 152, 154, 170, 171, 172, 187, 226
Aldabran giant tortoises 112, 135, 141
Aldenham Hertfordshire 35
Aldenham, Lord 40
Aldous Huxley 40
A-levels 38, 45
Alexander, Richard 202
Alexander, Sandy 198, 209, 210, 211, 216
Alexandria Quartet, The 206
Allen, Dale and Irma 278
Allerdale Council 240
Allicock, Sydney 251
Alta Vila 26
altruism 38, 40, 166, 168
Al-Yamamah 172
Amazon 21, 22, 253, 271, 272
America 318
American Ambassador 258
American hospitality 200
American Museum of Natural History 188, 208
Amerindian 89, 253, 272
Amirantes 184, 190
Amphibian and Reptile Conservation Trust (ARC) 205, 222, 252. *See also* Herpetological Conservation Trust
anaconda 42
Andes 271, 272, 273
Andre, Willy 128
anger 304
Anglo-Saxon 312, 317
Animal Dispersion in Relation to Social Behaviour 166
Animal Ecology Research Group (AERG) 106
animals 19, 20, 21, 22, 25, 30, 32, 37, 38, 40, 42, 43, 44, 46, 47, 50, 54, 55, 56, 59, 60, 63, 71, 78, 81, 86, 87, 88, 118, 120, 123, 124, 129, 133, 135, 137, 139, 140, 141, 145, 151, 155, 166, 172, 173, 180, 185, 187, 189, 190, 194, 198, 206, 222, 228, 229, 236, 272, 285, 301, 309, 310
Ann Arbor 104, 127, 153, 198, 199, 200, 202
Ansell, Frank 71
Anse Malabar 113, 114, 115, 116, 130, 142
Anthropology 220, 221, 223,

230, 294
antimicrobial 278
ants 5, 6, 22, 25, 50
Antwerp 312, 314, 315, 316, 317
Apple and Pear Research Council (APRC) 276, 277, 278
Arabian Oryx 44, 107
Ardèche 173, 174
Argo 231
Aristotelian 226
Arkley 51
Armstrong, Neil 56
Arnold, Nick 140, 141
arsenic 284
Article 6 of the Paris Agreement 247
asbestos 170
Ashworth, John 175
Asian Development Bank 259, 279, 280, 283, 286, 289, 293
Aske, Robert 38
Aspinall, John 43
asset strip 220
Astle, Bill 71, 74, 76, 77
Atahualpa 273
Athenaeum Club 9, 137, 264, 295, 297, 308
Atkins, Vera 9, 10
attack 64, 83, 109, 190, 214, 224, 282, 317
Attenborough, Sir David 30, 206, 266
Auckland 226, 228, 230, 231, 232, 262, 263, 264, 305
Auckland Foundation Fellow 263
Auffenberg, Walter 193
Auschwitz 10
Austin Mini 41, 63
Australasia 124, 163, 164, 301
Australia 4, 29, 70, 105, 130, 162, 163, 164, 165, 264, 270
Autoland 27
Aventurier 138
Avery, Mark 173
Avery, Roger 27
Avianco 26
awful Peace 315
ayam cemani 232, 297, 298
Aylward, Bill 250

B

Baboons 94

environmental lawyers 275

Environmental Management (GB) Ltd 300

environmental sex determination 111, 147, 149, 154, 180, 187, 220

environmental sustainability 242

Environment, Food and Rural Affairs Committee 248

epithelial cells 208

Eric 293

Erie, Pennsylvania 153

Esk Rivers and Fisheries Trust 58

Esmée Fairbairn Foundation 212, 217

Esslemont Road 61

Ethnobotany 220

Eton Fives 35

EU Common Agricultural Policy (CAP) 238

EU Emissions Trading Scheme (ETS) 164, 242

Europe 6, 27, 180, 196, 205, 211, 240, 248, 249, 250, 254, 255, 267, 269, 292, 314, 315

European 4, 28, 68, 80, 95, 138, 147, 149, 164, 175, 180, 205, 229, 230, 243, 246, 247, 256, 262, 272, 314

European MSc 262

European Space Agency 4

European Union 164, 246

Evans, Cecil 76

Evans, Dafydd 46

Evening Standard 300, 306

Everest 232

Everitt, Denise 212, 218

evolution 38, 40, 50, 59, 165, 166, 167, 168, 169, 175, 176, 184, 202

evolutionary ecology 30, 106, 165, 166, 191, 203, 211, 262

ewer 77

exams 17, 51, 176

Executive Director 46, 58, 208, 212, 216

Exocet 110

expensive 39, 54, 55, 171, 200, 209, 279

explorer 126, 234, 260, 301

extremely rare plants 189

F

Facts from Faeces 207, 208

Faeces 207, 208

Fahd, King 172

failure 126, 144, 221, 224, 230, 283, 309

Fairbairn, John 212

Fairfoot Road, Bow 316

fall guy 304

famous 1, 10, 20, 24, 41, 42, 43, 51, 64, 106, 107, 127, 135, 156, 185, 187, 190, 193, 201, 206, 207, 230, 260, 271, 300, 301, 306

Farakka Barrage 29, 283

Farmers' Club 222

Farnborough International Airshow 4, 239

Farne Islands 181

Farquhar 139

Farrier Major 222

fart 97

Fauna & Flora International (FFI) 197, 203

Fauna Preservation Society 197, 203

Fauvel, A.A. 132

Faversham 196

fees 39, 200, 216, 285

Fellow of the Royal Society (FRS) 56

female 21, 22, 23, 25, 26, 30, 40, 44, 49, 50, 68, 69, 87, 98, 107, 118, 120, 122, 125, 129, 133, 145, 146, 147, 148, 149, 168, 188, 189, 200, 203, 234

Fernie, Violet 17

fertiliser 179, 201

FFI 197

fifth columnists 6

fight 20

filariasis 69

Finale 310

Finch Hatton, Denys George 83

Firestreak 4

first day covers 190

First East Bengal Regiment 282

First Mate 109

First World Congress of Herpetology 130, 203, 205, 221, 222

Fisherian runaway 166

Fisher, John 54, 55

Fisher, R.A. 166

Fitter, Julian 197, 203

Fitter, Richard and Daisy 203

Flanders 312, 316, 317

fleas 69, 107, 311

Flemish 316, 317

flightless rail 105, 121, 150

flood 91, 171, 283

floozies 91, 92

Florence 195, 262, 266

Florence Evolution & Ecology of Social Behaviour Conference 262

Florence Postgraduate School of Vertebrate Behavioural Ecology 262

Florence University 262

Flying Tiger 292

food co-operatives 232, 252

Food Standards Agency 106

Forbidden City 294

Ford, Gerald 201

Foreign, Commonwealth and Development Office 68

Foreign & Commonwealth Office 57, 219

forest management 239

Forestry Department 281

Fornebu 104

fossilised coral 111, 123, 131, 146, 189

Fostering 23

Founder's Committee 210

Fox and Hounds Hotel 55

France 9, 10, 11, 18, 23, 63, 137, 138, 139, 141, 147, 179, 180, 192, 195, 206, 217, 313, 314, 315

Frank Lloyd Wright 200

fraud 23, 300

Freedom of London 17

Freeman 38, 39

French 10, 11, 40, 45, 123, 139, 172, 179, 180, 229, 313, 317, 318

frequency dependent selection 111, 144, 154

Frescon™ 54, 55, 105

fresh water 111, 137, 283, 284

Freshwater Turtle Specialist Group 130

friends 10, 16, 19, 20, 25, 27, 41, 61, 107, 112, 126, 127, 130, 154, 157, 163, 179, 197, 198, 200, 206, 207, 211, 226, 231, 237, 257, 258, 278, 292, 293, 295, 302, 305, 308, 309,

310, 311
Friendship Hotel 292
Friends of the National Trust
(Font) 235
frigate 139, 144, 172
frogs 214, 228
frontline soldier 301
FRS 54, 58, 106, 108, 170, 219,
223
Frye, Mary Elizabeth 311
Fryer, J.C.F 308
Fryer, Mark 240
Fulgheri, Francesco Dessi 262
Fullagar, Peter 105
Fundación Malecon 239
fundraising 209, 210
Furley Page 210
Fylkesmannen 104

G

Gaboon viper 70, 71, 124
Gaelic 24, 60
Galápagos 118, 131, 133, 134,
173, 183, 184, 185, 186, 187,
188, 189, 197, 203, 239, 262,
263
Galápagos Islands 133, 184,
185, 187, 203
Galápagos National Park
Service 184
Galbraith, David 144, 199
Galle Face Hotel 285
Game and Tsetse Control 102
Game Management Area
(GMA) 74, 77
Gandhi, Mahatma 24, 67
gang 95, 302
Ganges 29, 283
Gans, Carl 127, 203
Gansu 287
Garcia, Allan 273
Garcia, Fortunato Carvajal 284
Garoua Wildlife College 271
Garuda airlines 226
Gathorne, Dato Sri, Earl of
Cranbrook 158
Gathorne, Jason 158
Gathorne, Lord Medway 158
GATT 94 259, 280
GCSE 38, 45, 176
gecko 211
Geddie, Mary 30, 32, 33, 152
Gee, Ethel 3
Gellerman 52

Geneid, Robert 163
General Assembly 90, 130
General Assembly IUCN 130
genetically 133, 187, 278, 279
genetically modified (GM) 278,
279
genetic fingerprinting 199
Genghis Khan 291
genital mutilation 22
George II 313, 318
German 9, 64, 123, 195, 254,
256, 314
German Development Bank,
The (KTW) 271
Germans 9, 12
Ghurkha 12
ghutrah 28
Giant tortoise ecology and
behaviour 132, 139
giant tortoises 105, 110, 111,
112, 121, 125, 127, 130, 131,
132, 133, 134, 135, 137, 140,
141, 144, 145, 147, 148, 149,
164, 175, 181, 185, 186, 187,
188, 189, 191, 230
Gillot, Commandant 138
gin 25, 285
Girardet, Sibilla 226, 230, 231
Gladwin 45
Glenmorangie 61
glide 156
glitterati 31, 42, 45, 223
Global Environment Facility
(GEF) 286
Global Environment Facility
(GEF} 281, 285, 286, 288,
290, 292
glue-making 316
Goater, Barry 37, 39
Gobi 279, 287, 289, 311
Gobi Desert 287, 289
Gobin, Dane 253
Gobius, Ilkka 162, 164
godsend 80, 118, 126, 302
Godward, Maud 51
gold diggings 319
gold dust 24
goldfish 1, 52
Goldman Sachs 241
gold taps 126
golf 11, 12, 16, 24, 31, 35, 57,
210
Golf GTI 196
Goodwin, Harold 218, 274
Gorai River 29, 283, 284

Gorai River Restoration Project
29, 283, 284
Gorinsky, Conrad 90, 253, 255,
256
Gottschalk, Peter 267
Gouldian 32
Gould, Stephen Jay 167, 168,
169
Government House 132, 133
Government of Swaziland
(GOS) 276
government representatives
246
Government Research Assess-
ment Exercise 60
Gower Peninsula 51, 181
GP 1, 37, 44, 158, 224, 232, 267
GPS 275
Grace, John 294
grader 98, 99
granddad 18
Grande Bassin 129
Grande Passe 123, 138
Grande Terre 111, 113, 114, 115,
118, 139, 142, 144, 145, 146,
148, 172
Grandison, Alice "Bunty" 141
Grand Mentor 119
Great Barrier Reef 270
great bustard 291
great crested newts 214
Great Oaks Small School 257
Great Wall 287, 294
great white sharks 112, 123
greedy 160, 301
Greek Macedonia 182
Greene, G. 176
greenheart 89, 253, 255, 256
Green Line 35
Green Oscars 51, 195, 225
Greenpeace 270
Green Planet 299, 300, 303
Greenwood, Paul 141, 144,
176, 181
Greymouth 319
Griffin, David 116, 118
Griffiths, Richard 225, 266
groundwater 31, 284
grouper 123
group selection 166
GRZ 92
Guanacaste 153, 154
Guangchun, Lei 293, 294
Guatemala 184